From: _____

Date: _____

_____

_____

_____

THANKS, DAD, FOR EVERYTHING

Thanks, Dad, for Everything

Allison Yates Gaskins
a n d
Susan Alexander Yates

VINE
BOOKS

SERVANT PUBLICATIONS
ANN ARBOR, MICHIGAN

Vine Books is an imprint of Servant Publications especially designed to
serve evangelical Christians.

All Scripture quotations, unless otherwise indicated, are taken from the
HOLY BIBLE, NEW INTERNATIONAL VERSION®. © 1973,
1978, 1984 by International Bible Society. Used by permission of
Zondervan Publishing House. All rights reserved.

Published by Servant Publications
P.O. Box 8617
Ann Arbor, Michigan 48107

Cover design: Left Coast Design, Portland, OR
Cover illustration: Cecil Rice, Acworth, GA

98 99 00 01 10 9 8 7 6 5 4 3 2 1

Printed in the United States of America
ISBN 1-56955-068-9

LIBRARY OF CONGRESS CATALOGING-IN-PUBLICATION DATA

Gaskins, Allison Yates.
Thanks, Dad, for everything / Allison Yates Gaskins and Susan
Alexander Yates.
   p.   cm.
ISBN 1-56955-068-9
1. Fathers—Literary collections.   2. Fathers and sons—Literary collec-
tions.   3. Fathers and daughters—Literary collections.   I.Yates, Susan
Alexander.   II. Title.
PN6071.F3G37   1998
306.874'2—dc21   97-51271
                                             CIP

With thanksgiving for our two dads,
Sydenham B. Alexander
and John W. Yates II

With appreciation for the many wonderful friends
who have allowed us to tell their stories. Some of
their names have been changed to protect their privacy,
but all of these stories are true. We join you
in saluting these special men in your lives.

Contents

Introduction

It's a scary thing to be a dad. It's hard to provide for children, to protect little ones from danger, to make wise decisions on their behalf. It's hard to feel like you are doing a good job at the office and at home at the same time. There's lots of pressure, and it's not considered masculine to show weakness or to feel inadequate. It's easy to want to quit.

But dads don't quit. They keep on keeping on. Just as there are no perfect moms, there are no perfect dads. Instead, there are dads who have given it their best shot and failed, dads who have begun afresh and sometimes made more mistakes. Yet in the midst of it all, these dads have done many things right.

This book is to salute you, to honor you for what you have done right. You may be a dad or a big brother, a granddad or an older mentor in someone's life. You've had a hard job, an *impossible job,* but you've kept on and because of your endurance and God's grace, you've made a positive difference in our lives.

We thank God for you!

Me, a Father?

"*Congratulations, Mr. and Mrs. Gaskins. You're going to have a baby! Welcome to the wonderful world of parenthood.*"

Allison and I found out this news just a few weeks ago, and I'm still not sure how I feel about it. I mean, of course I'm excited and happy and everything, but I feel a little strange at the same time. It's hard to believe this is really happening. In fact, it's shocking. This pregnancy didn't come as a surprise. As a matter of fact, we'd been hoping for it, but when you actually find out that it's going to happen, and there's no going back, well ... it kind of throws you for a loop.

I've been reading a book about becoming a father, and something it says is both surprising and encouraging. It says that the most common feeling a man experiences when facing fatherhood is *grief*. I know that sounds crazy, but I'm glad that somebody else agrees with me!

I hate to admit this, but I'm *worried!* In some ways it seems like my life is falling down all around me. There were so many things I still wanted to do and now I'm going to be a father. Will my life ever be the same? No, of course not. Will I still get to live out my dreams? I don't know! Will I ever have freedom again? I hope so, but at this point I'm not sure. *Me*, a father? That's a really scary thought. How in the world will I know what to do? I've never done this before. They don't teach fatherhood in school. Will I be any good at it?

All these questions make me think about my own dad. I thinks he's one of the all-time greatest dads in the world. I wonder if he felt like this when he found out that *I* was on the way? He didn't know any more about fathering than I do, and he did a great job! If I can be a dad like him, I'll be just fine. I know some-times he found it difficult to be a father. He went through lots of hard times, both as our dad and in his personal life, but he trusted the Lord at all times and he's taught me to do the same in my life. Fatherhood is certainly something I can't do on my own. I'm going to need some real guidance—from other people, from my dad, and especially from my Heavenly Father.

I know that God has given us this little baby for a special reason, as his great gift to us. I'm still scared, but I know he will help me every step of the way. I may not know how to be a father, but I do know the greatest Father of all, and I know he has promised us that he will always guide us. He has told us that "He tends his flocks like a shepherd: He gathers the lambs in his arms and carries them close to his heart; he gently leads those that have young" (Isaiah 40:11). I need that guidance, and I'm so glad I can count on the Lord for it.

Thank you, Heavenly Father, that you are the greatest Father of all. Thank you that you are in charge of every minute detail of our lives. Thanks for the wonderful earthly father you gave me, and for the opportunity you have now given me to become a father. I'm relying on you to show me what to do!

Just Because You're Mine

~

When I was young I would have given anything to be a boy instead of a girl. Sports were my passion. In those days, however, boys' athletics got a lot more attention than girls'. Our neighborhood had twenty kids under the age of twelve, enabling us to create teams of every sort. Television was just appearing in homes and VCRs hadn't been invented yet, so a lot of our entertainment was left to our own creativity. This was not a bad thing! It wasn't unusual for four of us girls to challenge the boys to a game of football. It was tough, bloody, muddy, and we girls weren't above kicking or pulling hair occasionally to force our way through their front line.

Although I played just about everything, basketball was my favorite! Growing up in Chapel Hill, North Carolina, you just *had* to be a basketball fan! It was the fifties and the University of North Carolina (UNC) was about to win its first national title. Basketball was king, and oh, how I wanted to be a star!

Somehow, my father understood my passions. He took me to UNC basketball games. As we sat in the stands, he'd pull out a piece of notebook paper and begin his own statistics sheet. Clean O's were for missed foul shots, colored ones meant that the shot was good. He recorded everything and taught me how to do it as well. If we couldn't get tickets to the game, we listened to the radio at home and filled in our sheets together.

More than anything, I wanted a regulation basketball hoop in our backyard. I was sure that if I practiced enough, one day I'd be a famous player. Mom and Dad agreed that we could turn part of the yard into a basketball court, so Dad went to work marking it off and gathering cement and wood to build it. He even attached a floodlight so I could practice after dark.

Dad didn't seem to mind that his daughter wasn't interested in dresses and makeup. He accepted my "tomboy" ways, and I instinctively knew that he loved me just as I was. He wasn't the type of dad who shared his personal feelings. His generation just wasn't comfortable with that. But he was affectionate, and often showed his love in wordless ways. I knew he loved me. Once, though, I remember him saying, "Susan, I love you so much."

"Why, Daddy?" I asked.

"Just because you're mine," he responded simply.

It wasn't because I had been good. In fact, I was probably more trouble than I was good. The oldest of four children, I was strong-willed, bossy, and usually mean, especially to my siblings. Dad was no pushover, either. He was a firm disciplinarian when I needed discipline.

On another occasion he said, "Susan, I want you to know that I'll always be here for you. I may not always agree with what you do, but no matter what happens, I'll always be here for you."

In high school I made the varsity girls' basketball team. I wasn't the star; my best friend Jill was. But I played, and whenever we had a game my dad was there. He didn't coach me from the sidelines, but just quietly sat in the stands with a great big smile across his face. Whenever I'd look up he'd give me a thumbs-up sign or a nod of encouragement. If I played miserably he'd comfort me, and if I did well he'd be happy for me, but mostly he was content just being there. My performance didn't seem to matter to him. He was happy simply because I belonged to him.

Thanks, Dad, for communicating that you loved me just because I was yours. Your love has enabled me to understand that God loves me not because I'm a good mother or wife or friend (I'm usually not!) but he loves me simply because I belong to him. Your earthly fathering has made a tremendous difference in my understanding of the love my Heavenly Father has for me.

A Man Without Guile

W orking for your family—or, more specifically,
for your father—can be a stressful experience.
It can destroy relationships between the two of you,
or it can forge them. But no matter what, working
together exposes you to the *real person* each of you is.
Pretense falls away and you come to know each
other's faults, strengths, inconsistencies, and passions.
You get to know each other's raw character. Fortunately, in my case, working with my dad was
among the greatest blessings in my life.

Dad was an executive with a large chain of retail
stores. For nine years I worked in the same store with
him. Our offices were next door to each other. My
exposure to the retail business had actually begun
when I was twelve, when he asked me to help during
the annual July Clearance Sale! Then, after graduating from college, I came to work for Dad full-time.
He started me out on the loading dock and in the
receiving room. It may have seemed odd to some to
see the boss's son doing such menial tasks, but it
made perfect sense to Dad. He felt I should learn the

business from the ground up so that I would appreciate what each person did. Dad didn't feel a person's job determined his or her value. To him, each person was important. A vice president's job was no more important than a custodian's. It was simply *different*. Both were important for the success of the company. Dad's actions one morning particularly illustrated this.

It was early, before the store's doors opened for another busy day. Dad happened to be walking through the ladies' department when a frantic salesman approached him.

"What's the matter, Roy?" Dad inquired.

"Mr. Ogburn, we've got a bad leak in the toilet in the ladies' lounge and it's making a mess. I've got to hurry and find the custodian to clean it up."

Ten minutes later Roy and the custodian, laden with mops and tools, raced into the ladies' lounge to find Dad, his suit jacket hanging over the back of a chair, his shirt sleeves rolled up, and his tie tucked away. He was down on his knees with a rag in his hands, cleaning up the mess.

Dad's life illustrated the point that no job was too menial. He knew how to be an executive with a number of stores in his care; yet, he also knew that we are simply called to love and to serve others.

On another occasion a disgruntled employee

began to say nasty things about Dad publicly—things that were untrue. How I wanted to refute the gossip! But Dad's response was, "Son, if after all these years folks don't know me, then it's too bad. They should know by now that I'm not like what's being said. We just have to let it go and keep on doing what's right."

Dad never hesitated to admit his errors. If he disagreed with an associate, and that associate turned out to be right, Dad would always be the first to say, "I surely was wrong on that one. You were right, and I'm so glad!" Being right all the time simply wasn't that important to him. He was quick to confess, to apologize, and to praise others. Dad loved Jesus and he loved people. It was evident to everyone who knew him. How I admired him! How I loved him! What a man!

Dad's faith was at the core of who he was. On many occasions he'd come into my office, sit down in the easy chair, and begin to talk about his blessings. When he began to talk about his family, he'd often start to weep. He wasn't embarrassed; he was too natural for that. His faith in a loving God was completely genuine, and it overflowed into everything he did. When we renovated the main store, he had a small prayer room built. He wanted a place where employees or customers could slip away to read the Scriptures and to pray. This room, with its small kneeler and open Bible, was a symbol of Dad's big heart. It was used often.

When I think of Dad I think of a man in whom there was no guile. He was a man like the biblical disciple Nathaniel. A man with no pretense, who at the core of his being understood and illustrated what it meant to love and to serve.

Thanks, Dad, for modeling for me what it means to be genuine. Because we worked together, I saw you more closely than any other person, except Mom. Now, as my own son works in business with me, I appreciate your life and your legacy in an even deeper way.

Sentenced

"Sentenced. To twelve months plus one day in federal prison."

With that one statement from a judge, my life and the lives of our entire family were changed forever. I was only four years old and my dad was going to prison. My brother was seven and my sister was ten. Dad was a prominent lawyer in the South. We had a nice home, country club memberships, great friends, and went to church on Sundays. To an outsider we looked like the perfect family. But inside our four walls there was trouble—*real* trouble. Because of his testimony in a complicated, out-of-state legal case, Dad was indicted for perjury and found guilty.

It was a rough time for our family. Most painful were the news headlines: *"Prominent Lawyer McConnell Indicted for Perjury."* It seemed that the press delighted in stretching the bad news and in mortifying my parents by printing irrelevant, personal things. Mom cried a lot, and Dad was embarrassed and humiliated. Soon the lack of finances became a problem, so Mom went back to work. Thanksgiving and Christmas were extremely hard with Dad away in prison. We just didn't feel like a family without him.

It would have been natural for Dad to have justified his actions, to have blamed others, even to have run away. I'm sure he wanted to, but he didn't. Instead, he accepted responsibility for his actions. He wept tears of humiliation, not only for himself, but for the pain he was causing my mom and us kids.

After the first prison term, my dad was anxious to get things back to the way they had been before. God had other plans, however, and Dad was indicted again, this time by the state.

During this difficult time, after Dad had been indicted but before he was convicted, two men began to have a great impact on his life. George and Boyd invited him to join a home Bible study of the Gospel of John. Dad, on his own, also began to read the Book of Job. He finally realized that he couldn't run his life by himself. He got down on his knees and, with some trepidation, said to God, "OK, I'm going to give you 95 percent of my life."

Sensing a strange silence, he prayed again. "OK, God, you can have *all* of me." God took him at his word.

He was convicted again and during Dad's second prison term his faith really began to grow. God used this second time in prison for good. Once again, godly men surrounded him. Guys like Lyston, Larry, Trip, Vick, David, Jamie, John, Danny, Robert, and Norman went to visit him, studied the Bible with him, prayed for him, and encouraged him.

After Dad got out of prison, his life didn't change radically overnight. He had always been a good father. But there were *subtle* changes in his priorities that made a lasting impact.

Before prison, Dad's prayer life had consisted of hearing our rote prayers at bedtime. Now he had us praying for specific people and their needs, as well as thanking God for specific ways he had used our pain. Bible stories had never before been a part of our family life. Now Dad began to read *Little Visits with God* to us at bedtime. Soon he began to share specific Scripture verses that he was memorizing.

He and Mom started studying the Bible together. His relationships seemed to take on a new depth. His weekly meeting with a four-man accountability group became a top priority. He knew he needed a small group of men to whom he could be accountable— men with whom he could pray, study the Bible, and share honestly.

Many changes took place after Dad's imprisonment, but what has impacted me the most has been Dad's emphasis on truth. "Kids," he would say, "you know from all we've been through that telling lies is wrong. Your actions will have consequences. You have to deal with those consequences. When you get into a situation where you are tempted, always tell the truth, no matter if it's big or small. There's no such thing as a white lie. A little lie is a lie. Tell the truth. Truth is very important."

Today, as I work in a senator's office in Washington, D.C., I find that it's easy for me to stretch the truth in different situations. After all, half-truths are "the stuff" of real politics. But because of my dad, I'm more sensitive to my own powers of rationalization. Because of his example, I'm more desirous of fleeing temptation. More than ever I want to be a man of integrity.

Thanks, Dad, for being humble enough to admit your mistakes and to learn from them. You had the courage to own up to your errors and to accept the consequences of your actions. From you I have learned the importance of truth. I pray that I may emulate the man of integrity that you have become. You are my hero.

Finding Alfonso

It was early in the morning, and Chris was late for school again. He was digging through his dresser drawers like crazy, trying to find a pair of socks that were at least the same length, if not the same shade of grayish white! The pile on the floor next to him grew higher by the minute as he tossed mismatches aside. A few unexpected items showed up as he dug through the pile. There was a set of old keys he had collected a few years ago, and there was the Easter candy he had been hiding from his brother John. There was his favorite baseball card. *So that's where it's been all this time!* Chris pulled out a green sock and a muddy-colored one that looked like it hadn't seen the inside of a washer in years, but none resembled the white ones he needed for school.

In a last-ditch effort, Chris reached his arm all the way back into the dark part of the drawer to make a final sweep. His fingers closed on something hard and rubbery. It was definitely not the sock he was looking for, but this might be something far better! Expectantly, he pulled his hand out, and when he saw what he had grabbed, Chris dashed gleefully out of the room, his sock search already forgotten.

"John! John! Guess who I found! *Alfonso!* He was in my sock drawer! I found him!" His brother's eyes glinted with envy as Chris gloated all the way to the bus stop, not caring about his mismatched socks.

"I found Alfonso, I found Alfonso!" he gloated. "Nobody's found him in months! This is gonna be a *good* one!"

Alfonso, you see, was one of the greatest family secrets in the Yates household. He was a rubber alligator, approximately ten inches long, who disappeared and appeared seemingly at will. He often appeared in unexpected places such as the dishwasher, at the bottom of the outdoor garbage can, or underneath Mom and Dad's bed, only to be discovered when someone was doing their vacuuming chores. Rarely did Alfonso make his way into anyone's bedroom, and he had never crawled into anyone's dresser before! This made Chris feel extra important, because he knew that in some way *he* had been meant to find Alfonso.

What made the rare discovery of this alligator so special was the fact that the person who discovered him got a special treat from Dad for "rescuing Alfonso" from his hiding place!

"That darned alligator!" Dad had been known to

say. "He never stays at home in my desk! I am forever looking for him, and what would I do without you children to rescue him for me? Anyone who finds him certainly deserves a big reward."

When Dad got home that night, Chris was waiting for him at the door. No sooner had Dad set his brief-case down than Chris threw himself into his father's arms, waving the rubber alligator in front of his face.

"Look who I found, Dad! Alfonso was napping under my socks and I found him this morning when I was looking for a matching pair! I found him!"

"Well, that's a relief!" Dad smiled. "He's been missing for several days and I was beginning to get worried about him. I wonder how he found his way into your sock drawer? That's a pretty scary place, if I do say so myself. I don't think I'd want to be lost in there with all those smelly things! Maybe you should clean it out in case 'Fonso runs away again."

"Maybe so," Chris grinned sheepishly. "I suppose it would be nice to find out what else is lost in there!"

"You know what?" Dad asked. "I sure am glad it was you who found Alfonso. You see, I have these tickets to the Orioles baseball game Friday night and I just don't know what to do with them. Maybe we could go to the game together for your "Rescuing Alfonso Reward." Of course, we'd have to bring him along, too, otherwise he might run away again, mischievous rascal that he is. What do you think about that?"

Chris gave his Dad the biggest hug he knew how. "I'd love to, Dad! Just the two, I mean *three*, of us. That would be AWESOME! Do you think Alfonso likes hot dogs and popcorn?"

Dad smiled back, returning the hug. "Well, I kind of think he prefers bugs and mud and that sort of thing. But we could offer him some and if he doesn't like it, then there's all the more for you and me, right?"

"Right!" returned Chris. "I can't wait!"

Thanks, Dad, for your sense of fun! You kept me on my toes, never knowing when the next surprise would come my way. Not only did you go out of your way to spend time with me, but you made it into a game and a special event to remember.

Godfatherly Wisdom

❦

Sweating in her car outside University Hospital, Betsy tried to pray. *God, prepare me for this time with John. Help me to be an encouragement to him in his time of need. Help me to minister your love to him. In your Son's name, Amen.*

Betsy's godfather, John, was in the hospital for cancer, and the hopes were slim for his recovery. He was a young, vibrant man with a lovely wife and three daughters. It was hard for Betsy to imagine him as anything but the picture of health. A sophomore in college, Betsy still relied heavily on the love and guidance of this man, who had been a father figure to her since her own dad had left the family. John always knew exactly what to say to motivate and inspire her, and as she walked down the antiseptic halls toward the intensive care unit, she wondered if she could do the same for him at this time.

Betsy took a deep breath and gently pushed the door open. John's pale face lit up when he saw her, and with almost his usual enthusiasm he exclaimed, "It's about time you got here! This place is getting a little boring, and I was hoping you'd be along to brighten things up."

His cheerful greeting put Betsy at ease and she teased, "Well, it was a bit of a challenge to fit you into my schedule, you know!" Maybe things weren't going to be as difficult as she had thought. But behind the laughter in John's eyes, she could detect a seriousness.

Never one to beat around the bush, John said directly, "There's something I've been wanting to talk to you about. Tell me how you are—I mean how you're *really* doing."

This is backward, flashed across Betsy's mind. *I should be asking him how he's doing—he's the one who's sick!* She paused a moment and replied, "Pretty well, I guess," proceeding to give him a superficial run-down of her life at the moment. "Nothing too exciting," she concluded.

John listened intently and Betsy saw that he was digesting her words carefully. She knew he could understand without exactly being told that she wasn't really excited about her life. John knew her well, sometimes even better than she knew herself. As she waited for him to speak, she could sense that this was going to be a very deliberate conversation. John dove in with the penetrating questions that had always been his style.

"So, Betsy, how do you see yourself growing in your faith right now?" Betsy fumbled for an answer. That was a hard question. When she didn't reply immediately, he continued, "In what ways are you being a witness to the people around you? Specifically, how is your life reaching others with the good news of Jesus?"

As Betsy struggled to put words to her response, John looked at her with eyes full of compassion. He was well aware of the fact that these questions were hard to answer, and that they reached to the core of Betsy's existence. As Betsy tried to find an answer, she realized that John could see into her heart. He knew she was dissatisfied with herself and her life, and he was trying to help her understand the reasons why.

"I don't really feel like I'm growing in my faith, John," she replied honestly, although until this moment Betsy hadn't even realized that she felt this way.

"I'm involved in lots of Christian activities, but I don't feel like I'm being stretched and challenged. I don't even know very many nonbelievers. I guess you could say I'm hardly being a witness for Christ." John nodded to himself as if he had expected this reply.

"Betsy, it seems to me that you are allowing yourself to become stagnant."

Ouch! That hurts! thought Betsy, although she knew he was probably right.

John continued, "I know that you are a young woman of incredible talents and passions. I see you as a beautiful flower that has blossomed well in a small pot. But now that pot is too limiting. In order for the flower to grow, it needs more nourishment than a small pot can give. The flower needs to be dug up, to have its roots shaken out, and to be transplanted to a larger pot where it can plunge those roots deeper and find greater nourishment. If this flower isn't transplanted soon, it will just wither away and be another dead plant on a shelf instead of the lovely, fruitful blossom it was meant to be. The transplanting process isn't easy; it hurts. Sometimes the plant has to struggle before it revives itself. Do you understand what I'm saying?"

Betsy nodded, trying to keep the tears from her eyes. He was so right. John knew exactly where she was in her life. She *did* need a "bigger pot," but she was afraid of the transplanting process.

"I know you're right, John," she replied. "I'm just afraid to take the steps I need to make a change."

"Change is always scary, Betsy. But I know you, and I know what God can do in your life. Let's pray right now that he will give you the strength to step forward in faith."

As Betsy stepped back into the fresh air outside the hospital, she paused in amazement. Her godfather was clearly not going to live much longer, yet they had spent the whole visit talking about *her* needs! She had gone into that hospital with such different intentions. She had wanted to encourage John! Instead, in his characteristic way, he had taken the focus off of himself and had directed it toward Betsy. He had known that she needed sensitive guidance at that particular moment.

During their conversation, Betsy had completely forgotten her original intentions for the visit, and John didn't even seem to notice that he was lying in a hospital bed. That was so like him. He had always done that for Betsy—given her gentle and loving wisdom when she needed it most, regardless of his personal circumstances.

Thanks, John, for the fathering you gave me during your life. At a crucial moment in your illness, you thought not of yourself and how you were feeling, but of my needs. You challenged me to grow in ways that I couldn't see for myself, and your faith in me has given me the strength to go on even now that you are gone. I'm so blessed to have been your goddaughter!

A Change of Heart

"**S**o, when are you going to get a real job, Son?" His father's caustic words burned in Derek's ears. "When are you going to do something grown-up, and earn a real living for yourself and that wife of yours?"

Such painful statements were a common refrain in Derek's family. Casually tossed phrases stung Derek's memory, reminding him of his father's disapproval. It wasn't surprising, then, that when his dad suggested the two of them spend some man-to-man time together, Derek was wary. He anticipated more criticism of his chosen profession as a full-time youth minister.

Derek's father was a highly successful businessman for whom the pursuit of wealth had always been a consuming passion. He understood neither Derek's deep love for the Lord nor his desire to serve God by working with teenagers. To Dad, youth ministry just seemed like a postponement of "real life." He considered it a phase his son was going through and hoped Derek would soon move past it!

To Derek and his wife, however, ministry was a lifelong commitment—something they felt with all their hearts that the Lord was calling them to pursue. Derek had all but given up trying to explain this to his father, yet he still prayed that one day his father would understand.

Right now, however, his dad seemed to operate on a completely different level. He saw contracts and numbers where Derek saw changed lives and kids turned to God. Hence, it was a very hesitant son who agreed to an afternoon outing with his father. Derek feared that this time together would only lead to another one of those "discussions" where Dad tried to make him "see the error of his ways" and change his career path.

As they drove through the countryside, Dad broached the subject first. "There's something I've been meaning to speak with you about, Son."

Derek felt himself tense up immediately, but managed to sound nonchalant as he replied, "Oh, really? What's on your mind?"

"You may not have noticed this, Derek, but for a long time I haven't been very proud of your career choice." He paused, and Derek found himself thinking, *May not have realized it? Who does he think he's kidding? Subtlety has never been one of Dad's gifts!*

"Well, actually I have been aware of that for a

while, Dad," Derek replied, trying to keep a defensive edge from creeping into his voice.

His dad continued, "I've often thought that you chose foolishly, pursuing a job in a church when you could be using your excellent mind for something so much more lucrative and prestigious. I've always thought you were selling yourself and our family short by going into ministry."

Here it comes, Derek thought, bracing himself for the next stinging blow.

"Well, Derek, I want you to know that I've changed my mind," Dad stated simply.

"Excuse me?" said Derek, certain he had misunderstood. It was Dad's unwritten rule never to change his mind on things he considered important.

"I have completely changed how I feel about you and your chosen career, Derek, and I feel I owe it to you to apologize for having been so critical of you until now."

Derek was caught so off guard that he could hardly comprehend what his father was saying. "What exactly do you mean, Dad?" he asked tentatively.

"Well, honestly, it's been kind of a long process, Son. Your mother and I have begun going to a church where they talk a lot about our personal relationship with God. We're learning that he has a special plan for each of our lives. It's really been fascinating and I'm learning a lot of things I'd never thought of before, like the fact that God has a 'calling' for each of us, something that he has designed specifically for us to do with our lives. If we listen to him, he will clearly direct us down the path, and we won't be satisfied unless we follow his leading.

"I'm starting to realize that this is what you are doing in your ministry. You *are* fulfilling God's call on your life. He gave you the desires and talents necessary to work with kids and to share his love with them. For you to do anything else would be to deny God's plan. In a way I envy you, Derek. I have never thought about this in my own life until now. I have pursued my own goals over the years without ever once considering that God even cared about them, let alone that he might have had a special plan for my life. But I know that you have thought about all of this, and that you have confidence that you are doing exactly what God wants you to do. I think that's an incredible gift, and in spite of the way I have felt in the past, I'm proud of you for it."

The passing countryside was just a blur to Derek as he sat processing all that his father had just said. He had never even dreamed of hearing such affirmation from his dad! He had given up even hoping that his father would one day understand, and had resigned himself to living without his father's blessing. This conversation was truly a gift from the Lord. It never could have happened without intervention on God's part!

"Dad, you don't know what it means to me to hear you say these things. It has always hurt me that you have disapproved of my choice of a life's work. I was afraid I'd have to learn to live the rest of my life knowing I had disappointed you. Thank you for being willing to change. It means the world to me to know that I have your blessing."

Thanks, Dad, for being humble enough to hear God's voice and to understand our different perspectives. Thank you for your willingness to change, and not only to accept me in my calling, but to encourage me in it as well. It gives me great joy and affirmation to know that I have your blessing now.

Sweet and Bittersweet

M y senior year in high school had finally arrived, and with it came a bundle of tangled emotions. I was stressed out trying to meet college application deadlines, fearful I wouldn't be accepted anywhere, anxious about leaving home, and frustrated at trying to juggle my extracurricular activities and still get everything else done! In addition, I could sense that my parents, especially my dad, were going through the early stages of "daughter-withdrawal" that come with sending your eldest off to school.

Finally, one chilly February day, a fat letter arrived in the mail from my number-one college choice. Fat letters are the encouraging ones—they herald acceptance, whereas the skinny ones usually read something like this:

"Although we appreciate your interest in our college, we had so many applicants this year that we regret to inform you ..."

All high-school seniors dread skinny letters. This time I had been fortunate, and I was thrilled! The only drawback was that this college was very far from home. Although my parents were obviously happy about my acceptance, I could sense a deep sadness in Dad. I knew he was missing me already. It was a bittersweet moment.

The same week that my college acceptance letter came, I got some more good news. I had been chosen to sing the soprano solo in a Bach cantata performed by our community choir and orchestra. This was an honor, because singing had always been one of my greatest passions—a passion I inherited from my dad.

I soon discovered that the choir director was looking for tenors to join the group. *Dad has a bright tenor voice,* I thought, *and he loves music. Maybe he would do this with me. It would be a special way for us to spend a little time together before I go to college!*

Dad was pleased when I asked him, and he happily joined the choir. Every Tuesday and Thursday I picked him up at work and we drove to rehearsal across town. After rehearsal we'd grab supper at our favorite café. Both of us wanted to make the most of these last days together.

Over soup and salad we'd discuss our family's German heritage and our common love of music. We'd talk about the ways that music fed us spiritually. For both of us, singing was a very moving spiritual experience, and singing in a Bach cantata was especially so. The 131st Cantata, which we were performing, is based on Psalm 130, "Out of the depths I cry to you, O Lord." To both of us this particular piece of music connected us to our ancestors. Because of our German heritage, we felt called to faith out of the depths of a painful period of history. During those evenings in the café, we had many memorable conversations about our common love for this music and the ways in which God has given us the ability to express our love for him vocally.

Finally, the evening of the performance arrived. It was a night that marked a turning point in our lives. Dad had always been the leader in our family and the one to whom I had turned for guidance. But on that evening, for the first time, I was the leader. I was the soloist in front of the choir and Dad was in the background, singing a supporting role. For both Dad and me, it was my official "debut," my time to shine as he proudly looked on.

Little by little over that month of rehearsals and café conversations, I had grown up, and Dad had learned to let go. I sang my heart out for the performance, and I could hear his voice behind me shining out from the choir. I knew he was so proud of me he could have burst! This was the best "musical high" I have ever experienced.

After this experience, we began to have a better perspective on our changing relationship. As I left for college I knew my dad would still be a vital part of my life, but now his role had changed. He would no longer always be out in front as the soloist and leader, he would now be supporting me less visibly, from the choir of life. It was a very tender time for both of us.

Thanks, Dad, for being there for me. I know it has been hard for you to let go of your first child. Thank you for sharing my love for music. Your supporting role in my life continues and I am so grateful to know that you will always be backing me up, not only in music, but also in life!

The Pedlowe Family Creed

⬡

I f you walk into the Pedlowes' house, it won't take you long to realize that theirs is a special family with some real values. When I first entered their home, I was struck by a framed wall hanging that read "Pedlowe Family Creed." Below were listed four values this family chooses to live by: Love God, Love People, Work Hard, and Be Honest.

After talking with the three oldest children (at eight months, the youngest, Emily, didn't have much to say yet!), I quickly came to realize that this was indeed an unusual family. They were a family with a mission! I asked Drew (age eight), Kelsey (ten), and Katie (six) what they had learned from their daddy, and then listened for the next hour and a half!

Katie, always the first to speak, piped up right away. "He teaches us the Pedlowe Family Creed: Love God, Love People, Work Hard, and Be Honest," she said, all in one breath. This was exactly what the sign on the wall in the kitchen said, and it was quite clear that these values were taken seriously by the Pedlowes. No one remembered where they came from ("I think Mommy and Daddy made them up," was the consensus), but all of the children had known them as long as they could remember. These were not empty words to be recited piously, either. The kids were quick to explain exactly what each of them meant, and especially how their father had helped to demonstrate the family creed.

"Daddy teaches us to love God when he prays for people and when he goes to church with us. And he teaches other people about God. We even gave a Bible to our grandpa who doesn't know Jesus."

Clearly, this was a family that didn't rely on "Do as I say, but not as I do." This was a family where the kids learned by example.

Drew explained to me that his dad also was teaching them to "Love People."

"Yesterday we went to the bank and there were a man and lady there whose car had broken down. We saw them and Dad stopped our car. Other people drove by, but we got out and helped them push their car into a parking lot and out of danger. That's what it means to love people."

"And Dad shows us what it means to work hard, too," Kelsey, the eldest, added. "We wanted to have a fort in the backyard, so Dad decided that we should help build it. It was hard work, but we all worked together on it and now we have a great fort." (Their fort truly is the best in the neighborhood!)

"We also have chores to do in the house and yard. That helps us learn to work hard. We all have our own baby trees that we bought with Dad and planted in the yard. I have a dogwood, Drew has a Japanese maple, and Katie has an evergreen. Emily doesn't have one yet 'cause she's not old enough to take care of it. We have to be responsible and water the trees and take care of them if we want them to grow up strong."

The value of honesty is often a difficult lesson to impart and to learn. But even in their youth, the Pedlowe children had a very clear understanding of what it meant to be truthful, and of the consequences when they weren't!

"We can't get away with much," Kelsey confessed. "If we're dishonest, Mom and Dad always know and we'd better confess or *else!*" I asked the kids if they thought their dad was an honest person, and all of them vigorously nodded their heads. "Pedlowes always tell the truth," Katie reminded me.

Drew recently had the opportunity to put this into action with his dad, when on the way home from a hardware store Drew realized that they had taken eight bricks, but had only paid for six. When he brought it to his father's attention, Dad felt terrible about the mistake. They both decided that the honest thing to do would be to go right back to the store and pay for the extra bricks. And that's what they did. The bricks were not costly, and many people would have simply tossed the mistake aside. But for Drew and his daddy, this was the perfect opportunity to put into action their value of "Be Honest."

As we concluded our conversation, I asked each of the kids what their favorite thing was about their dad, and what the most important thing they had ever learned from him was. The "favorite things" were simple, but telling, about a father who truly cared for his children.

"My favorite thing is taking trips together," explained Katie. "I like going to the amusement park or the beach and spending time together."

"And mine is when Dad took *just me* to play golf with him!" Drew remembered, his face shining at the thought. "And one time he took me *and* my friends for a day of golf!"

Kelsey especially liked the days when just she and Dad went out together.

The things they had learned from their father were many, but each child had a favorite. "Dad teaches me to do what the Lord would do," Katie said. "He taught me Philippians 2:5, 'Your attitude should be the same as that of Christ Jesus.'"

Drew agreed with his sister that this was important,

but said that the best thing he had learned from his father was to always tell the truth, even when it's hard. Kelsey summed it all up with this thought, "We should ask ourselves 'What would Jesus do?' and live every day doing our best as if Jesus might come. That's what Dad does." All three of the Pedlowe children nodded their heads in agreement.

Thanks, Dad, for giving us a clear statement of what is true and important. Ever since we could speak, we could recite our family creed, and because of your example, we understand what it means to turn these words into actions.

Mentor of the Year

I t was one of the worst days of my life. Having just graduated from high school, I had finally landed a summer job with a construction company. The pay was good and I was learning a valuable trade, but my coworkers were a vulgar group of men. Their language made my tough high-school buddies look like a bunch of Goody Two-Shoes. But it wasn't just their coarse language and jokes that irked me. They began to pick on me. Then the abuse turned nasty and one of the men started shoving me around. My held-in hostility finally exploded, and I landed a hard right on the man's cheek.

I came home feeling terrible. As a Christian I knew my actions had not been right. I could have handled the situation in a better way. But I also knew that I couldn't go back to that job. I was ashamed, depressed, and anxious. On top of everything else, my mother, my sister, and I were having to move into a small, two-bedroom apartment. My dad had deserted us years before and finances were very tight. I knew I had to make good money that summer if I wanted to go to college in the fall. Life was hard enough for my mom and my sister. I was trying to be stoic for them, but I was about to fall apart myself. Not wanting to cry in front of my mother, I shut the door to my room and picked up the phone to call Nick.

Nick was the owner and publisher of our small hometown weekly newspaper. I had met him four years earlier when I needed a part-time job. Nick agreed to take me on as reporter for the sports section, where I was to cover the high school athletic programs. Sports were my passion and I had played both varsity basketball and tennis.

It hadn't been unusual for Nick to show up for my games, sit on the sidelines, and snap pictures of me to go with sports stories for the paper! Nick himself had been a semipro baseball player. He didn't especially like tennis, but he came to my matches anyway. He came to watch me even if there was a baseball game being played at the same time as the tennis match. Nick wasn't just my employer; he cared for me. I knew that I could call him now and tell him about this difficult situation at work.

Struggling for control, I dialed Nick's number. As I told him what had happened, he listened. He didn't seem to mind my tears. He understood.

"Nate," he said, "Why don't you come to work

for me full-time? I'll create a job for you called 'Editorial Assistant.' You can sell ads for the paper."

The very next day I started work for Nick. It happened to be the same week that the paper had its annual staff party. Even though I'd only been there a few days, I was invited to the party. At the party Nick gave out different awards. Boy, was I surprised to receive the "Editorial Assistant of the Year Award"! Of course, I was the *only* editorial assistant! Instinctively Nick knew that I needed to feel a part of things.

I was not the only young man that Nick cared for over the years. There were others, some of them boys from troubled homes, who simply needed extra support and encouragement. Nick and his wife did not have children of their own so they simply "adopted" boys that needed some extra attention.

Even though Nick was my dad's age, he didn't try to replace my dad. Because of my parents' divorce, my relationship with my dad was very painful. He lived in a different state and did little to stay in touch with me. Yet Nick encouraged me to keep communication channels open with my dad. He encouraged me not to become bitter but to keep praying for Dad.

Nick became like a wise older brother to me. Although he was not wealthy, he loaned me money when finances were tight. He helped me think through college choices and when I left for college he stayed in touch by calling me every Tuesday night just to check in and see how things were going. He taught me the newspaper business and during summers I continued to work for his paper.

Now, as I pack to return to college for my senior year, I know I'll be picking up the phone again each Tuesday to chat with Nick when he calls. It reassures me to know that he'll be glad to hear my voice, and will be happy to talk about *anything* that's on my mind.

Thanks, Nick, for mentoring a young teenager. Your care has demonstrated for me and for other young men a picture of open arms and understanding. Your big heart, your sacrifice of time, and your unending encouragement have helped me through some tough times. I hope that one day I can make a positive difference in a young man's life like you have in mine.

Celebrate!

I remember what it was like when I was a teenager, returning home after being out of town. As the car got closer to the house, my excitement would begin to build. Eagerly, I would push the speed limit. *Hurry, hurry,* my emotions seemed to say. I couldn't wait to pull into the driveway, honk the horn, and watch the family race out the door to greet me. I could just see the huge smile on Mom's face and the shine of Dad's bald head, his big grin spreading from ear to ear.

As I covered those last few miles, I would picture Dad looking at his watch and gazing out the window. He would have calculated the miles I had to drive, and would have guessed my arrival time. If it was summer he would have mowed the lawn and planted fresh flowers. If it was winter he'd have a fire all laid. And he'd be sure to have a clean shirt on. It would be a little out of style but he wouldn't realize that, and I didn't care.

Even though Dad was a busy physician, he always arranged his schedule so that he could be home to greet me. I didn't appreciate the trouble he went to at the time, but now, with five kids of my own, I do. Somehow Dad knew that just being there to greet me communicated volumes. Now I realize that Dad was turning a *greeting* into a *celebration.*

In my own life it's so much easier to keep doing the laundry, fixing supper, or working in my office than it is to get up and greet my family as they arrive home. After all, life is so busy. And the kids don't seem to appreciate my efforts. Is the greeting that important anyway?

Yes, it is!

Dad's greeting gave me a sense of belonging. In a world where there is a tendency to take each other for granted, he made me feel special. He communicated to me that I was worth celebrating.

A greeting is such a simple thing, but it reaps big dividends. I've found that it's the little things in life that often have the greatest impact.

Even today as an adult, I am still overwhelmed with those childhood feelings of anticipation when I pull into the driveway of my parents' home with my own kids and honk the horn. I know Mom is waiting to rush out the door with joyful hugs. It's harder now, though, because Dad isn't there anymore. He's in heaven, and oh, how I miss him. So now when I go home, I'm overwhelmed with tears—tears of sadness and tears of gratefulness. My mind is flooded with flashbacks of all the times he *was* there to greet me. In my mind's eye, I can still see him clearly. I can almost feel his arms around me, and I remember his steadfast love for me.

Now I imagine him in heaven, just waiting for me to join him so that he can give me a big welcome-home hug. His enthusiastic greetings were always so heartfelt! I didn't appreciate them at the time; I just took them for granted. Now I know they were a celebration, a simple foretaste of the glorious celebration that awaits us as believers reunited in heaven.

Thanks, Dad, for being there to celebrate my home-comings. Your greetings were worth the trouble. They made me feel loved and special. Your example has encouraged me to take the time to greet my children and my husband when they come home. Our greeting in heaven is going to be the grandest celebration ever.

I can't wait to jump into your arms again.

Just a Regular Guy

❦

It was one of those typical late-night jam sessions in the dorm; a bunch of smelly college guys in dirty t-shirts and gym shorts sitting around joking about how they would one day be great successes.

"When you guys need to invest your millions, you'll have to come to *me* on Wall Street," the first one challenged.

"Maybe I'll give you my business," the budding entrepreneur laughed. "In ten years I expect to be CEO of my own corporation!"

Not to be outdone, the campus politician jumped in. "Who knows, but in a few years you guys might be visiting *me* at the White House!"

In this particular Ivy League dorm room, these dreams weren't all that unrealistic. As others joined the conversation, the guys began to discuss seriously the hard work and sacrifices that would be necessary for them to have any chance of fulfilling their dreams. A clear focus, connections, finances, and a commitment to long hours at the office would be required. Certain things would have to be postponed: vacations, a social life, relationships, family time. How important was success? What would be the cost of success? When would the cost become too high? What constituted success anyway? These were difficult questions, with no easy answers.

"We each have to ask ourself what really matters in life," Rob interjected as he looked at his friends. As he considered how to answer his own question, his thoughts turned to his dad.

In most people's eyes, my dad would be considered successful. He's a lawyer, he's a secretary in the Governor's cabinet, he's a leader in the church, and he's a good family man. But most important to me is the fact that he's my friend. That friendship has not been built without sacrifices on his part.

When I was growing up, Dad made it a point to be home for dinner. Nearly every night we ate together as a family, and Dad always asked us questions. He wanted to hear about my wrestling practice, Mom's Bible study, my sister's soccer match, and my brother's math project. And, boy, did we debate! Politics, faith, social issues—we covered them all.

At that point in my life I didn't think family meals were any big deal. Actually, some evenings I wished I could just grab something out of the fridge, zap it in the microwave, and eat whenever I wanted. Many of my friends got to do their own thing for dinner and their dads were hardly ever home. But my mom and dad had a different agenda. They wanted to build relationships. Family meals provided a time to work on these relationships.

Dad came to my wrestling matches, took me camping, and challenged me to think through my needs and academic goals for each year. He and I worked on rebuilding a car together. We still haven't finished it, but we've learned some great lessons working together!

During those years Dad turned down some offers from bigger firms, and he said "No" to attractive financial opportunities. Instead he made the decision that time with us kids was more important than having the most exciting job or being a bigger financial success. He knew that in the long run, it was family that mattered most.

I didn't appreciate what Dad was doing, all those years. In fact, sometimes "family time" was a pain in the neck. But now as I talk with the guys, I'm beginning to see things a bit differently. Several of these guys have a dad with an important, high-profile job, a dad who's made it on the fast track, or a dad who's been very busy becoming a success. Often this means that they have a dad who hasn't made time to build a close relationship with his son.

"Hey guys," Rob interrupted his reverie, "my dad's coming up this weekend to visit. Is it OK with you if he bunks in with us again?"

"Sure, Rob. I think it's cool that he comes up to visit, and that he stays with us and sleeps in a sleeping bag. He doesn't even seem to care that the bathroom for us forty guys is totally nasty! Your dad is just a regular guy. He's fun!"

Thanks, Dad, for modeling that no amount of success on the job is worth sacrificing family relationships. When I have a family I hope I will be able to make the difficult yet wise choices that you have made and develop a friendship with my son like the one we have. One day, I hope he'll want me to come stay in his messy dorm room!

Mr. Churchill's Advice

I'm only nine years old, so I haven't actually known my dad for very long, but he is a very special person in my life! When he isn't busy building new diners (he's the CEO of a restaurant chain), or playing with us kids, he likes to work in his home office. Sometimes I go there and sit in his big cozy leather chair. It's fun to spin around and around in it. If his desk is messy, I put his papers into neat piles, and I always look at *The Saying*. It's printed in black calligraphy and framed right above Daddy's desk. A man named Winston Churchill said it. He's Daddy's hero, and this is Daddy's favorite quote:

> *Never give in. Never give in.*
> *Never, never, never, never*
> *in nothing great or small, large or petty,*
> *never give in.*

Every summer since I can remember, we have gone to the beach for our family vacation. My dad loves physical activity and is very competitive so we play tennis and have bike races and bodysurf. When I first learned to bodysurf I was really scared. The waves were so big and unpredictable, and sometimes the undertow pulled me in directions I didn't want to go. I wasn't at all sure I wanted to surf, but Daddy kept encouraging me. He said, "You can do it, Melissa. I know you can."

So I would try, and a big wave would knock me down. But Daddy was there with me and he'd say, "You almost got it. Let's try again." One time I scraped my knee against the sand and it really hurt. I wanted to quit, but he wouldn't let me give up. He kept telling me how proud he was of me, and how much fun it would be when I got it. And you know what? He was right. I did learn and now I love to bodysurf!

I had a problem in school this year. My mommy was out of town and I had a lot of homework. Math homework—UGH! Two whole pages of long division! It was horrible. I just couldn't understand it or figure out how to do it. One night I was very upset. I told my dad I just couldn't do it and that I wasn't going to try any more. He said, "Melissa, don't give up." That night I didn't especially like Mr. Churchill.

Because it was already late, Daddy promised to help me with the math in the morning, before school. We got up extra early and we both had trouble with the math. Daddy even had to use the calculator! We didn't get all of it but we got most of it. When I got to class, I was glad Daddy hadn't let me give up.

This year Mommy and Daddy celebrated their seventeenth anniversary. I wanted to surprise them by making them a banner. Daddy has a really good computer in his home office he lets me use sometimes. I waited until my parents were busy, then I slipped into his office to work on my surprise. I was able to make a huge banner with lots of colors that said "Happy Annavarsary, Mom and Dad!"

I was very excited about my project *until* I saw my mistake. I had spelled "anniversary" wrong. I didn't know how to fix it without losing all my work, and I didn't want to ask Mom or Dad to help me because it would spoil the surprise. I thought my banner was ruined! I felt like crying. Then I looked up above Daddy's desk at Mr. Churchill's saying. *"Never give in ... "*

OK, I said to myself, *I won't give up. How can I do this?* I thought for a long time and I didn't quit. Finally it came to me how I could fix it. It turned out great. My little brother Bret helped me put up the banner. It was ten feet long! Mommy and Daddy were surprised and excited when they walked into the family room and saw it!

That day I decided Mr. Churchill might be right after all.

Thanks, Daddy, for teaching me never to give up. You are always so positive and you don't quit even when things are hard. You encourage me and you are helping me learn not to give up. I am so glad you are my daddy.

Big Brother

Hurrying home from school, the little guy slammed the front door and tossed his papers on the floor. Then he noticed the letter propped on the hall table—the place of prominence for important messages. Looking closely, he saw with surprise that it was addressed to him. He could hardly restrain himself as he began to tear open the letter.

Hey Brother,

I'm so glad you're coming up Saturday to see me. I'll feel like it's partly my birthday too.

Hope you had a nice party Friday afternoon. Didn't we have the greatest time together when Mom and Dad went away? Remember how we went to the ballgame and all the questions you asked and all the ice-cream cones we had? And remember how you and Sammy and I went swimming? Boy, I really enjoyed that weekend! And you only wet the bed once—of course, that time you nearly drowned both of us!

I just want you to know that I think that you're the greatest little brother a guy could ever hope to have—a brother who's so honest and fair at all times. When something bothers you, you just say, "Now, God, I don't know what to do. I want you to take this and work it all out for the best." And boy, be will, too! Aren't we glad that God loves us so!

Hope you are getting along fine in school. I'm so glad I went over and saw your new school. It surely is fine and pretty. I know you like your teacher lots. I remember how much I enjoyed third grade. I know you will, too.

Looking forward to seeing you on Saturday. Eight years old! I just can't believe it. You are really growing up. Be a good boy and look after everything for me.

Much love,
Your brother

This older brother taught his little brother to throw a baseball and to ride horseback. He gave him special books, read the Bible with him, and prayed with him. He always made his little brother feel like his equal rather than just a "kid brother." The relationship they established continued to grow, and when the younger brother's college sweetheart dumped him for someone else, his big brother comforted him. Years later when he was married, had a bunch of kids, and was financially strapped, his big brother bought him an automobile.

Did the encouragement of a brother who was ten years older have an impact on this little boy? It certainly did. This big brother has been a hero and an encourager to his little brother all his life. What greater gift could one receive from an older sibling?

Thanks, Brother, for loving me. You could have ignored me or cast me aside as the irritating kid I know I often was. Instead, you took time to encourage me and to let me know that I was somebody special. You have always been a role model to me. I pray that I will be able to teach my children to love one another in the same way that you have cared for me.

The Dad of the Neighborhood

 ❧

Snow was falling and piling up on the lawns, streets, cars, and bushes. It was 7:45 A.M. and we had already heard the thrilling news that school was *canceled* due to dangerous road conditions. I'm not sure who was more excited, we kids or our dad! *We* were always looking for an excuse not to go to school, and *he* was always looking for a reason to stay home and play with us. Because the weather was truly treacherous, he could in good conscience cancel his real-estate appointments for the day and spend it the way he most loved—being one of the kids!

Our dad is one of those fathers that every kid loves. He has a mischievous twinkle in his eye that often gives away his fun-loving nature—even when he's trying very hard to "be serious." His enthusiasm is infectious, and all of the kids in our neighborhood have long since adopted him as their own. He has sort of become the "Dad of the Neighborhood." When other people's fathers are absent, or too busy with work to just hang out with them, kids flock to our house.

So, it wasn't surprising this snowy morning that by about 8:30, a dozen of the neighborhood youngsters were at our front door, clamoring for my dad!

"What are we going to do today, Mr. G?" Rick asked breathlessly.

"Can we go to the lake?" panted Andy as he ran up the front walk. Dad just chuckled and his eyes danced.

"Did you keep your promise?" I chimed in.

"Have you no faith in me, boys?" he teased. "Of course I kept my promise. Look in the garage and see what I have waiting for you!"

Over the past few weeks as we kids had been praying for snowy days, Dad had been preparing for them. He had scoured thrift stores and secondhand sports shops to come up with a collection of not-new-but-still-useful hockey sticks. He had finally accumulated enough so that, by supplementing his collection with a few kitchen brooms ("Don't tell Mom!"), we could outfit two neighborhood ice hockey teams!

We lived right down the street from a lake that froze deep enough to skate on, and we had been wanting to take our competitive spirits to the ice for a long time. Dad was definitely the ringleader in this exciting escapade. He quickly helped divide us into fair teams, explained the rules, and we all headed to the lake.

As we crunched down the path, Mike from next door said to me, "I sure am glad your dad likes to do things with us. He always thinks up fun things for everybody to do!"

"He is pretty cool most of the time," I replied proudly.

"I'll never forget your birthday last year!" he continued. "Remember how he took all us guys out to the country?"

"Oh yeah, that was great!" I recalled. That had been another occasion when Dad had rounded up all the neighborhood guys for an adventure. He took us—and all our camping gear—to my grandparents' farm, where we camped in the woods for the weekend. We chased each other like wild animals, collected firewood, cooked our own dinners over a fire under Dad's supervision, and just generally had a great time being guys. We all liked to remember it as a very "manly" weekend, especially since it was in honor of my twelfth birthday.

Out there in the woods, Dad taught us how to shoot BB guns. Mom wasn't excited when she learned about that one, either, but we thought it was really great—all except for Andy, that is. He was accidentally shot in the seat of his pants. He was OK though, and he toughed it out. It really was a great weekend.

"Maybe we could do that again sometime," Mike said wistfully. "I like hanging out with your dad. He talks to me like he really thinks I'm someone."

"Well, that's 'cause he *does* think you're someone!" I explained. "He really likes you and thinks you're a pretty cool guy. He's told me so. He likes all of my friends. He just sometimes kind of thinks of all you guys as his kids!"

Mike nodded in agreement. "I can tell. He treats us just like he treats you and your family. Your house is the neighborhood hangout. I feel so at home with you guys."

At that, the conversation ended. We had reached the lake, and besides, twelve-year-old guys don't talk much about that kind of emotional stuff anyway. Still, I knew what Mike meant. My dad really was like a father to a lot of my friends. I didn't mind. It was great that they liked him, and that he liked them, too. As I shoved off onto the ice, I felt proud of my dad. He's a pretty good guy.

Thanks, Dad, for being someone I can be proud of. Thanks for hanging out with my friends and me so much. They really like you and it makes me feel important. We love the games you play with us and our manly camp-outs. I wouldn't trade you for anybody else's dad!

Sweating It Out

When Kristen was two, her parents divorced. Dad left home and Mom became the center of Kristen and her sister's little universe. They played together, laughed together, and loved each other enthusiastically. That's why, when Kristen turned five and Mom told her that their friend Don wanted to become her new daddy, Kristen was furious! She didn't want to share her mother with *anyone!* They had too much fun together as "the girls."

Having a man live with them simply couldn't be any good at all. Despite Kristen's vehement protest that it "just isn't fair!" her mother married Don and left on a honeymoon. Kristen doubted they'd come back from the trip at all, because it was obvious that Mommy loved someone else now, so she wouldn't really care about Kristen and Holly anymore.

When, to her great surprise, Mom and Don did return from their honeymoon, a small battle began to flourish in their house. It wasn't a struggle evident to many people. The battles were mostly waged in Kristen's little heart. She didn't really want a daddy.

Mommy had been fine on her own. It was hard to know how to talk to this grown-up man. How could he understand little girls? Would he be any fun to have around the house?

As the years went by, Kristen accepted the fact that Don was now her daddy. She called him Dad, and tried to get along with him without causing too many ripples in the relatively smooth family waters. After all, Mom was really happy, happier than Kristen ever remembered her being, and Holly, her sister, liked Don a lot. It was just hard sometimes for Kristen. She couldn't find any common ground with this man who was her "dad."

As Kristen matured into a bright young twelve-year-old, she realized that she differed from her Mom and her sister in a pretty significant way. They hated sweat, and Kristen *loved* it! She was a true athlete! She loved competition and she loved using her body to do thrilling things like run, skip, jump, and follow a ball down the field. Mom and Holly couldn't understand this. To them athletic activities were not enjoyable. Don, however, could relate to this side of Kristen. He knew the excitement of pushing oneself to the limit physically. He knew the thrill of victory.

Students in Kristen's elementary school competed every year for standards of fitness. The "Presidential Physical Fitness Test" was a national competition and

Kristen really wanted to excel in it. She wanted to prove to herself and to her peers that she could compete on a national level with other young girls and do well. Mom and Holly were happy for Kristen to have such a lofty goal, but they didn't quite understand what it meant for her to cut her "shuttle run" time by eight-tenths of a second, and to sustain a "flexed-arm hang" for twenty-nine seconds. To Kristen's excitement, however, Don understood. He said that he would help her reach her fitness goal. This was something they could do together.

Kristen wasn't in the habit of volunteering to do things with Don, but she quickly realized that he could be her key to athletic success that sixth-grade year. Thus began six months of mini-training-camp for Kristen and her "dad"! Every evening when Don returned from work, he and Kristen went running together. He timed her and encouraged her with her sit-ups. He raced her up and down the block to improve her quick-starts for the fifty-yard dash and the shuttle run. Perhaps the most precious moments of building their new relationship came when Don helped Kristen master the flexed-arm hang. He cut the ends off of a broomstick, creating a bar, which he held just above Kristen's head. She stood on a chair, clasped the bar, and hung with her chin just above the bar for as long as she could, while Don held it tightly in his arms. Sometimes when Kristen kicked her legs for that last gasp of strength to hang on, she kicked Don in the shins, but he never complained. As long as she could hold on, so would he.

In the spring when it came time to actually compete in all of these physical fitness categories, Don was Kristen's main cheerleader. All their work that year paid off! Not only did Kristen achieve the highest presidential standard, she nearly set school records as well! That was only the beginning. From that point on, Kristen had the confidence and encouragement to push herself toward her goals. She ran competitively all through high school, and kept training with Don after he got home from work.

Now, as a mother herself, Kristen still loves sports and still pushes herself to excel. Reflecting on that pivotal elementary school year, Kristen sees several turning points in her life.

"That's the year I really fell in love with sports, and it changed who I was. But that's also the year that I found common ground with my dad. We had something in common that I didn't share with my mother or my sister. He could encourage me in ways that nobody else could. That year drew us together in a new way, and we've continued to become closer ever since. Don has truly become my dad. He walked me down the aisle at my wedding. He is still my cheerleader and a favorite running partner! I understand now what he did for me and for our relationship that year. I'll never forget the picture of him holding that chopped-off broomstick for me, just so I could practice the bar hang. He held me up in so many ways as he stuck by my side that year. He has *never* stopped holding me up and encouraging me to pursue my dreams."

Thanks, Don, for not giving up when I didn't want you in my life. I am glad that you married my mother, and I am so glad that I can call you Dad! Thank you for persisting when we finally found common ground, and encouraging me in ways that only you could. I won't forget how you held me up that year, both as a struggling girl on a chopped-off broomstick, and as a child who was learning to love you.

Attitude of Gratitude

Dad was fairly bursting with enthusiasm when he walked into the house. "Guess what, kids!" he exclaimed. "I was able to sell the tractor! God has provided for us again!"

Our family's finances were tight. Mom was sick most of the time and Dad often worked two jobs to provide for us. With Mom's medical bills and five children, there were lots of expenses.

My dad grew up on a farm in the Midwest. He left school after the eighth grade in order to help out with the crops, but his education didn't end when school ended. He continued to read, especially philosophy and religion, and he became self-educated. He loved the writings of the Reformers, and around the dinner table he would engage us in lively discussions of great ideas and ponderous questions.

During my teen years, Mom was continually ill. Dad took care of her. He always arrived home in time to fix a family dinner and spend time with Mom. He took on many of the responsibilities she couldn't manage. He was the one who came to our school programs, drove us to our activities, dealt with our teenage rebelliousness, and wrote us letters when we were away. Looking back, I'm sure his life was not easy, but I didn't know it then.

Dad could have complained. He could have said, "It's not fair." He could have felt that Mom was a burden. He could have complained about the financial hardship. He could have moaned, "Why me?" But he didn't, and so we didn't. We kids never felt Mom was a burden. We simply pitched in and helped and enjoyed the times when she was healthy. We didn't realize we lacked materially. We knew things were tight, but they had always been tight. Sometimes Dad worried. He had bad days just like anyone, but usually he made the decision to be grateful for the things we *did* have.

Dad chose to have an "attitude of gratitude" toward what God had given him. He took particular joy in the simple things in life. For example, he was fascinated by weather. When a tornado rolled across the Michigan plains he would watch, exclaiming in awe at the incredible power of God's creation. When the peppers and tomatoes ripened he was thrilled, and proudly displayed them on the kitchen table. When he came in from work he entertained us with stories about his latest building project. (He was a contractor.) He always said how thankful he was that he was able to work and what a gift it was to have a job. When we had a financial need, he simply asked God to provide and then waited expectantly. The sale of the tractor was simply another one of God's provisions for us.

Dad not only lived in gratitude, he encouraged *us* to live with gratitude as well. As a young teen I became aware of my legs. Oh, how I hated them! I wanted movie-star legs, and mine weren't. I was self-conscious and embarrassed. Understanding my misery, Dad put his arms around me. "Esther," he said, "I think you are beautiful. Don't be concerned about your legs. Be grateful that you have two legs that work. You can run, walk, skip, and do just about everything you want to do. It's a tremendous blessing."

I still didn't like my legs, and at that time I didn't feel very grateful for Dad's advice. Even so, his example of being grateful for what you have instead of complaining about what you lack was taking root in my life, though I didn't realize it then.

It was years later that Dad's lesson impacted me in a more dramatic way. My husband and I realized that we were not going to be able to have our own children. Crushed expectations and tremendous sadness overwhelmed both of us, but we were not devastated. Instead there was a sense that God would provide, and we were simply grateful that we had each other. In his time we were able to adopt a little girl, the joy of our life, and we were grateful.

Thanks, Dad, for modeling for me the power of a grateful heart. Even when I didn't realize it, your example was seeping in, taking root, and preparing me for the times in my life that I would appreciate this important principle.

Dusty Golf Clubs

❦

Being an executive in a large retail chain is demanding. There's always pressure to increase the bottom line; pressure to expand and grow; pressure to beat the sales figures for the same day last year; pressure to beat the competition with the latest items; pressure to please the big stockholders.

The pressures at work aren't the only ones, however. There's also the pressure to be a good husband; to be the dad your kids need; to provide for your family; to encourage them. And then there are the community responsibilities and church responsibilities.... It never seems to end. Some days it's good just to get away from the pressures and play golf.

That's what Ogburn did. And it was good. Golf provided time for him to relax and unwind. On Wednesdays he took the afternoon off and headed to the club to meet his regular foursome. Saturdays were work days at the store but on Sunday, after church, he was back on the course, hitting those long drives. His was a full life—a busy life. But when Ogburn and his wife had two little boys in three years (and later a daughter and another son) life suddenly got a lot busier. It became harder to squeeze in those Wednesday and Sunday golf games and be at his sons' ballgames too.

One of Ogburn's favorite people was his mother-in-law, Toler. She had a delightful sense of humor. She was unusually interested in his business. He had a tremendous respect for her. Because she lived just an hour away, she came often to visit. Whenever she came, she and Ogburn relaxed in the den and talked.

One day when Ogburn came home from a round of golf, Toler asked him if he'd take her out to ride in his new car. As they drove around she said to him, "Ogburn, you have these two precious children. I know how much you love them and they love you. I know how much you want to be a good father to them and how much you want to be close to them when they grow up. But Ogburn, if you don't spend time playing with them when they are little, they won't want to be with you or talk to you when they are bigger. You might want to consider putting away those golf clubs and finding something you can do with these little boys."

The very next day Ogburn put his golf clubs in the closet. On Sunday afternoon, instead of heading to the golf course after church, he and his wife and sons climbed into the car and headed to the country. This quickly became a Sunday afternoon routine. Picnic basket in hand, they began to look for a little farm to buy, a place where they could find refuge from their busy lives and just be together.

After months of looking they found just the right place. There was a pasture and a creek, so they could have animals, and a very old house in need of work. No indoor plumbing, no electricity, no heat, but lots of potential! Best of all, it was just fifteen minutes from their home in town, so they would be able to come out often.

For the next twenty-five years Ogburn spent Wednesdays and Sunday afternoons with his growing family at the farm. Fixing up the old place, his kids learned basic carpentry. Watching sheep and cows give birth, they learned the facts of life. With Dad at their side they learned to ride horseback. It was at the farm that prayer meetings were hosted, church picnics were held, and many significant spiritual steps were taken. It was here that close relationships between a dad and his kids had time to develop.

While his golf clubs collected dust in the closet, Og's relationships with his children blossomed into tight friendships. These relationships forged a legacy that has continued to the third generation. I know this well because I've watched my husband, John, who is Ogburn's youngest son, build friendships with our five children at our own small farm.

Thanks, Ogburn, for being willing to listen to the wise advice of your mother-in-law and for acting on it. You put aside your own immediate desires in order to have time to work on what really mattered—your relationships with your children. Your example as my father-in-law is still having an impact today in the lives of your children, grandchildren, and great-grandchildren.

Giving Away Daddy's Little Girl

Most girls like to write letters, and we almost always save those we receive. Sometimes, when cleaning out my old boxes, I may throw away a few of those old letters—like the ones from jilted boyfriends, relatives I can't remember, and girls with whom I am no longer close—but there are some letters I will never throw away. The following is one of the most precious in my collection of "special papers." It's from the man who was number one in my life for my first twenty-three years. I know it was a hard letter for him to write, but it means the world to me.

October 20

Dear Allie,

As you now know, Will and I had that special "talk" about you a few weeks ago and I've just been waiting for him to find the time to finally ask you to marry him. I hope that by the time you read this you will have said "Yes!"

I want you to know how wonderfully happy and peaceful I am about this. We have always felt that Will is an exceptional young man and while I guess I have struggled some emotionally with the idea of "giving" you, my angel, over to some other man, still it hasn't been because of any hesitation about Will. And now that I'm adjusted to the idea, I'm fired up and ready to move! When you and Will decide, before God, that you are ready to marry, the time will be right, and Mom and I will do all we can to help you decide about all the details.

I am so impressed by Will's maturity and strength. I can't think of any ways I would want to change him. And when I think of him becoming a son to me, it brings me such a deep sense of gratitude and joy I can hardly describe it. He is clearly one in a million, chosen and anointed by God for a very special purpose. The goodness of God to me and to my children, as I ponder these things, is so overwhelming.

I love you so much, Baby. You are so precious and fine. God has blessed you exceptionally with grace and beauty, wisdom and good sense, a fine mind and rare temperament. I'm so proud of you both I'm about to burst! Thinking about you as a grown woman, beginning your adult life with God and with a husband, seeking to serve God together, is a breath-taking thought. I'm confident that the years ahead will be full of blessing and purpose. God has marked you as his own.

Much, much love,
Dad

Thanks, Dad, for giving me this written expression of your heart. I know I'll never understand what it meant to you to "give me away," but it fills me with joy to know that you love me and Will enough to give us your blessing. Thank you for the years you have prayed for both of us.

Your letter will always be a treasured gift to me.

Especially Chosen

My grandmother had died and I was at her house helping to clean out some of her things. She and I had been very close, so this wasn't an easy job. Even though she'd been sick for a long time, I couldn't believe she was actually gone! It still seemed so sudden. Sorting through a box of papers, I noticed an old letter with "private" written on it. It was a little faded, and I couldn't make out the handwriting. Not knowing whether to throw it out or save it, I opened it to read it and decide.

At first the letter didn't make sense to me, but then all of a sudden I was overwhelmed with conflicting emotions. I was reading a letter from my birth mother. Weeping and shaking, I picked up the phone and called my mom.

It wasn't that I was surprised to find out that I was adopted. I had known that as long as I could remember. It was just that finding the letter made my birth mother seem so much more personal. I wanted to do what I had done all my life—run to Dad—to find out why he and Mom hadn't given me the letter. It was written to me.

When I got through to my mom, she was concerned that I might be upset with her. Mom explained that she and Dad had planned to give me the letter on my eighteenth birthday. She was sorry that I found it the way I had.

"Tami," she said, "You know how much we love you. You are our precious daughter. We'll work through this together." My mom became very talkative because she wanted to make sure I wasn't upset with them. When I asked my dad about it (after he returned to Grandma's house) he just smiled and hugged me. *That* was all the reassurance I needed. He seemed to know I didn't want to talk right then, I just wanted to cry.

My relationship with Dad has always been special. There has never been anything we can't talk about. One of my earliest memories is of Dad and Mom explaining to me that I was special because I *was* adopted. They had longed for children and because Mom had not become pregnant, they'd prayed for God to choose a special baby for them. They loved to tell me the story of going to the hospital when I was born and bringing me, their especially chosen baby, home. As I grew up we prayed for my birth mother, thanking God that she brought me into the world and praying that she would know his love.

Of course there were times when I was little and wanted to get my own way that I'd say, "Well, my real mother or father would let me do this." Dad and Mom just laughed it off and I quickly learned that kind of manipulation wouldn't work.

Later, when I wanted to discover my "real" parents, they promised they'd help me if I still wanted to when I turned eighteen. They were never afraid to talk about *anything* with me. They were convinced that I was chosen by God to be their precious daughter.

Dad has always been good at talking and listening. Nothing embarrasses him or makes him feel uncomfortable. He doesn't get uptight. I can talk to him about periods, boys, dating, faith, friends, you name it. He likes hanging out with me and my friends. He likes me to pick out his clothes so he'll be sure to fit in.

He taught me to drive and to throw a baseball. He stayed up with me at night studying history, took me and friends camping, and he didn't even mind when the tent caved in or when we spilled soda all over the place. His sense of humor makes him fun to be with and comfortable to talk to. His quick laughter puts everyone at ease.

Recently he asked me about this older guy I had a

crush on. I told him all about the guy and why I liked him. Dad wasn't interrogating me or being nosy. He was just being Dad. He was just interested in me.

When I get married, I want to marry someone like Dad, someone who is a good communicator and who makes me feel especially chosen, just the way he has.

Thanks, Dad, for always being open to talk with me. I've always felt like I could talk to you about anything. You have given me the security of being chosen, and in your love, I catch a glimpse of the special love God has for me.

Winter Walks and Poetry Talks

It's a funny thing, but I always imagined that Robert Frost might look just like my dad. Dad has huge, hazel eyes full of warmth, a shiny bald spot on the top of his head, and an unusually youthful face with a large nose and pink cheeks. This resemblance to Frost is purely imaginary, but it symbolizes a bond between my dad and me that became stronger and stronger as I grew up.

Minnesota winters are long and dark and bitter cold. Temperatures routinely fall below zero, and no one goes out at night unless he has to—no one except Dad and me, that is.

As a young child, one of my fondest memories is of Dad calling in an excited voice, "Punkin, get your coat and let's go explore the night!"

Off we'd go, tightly wrapped in coats, hats, and mittens. A jet-black sky would be our canopy and the stars our light. As soon as our eyes grew accustomed to the darkness, Dad would begin to point out the silhouettes of the trees against the black sky. We'd laugh as our boots crunched the snow and we'd have fun making puffs with our breath. Dad might whistle a favorite tune or we'd talk about the beauty around us. Sometimes we would just walk in companionable silence.

Nature, words, and music were his three loves and he shared them with me. His favorite was poetry, and often we'd curl up together to read Robert Frost. Dad knew many of his poems by heart and on our walks he would recite them for me. By the time I entered middle school, I'd caught his love for words. Often, I would go into the woods by myself to write my own poems.

Language and music became my companions during my turbulent teen years. Those years were especially hard for me as I watched my parents' marriage fall apart.

Neither Mom nor Dad spoke ill of the other to us kids. Instead they each made it very clear to us that the problem was with their relationship, and not with us girls. Again and again they told us that their love for us had not changed. Both worked hard at continuing to build strong relationships with each of us, and both made an effort to spend time with us. I knew their sadness. They didn't hide it, but they didn't dwell on it either.

During those years, Dad often took me out on dates. We frequently went to breakfast or to the movies. He listened to my heartaches. When my adolescent heart was broken and I cried, "Dad, why don't boys like me?" He gave me hope saying, "Honey, those guys aren't good enough. One day you will meet a boy who really values you." Dad made me feel like a treasure—an individual with great worth.

My teen years were difficult and my parents' pain was great. As Dad always said, "Life isn't easy." Yet there was still the shared bond of poetry, music, and language. Dad made it a point to continually strengthen that common thread between us. He'd often remind me of some of his favorite Frost lines:

> *The way a crow*
> *shook down on me*
> *the dust of snow*
> *from a hemlock tree*
> *has given my heart*
> *a change of mood*
> *and saved some part*
> *of a day I had rued.*

It didn't really surprise Dad when, in my thirties, I published my first book. He understood my love of words and I knew he was especially proud of me. I had caught his love. And I had learned that when we nurture a common love, we build strong cords that enable us to stay close through hard times.

Recently I gave away one of Dad's treasures—his old, battered copy of Robert Frost's poems. I gave it to my son, for he, too, has caught a love for words, a love that now binds three generations.

Thanks, Dad, for giving me your love of words, poetry, and music. You didn't force it on me. You simply shared your joy in it with me, and I happened to catch it. This common thread we have shared has grown into a strong cord that kept us close during difficult times. Now the cord is touching your grandson, binding the three of us together in a special way.

Late-Night Ice Cream

It was well past my bedtime. My brothers and sisters were sound asleep in their rooms, but I was still wide awake under the covers. I was listening for the familiar sound of my dad's car pulling up in the driveway, signaling that he was finally home. *It's almost time!* I thought as I saw the clock on my bed-side table glowing 10:15. Mom's light had gone out about twenty minutes earlier, so I knew she was probably fast asleep. She always tried to stay awake on Monday nights, but sometimes Dad's meetings went too late even for her. Besides, she didn't have the same reason I did for staying awake!

I heard a car door shut and then the front door squeak as Dad tried to open it quietly. I scurried out of bed, pulled on my slippers, and glided down the stairs. He was taking off his tie and smiled mischie-vously at me as I slipped through the door of his study.

"I'm glad you're still awake, Allie," he said. "I've been looking forward to this all day! Is there any-thing for us tonight?" I bounced eagerly on my toes, ready for our weekly treat. "There sure is! Breyers vanilla—your favorite!" A huge grin spread across his face.

"Did you help Mom with the shopping today?" he asked with a knowing wink.

"You bet!" I grinned back proudly. "Let's go!"

We sneaked quietly into the kitchen, turning on as few lights as possible. We always pretended that Mom didn't know what went on on Monday nights after she innocently went to sleep. That was half the fun! I'm sure she had probably figured us out long ago, but she let us have our special time each week without reminders that "Tomorrow is a school day!"

As Dad and I scooped heaping bowls of ice cream, we chatted about the day. He told me some of the things that he and his committee had discussed at their meeting that night. I didn't really understand all of it, but it felt good to listen anyway, because Dad always talked to me like a real grown-up. He asked me how my tennis lesson had been that afternoon, and what I had learned in social studies class. We talked about who I sat with at lunch, and he reminded me that it was always nice to try and sit with people who looked lonely. He told me about a horse he had seen earlier that week, and how beautiful it was. Mostly, we just talked about simple things, and enjoyed our ice cream. It felt like there was no one else but the two of us awake in the whole world, and I loved every minute of it!

I truly loved ice cream, but we could have been eating cold spaghetti for all I cared. The real treat for me was having this private time with Dad. In a house as full of children as ours was, there wasn't a lot of Dad to go around, but he always found ways to make each of us feel special. None of the other kids ever shared late-night ice cream dates with him. That was *my* private treat! Even now, as a grown-up, I still love to go home to Dad and have a bowl of ice cream and an easygoing chat about life.

Thanks, Dad, for indulging with me! I got my love of ice cream from you, and learned a lot in the process! I learned about you and the things you love. I learned that you look forward to spending time alone with me as much as I look forward to being with you. I learned that you care about the small details of my life, and I learned that a late-night treat with Dad is a simple way of building a significant friendship.

Honor Your Mother

When I was growing up, my dad was a naval aviator who flew in and out of Norfolk, Virginia. He loved his job, especially when he had extra time to fly over the beautiful Northern Neck area of Virginia. Clean, clear rivers framed by lush pastures brought him great joy, and he began to hunger to own some of this land.

One of our favorite family activities was searching for property together.

After two years of exploring and looking, my parents found *their dream:* fifteen acres of land along a great river just waiting to be fished. Their long-range plan was eventually to build a house for themselves and then divide the acreage into four lots, one for each of their children. When they looked into the future, they envisioned a Heerwagen family community, with children and grandchildren playing together. The more they talked and planned, the more their dream became my dream as well.

Because I was the youngest of four I was around after the big kids left home. I was Dad's "baby girl," and the two of us were especially close. We spent lots of time talking together about all sorts of things, including *the dream*. I knew he loved me and I knew he loved Mom. They operated as a team. He had tremendous respect for her and I knew that as hard as I tried, I couldn't work them against each other. When I ran to Dad for permission for something questionable his response invariably was, "What did your mother say?" The way he honored her in everything instilled in me the habit of honoring her as well.

When Dad was sixty he was diagnosed with cancer. We were devastated. Three of us kids had become engaged that year, so it was a very emotional time for the family. A couple of months before he died, Dad walked me down the aisle to give me away in marriage. At the time I didn't completely realize how sick he was. He didn't want to ruin my wedding.

Two years after Dad died Mom called to tell me that she had sold nearly half of their property. Hearing this news, I burst into tears, sobbing uncontrollably over the phone. In a sense, I was reliving his death. Mom's news shook me with the realization that Dad's dream would never come to fruition, and that our family would never be the same without him.

In my pain and desperate desire to cling to Dad, I made my mother promise right then that she would retain one lot for me. She agreed. Six more years went by before Mom asked me to reconsider selling. For many good reasons she felt strongly that we needed to sell all the land.

Deep within my heart I knew that I needed to bring closure to this situation. For years I'd held onto the land and with my husband Jim had dreamed of building a retreat center there for our family and friends. How we wanted our two little boys to enjoy the romance of the tidal waters, the freedom of fishing, the tranquility of the setting, and the realization of their Grandad's dream.

Now, with Mom's request heavy on my mind, Jim and I set aside a weekend alone to camp on the property and pray about how to respond. It was a glorious late August day, just right for camping. We arrived on Friday in time to set up our tent and enjoy a quiet retreat together to consider Mom's request.

By Saturday afternoon I wasn't quite as determined to hold onto the land. A certain verse of Scripture kept coming to mind:

"Honor thy mother."

Mom was convinced that it was best to sell.

"But what about honoring my father?" my heart screamed. "What about *his* dream, *his* vision? What about *my* need for this connection to him?"

Then it dawned on me. *To honor my mother would*

be honoring my father. He would want that more than anything else. More than preserving his dream, more than building a family community. In honoring my earthly father I would be honoring my heavenly Father.

With this realization came a deep sense of peace, the kind that God alone can give. I knew this was his answer.

With Jim's agreement I phoned my mom to tell her to sell the land. Her relief confirmed my decision. How grateful I am to her for letting me go through that painful process. How thankful I am to God for answering my prayer for guidance and in the process teaching me a valuable lesson.

Thanks, Dad, for giving me dreams. And yet, thank you also for instilling in me from a young age that honoring my mom is more important than clinging to my dreams. You have taught me in a fresh way that when I choose to honor my Heavenly Father by obeying him, he will take care of all the other things (like dreams) in the way he knows is best for us.

Welcome to the Family

"I'm in love!*"* I said to myself. *"I can't believe it. I think this is really it!"*

Jim and I had been friends for several years, but within the last year we'd begun dating seriously. Recently we'd both become more sure than ever that we wanted to spend the rest of our lives together. Because he was in another state in graduate school and I was finishing college in our hometown, ours was a long-distance romance. He got home as often as he could, but between visits we ran up huge phone bills.

Jim's parents lived close to my campus, so I saw them often. I suppose I could have felt awkward spending time with the parents of the boy I was serious about, but in this case it didn't seem so. Jim's parents made me feel welcome and comfortable. I knew they liked me. But it wasn't just me that they liked; the very atmosphere in their home radiated acceptance. The message for all of the kids who visited was, "If you're my child's friend, you are welcome here." Their spirit wasn't evaluative or critical, just open and welcoming. Their lifestyle was simple and genuine.

Jim's dad, Bill, was easy to talk to. He was also thoughtful and creative. I loved to slip into the kitchen to see the family blackboard. Every morning, Bill rose early and wrote a thought for the day on it. Some days it was a Bible verse, others a simple word of wisdom. Coming up with something different each day took a lot of creative work, but Bill didn't fail. Every day there was a special message for the family!

Jim was still away at school on his birthday, but that didn't stop his parents from celebrating. They invited me to a birthday dinner in honor of their absent son! I suspect they knew I might be missing Jim, so they had me come to a party. We laughed as we looked at slides of Jim as a little boy. One picture of him sitting on their wooden steps reminded them that Jim was a "handyman" even as a small boy. He had tried out his new saw on those very same steps. By the time his parents had discovered his "project" the steps were beyond repair!

Being with his folks and having fun even without Jim made me feel all the more welcomed into this special family. Since I didn't have a car, Bill would come for me, and at the end of my visit he would take me back to campus. Those car rides enabled us to get to know each other better. One trip home will forever stand out in my memory. I had eaten a lovely dinner with Jim's folks. Now it was late on a cold, snowy night. Jim and I were soon to become engaged. As Bill pulled up to campus, he stopped the car and turned to me with an unusually thoughtful expression.

"Ann," he began, "ever since I accepted Christ as my Savior when our kids were younger I have been praying for God to bring Christian spouses for my children. I've prayed especially for Jim that God would bring into his life a wonderful Christian girl, and I have no doubt that you are the answer to my prayers."

That statement made a powerful impression upon me as I prepared to marry Jim. I realized that I was the answer to a father's prayer for his son. It was the greatest wedding gift that could be given. But Bill's words were more than a one-time gift. They were a promise of protection. Over the years, when tough times have come in our marriage and I have wanted to "quit," I have remembered Bill's gift. It has reassured me and given me the discipline to work through our difficulties, instead of withdrawing.

Today as I look at my teenagers, Mark and Laura, I pray for *their* future mates and I pray that somewhere they, too, have a future father-in-law who is praying for them. I know their grandfather Bill is.

Thanks, Bill, for praying for me, your daughter-in-law,
before you even knew me. Thanks for welcoming me
into your family and for giving me the most special
blessing a father-in-law could give—
your prayers and your acceptance.

A Man of Conviction

⌒

Stuffing the last bite of toast into my mouth and wiping the jelly drippings with my sleeve, I jumped out of my chair and headed into the den. It was *that time* again. Our daily after-breakfast-before-school routine. I didn't argue about it. There was no point. The habit was too ingrained in me. In fact I'd never known a time when we didn't do it. It was just part of being a member of the Tucker family.

Curling up in my regular spot on the couch alongside my twin sister and two brothers, I waited as Mom pulled out the old, family Bible storybook and began to read a brief selection. When she finished, we got down on our knees and Dad led us in prayer. Each of us prayed our own prayer, whatever we felt like talking to God about, and then with quick "Amens" we rushed out to carpools and buses for school.

Our family devotions weren't a big deal, they were simply a regular habit that grew out of my parents' convictions. Both Mom and Dad had a deep faith—a faith that was the foundation of our family. Family devotions weren't something Dad insisted on because he thought "we kids" needed them. He knew *he* needed them too. Each night after everyone else was in bed, I could see across the hall to Mom and Dad's bedroom. There I'd see Dad kneeling beside their bed praying.

Sundays meant church. In the morning we went to a formal service. In the evening we went to a more relaxed service at the Salvation Army, where we'd hear glorious testimonies of God's work in individual lives. Occasionally, I'd peek at Dad and glimpse a tear trickling down one cheek as he listened to someone sharing how God had worked in his or her life.

Dad was a firm disciplinarian. One thing that would make him really angry was if we talked back to Mom. We could count on swift punishment for that action. He simply would not tolerate disrespect. "You may disagree with us, but it must be done with respect," he always said. We quickly learned that we couldn't get away with verbal abuse, and although I didn't like it at the time, my respect for him and for Mom grew.

Dad's faith wasn't compartmentalized. Instead, his inner convictions impacted every area of his life and ours. When my sister and I wanted trendy shoes, Dad said "No."

"But *everyone* has them!" I wailed.

"We're not everyone," he responded, "and those shoes aren't good for your feet."

When my sister and I were teens and involved in a series of parties celebrating our social debut (an old southern tradition), Mom and Dad were asked to co-host a party with some of the other parents. As plans for the party materialized, Dad realized that the other parents planned to serve alcohol. After all, this was what *everyone* did. He went to the other hosts and simply said that he and Mom did not feel it was right to serve alcohol to teenagers, and if the other hosts decided to do so, he and Mom would have to excuse themselves from hosting. He was polite in apologizing for the dilemma that this posed for the others, but he knew he had to be true to his convictions. In the end the other parents agreed with him and we had a wonderful, alcohol-free party.

Even though Dad may have seemed rigid to some, he did have a good sense of humor. Once, when he was trying to cut back on sweets, I wrote out Bible verses on the dangers of gluttony and taped them to the ice cream he had in the freezer. Later, I found taped to my mirror a verse from 1 Timothy 5:13 warning against the dangers of being a "busy-body!"

Dad also taught us to be thankful. "Kids," he would say, "you can never thank your mother enough for what she's done for you." When I was about ten, he came to breakfast one day and said to Mom, "Honey, you've been cooking big breakfasts for many years. We are so thankful to you for working so hard. Now it's my turn to cook breakfast."

Dad began to cook every day! It took him a while not to burn the toast and to get the eggs just right, but his act of thoughtfulness in appreciating Mom was another example of his inner convictions making a genuine impact upon the way he lived his daily life.

Thanks, Dad, for being a man of convictions. Your hunger to live out the faith that God has called us to has given me the desire to be a woman of conviction. Your example in standing for your beliefs has given me the courage to take unpopular stands for what I know to be God's truth. I pray that my children will have the strength of character that you have.

All-Night Spellers

༄

Fourth grade was hard, *real* hard, for young Dave, and spelling was the hardest thing about it!

"Illegibble. Ulegibel?" No matter how hard he tried, it seemed like he could never get the word "illegible" right. And there were so many others he couldn't get right either! He clenched his teeth, squeezed his pencil as tightly as he could, and tried once more, with his teacher breathing down his neck. "Ilejibel?" Her hand clamped down on his thin shoulder blade and he knew it still wasn't right. Dave's heart thumped down to the pit of his stomach.

"Well, Dave," she sighed, "You'll have to write it out twenty-five times this time. And if you don't get it tomorrow, that's five times twenty-five, and five times that the next day. I hope you know your multiplication tables better than your spelling words." Dave's ears started to burn. "You owe me more words than I care to count, and I want you to hand them *all* in tomorrow, correctly spelled." At that precise moment the bell rang, rescuing Dave from the further humiliation of tears, which were quickly rising to the surface. "TOMORROW, DAVID!" echoed in his ears as he ran blindly out the classroom door.

As he trudged home, mentally calculating how long it would take him to spell all those words correctly, Dave's pace got slower and slower. For every word missed on a spelling test you had to write it five times correctly, and if you missed it again, like he had today, you had to write it five times five times, and so on. Miles of misspelled words stretched before Dave's eyes.

The problem was that he just couldn't seem to get them right, no matter how hard he tried! This time he was really sunk, because he not only had "illegible" to copy tonight, but also five other words that he'd been getting wrong for so long that he was going to have to copy them more than three thousand times! There was no way he could do it! He would just have to quit school. That was the only way he could escape.

So far, Dave had managed to keep from telling his parents about this awful problem, but this time Dad was sure to find out and Dave really didn't want that! Dad always expected him to do his best at everything. This was a humiliating problem. He *should* be able to spell. What was wrong with him?

All through dinner Dave kept his eyes on his plate,

dreading telling his parents that he couldn't go back to school. He'd just have to become a nine-year-old dropout. Maybe he could get a job somewhere.

"Dave, is something wrong?" Mom asked with concern. "You haven't said a thing all through dinner." Dave gulped, and screwed up all his courage. There was no point in hiding it—they'd find out eventually anyway.

"Well, I'm afraid I'm going to have to quit school," he said as calmly as he knew how.

"Oh really?" Dad's eyebrows shot up. "And *why,* exactly?"

"Because I'm a spelling failure," Dave mumbled under his breath.

"Let's get one thing straight," Dad replied calmly. "No son of mine is, or ever will be, a failure. We love you no matter what. Now, what precisely is the problem you're having?"

As Dave explained his miserable situation, a twinkle appeared in his father's eye. In his misery Dave didn't notice it, but he was surprised and relieved when at the end of his teary explanation Dad said, "Well, it looks like we have only one solution to this problem. I'm going to have to help you with those words!" Dave couldn't believe his ears.

"Really? You mean you'll write the words with me?" Dave asked, hope rising quickly in his chest.

"Not exactly," Dad replied. "This is still your problem, and you have to do the assignment. I can't do your work for you. But, I'm going to encourage you all the way through. We'd better get started, though. I'll help Mom with the dishes, and you go sharpen about ten pencils and get a pad of paper. We've got some work to do!"

All through that night, Dave wrote his spelling words. He wrote "illegible" so many times he started getting it right without thinking about it. Even the other words came naturally after a while. And Dad sat by his side *all night*, encouraging him and even making it fun. Dad set goals for Dave. After he wrote two hundred words, they went outside and shot baskets for ten minutes. After five hundred, somewhere around 11:00 P.M., they snuck out to the nearest gas station and got huge Cokes and candy bars. "Sometimes sugar helps you get the job done quicker!" Dad teased. It seemed as if he were actually enjoying himself! Having Dad around helped Dave a lot. When Dave got sleepy and his eyes drooped, Dad tried out his new jokes on him and Dave had to laugh at how silly they were. "Don't become a comedian, Dad!" he joked. "Don't become a professional speller, Dave!" Dad kidded back. It was all in fun.

"You have to laugh at these things, Dave," his dad explained. "Sometimes it's too easy to get down on yourself for things you don't do well. But always remember, there are hundreds of things you're just *great* at! Nobody can be perfect at everything."

Sometime not long before dawn, Dave finished his last word. Dad cheered for him and carried him around the dark house on his shoulders. "Congratulations, Son! You are now an official All-Night Speller. There aren't many of them in this world!"

Dave gave Dad a sleepy smile and a hug. "Thanks for helping me and for not being mad, Dad. I still may never be a good speller, but at least we got the job done, right?"

Dad smiled. "That's right, Son. I'm proud of you for sticking it out and finishing. I knew you could do it!"

Thanks, Dad, for reassuring me that I was not a failure. You turned my sense of worthlessness into a powerful lesson of perseverance and doing one's best. You encouraged me like no one else could, and you kept me from giving up. I couldn't have done it without you!

The Key to Your Heart

❧

Knock, Knock! Someone pounded on the front door and a muffled voice called out, "Is my date ready yet?"

"Yes, she is. Come on in!" Ann laughed and opened the door for her father, who had stepped outside only seconds before.

"My, aren't you looking lovely tonight!" he exclaimed, presenting her grandly with a bouquet of roses. "Would you do me the honor of accompanying me to dinner this evening?"

"Why certainly," Ann replied, smiling and rolling her eyes slightly. At fifteen, she was alternately amused and annoyed by Dad's sometimes silly ideas. "Let me just put these in a vase and we'll be off. They're really lovely, by the way. Thank you."

"Not half as lovely as you are ..." Dad whispered to her retreating back, as she headed off toward the kitchen.

Several hours later, comfortably installed in an intimate booth at the fanciest restaurant Ann had ever seen, they made their dessert choices and settled back into the cozy chairs. Dad sighed happily and loosened his belt a few notches. Ann squirmed. She had had about enough of this ladylike stuff and was ready to jump into some comfy blue jeans. Dad cleared his throat and she looked up, expectant. Dad never did things without a reason, so she knew that there had to be some sort of motivation for bringing her out on this "date." What could he be planning? She squirmed a little more as he cleared his throat and said with a serious tone, "Annette." Hearing her full name, Ann knew that something big was up. She was pretty sure she wasn't in trouble. So what could it be?

"Annette, you are a beautiful young woman. You are outwardly appealing and inwardly lovely. Your pure heart and love for the Lord shine through you. Your mother and I are so proud of you." Ann blushed at all this praise.

"Mom and I have prayed that these qualities and others would develop in you ever since you were a baby. I wanted to bring you out tonight to celebrate the godly young woman you are becoming, and to talk with you about what this will mean in your life as you mature and grow. I understand that it is really hard to be a teenager today, and even more difficult to be one that is pure and right in God's eyes. I want to take this opportunity to share with you some of the specific things I am praying for you, and to tell you what some of God's standards are for your life, particularly when it comes to dating, love, and marriage.

Marriage? Who's getting married? Ann wondered to herself. But she kept her words inside and instead took a bite of the chocolate sundae that had just been placed in front of her. "I'm listening," she managed to say through the hot fudge and nuts, and her dad continued.

"Ever since the day you were born, I have prayed that God would one day bring the right man into your life for you to marry. I know that it probably seems like the distant future now, but one day it won't, and I want you to know that we've prayed for this special man for fifteen years, and will continue to pray for him! I truly believe that God has a special person chosen for you, and that when he decides the time is right, God will bring this person into your life. Isn't that exciting to think about?"

Ann nodded, still trying to manage the sundae.

"Believe it or not," Dad continued, "the Bible has a lot to say on the subject of dating and marriage." Ann looked up, her interest piqued. Dating, after all, was a little more relevant to life right now than marriage. "The Bible speaks of ways that we can prepare for the marriage God has intended for us, and that should affect how you as a Christian approach dating.

Let me show you some of the verses I'm talking about."

Dad pulled out the flattened Bible that he always carried in his back pocket. It was slightly curved from years of being sat upon.

"Here in Jeremiah 29:11, God says that he knows the plans he has for us, plans to prosper us and to give us a future and a hope. He *knows* who he is saving to be your husband, and his choice is a good one! Then God reminds us in 2 Corinthians 6:14 not to be 'yoked together' with unbelievers. That means that he wants you to date and marry a man who believes in him and loves him as much as you do.

"This is all part of God's perfect plan for your life. And there's one more important guideline that we're given in the Bible about dating and marriage. We are clearly told in Hebrews 13:4 to honor marriage, and to keep the marriage bed pure. In order to do this, we are only to have sexual relations within marriage. Now, I know this is not a very popular view in today's world, and that it's a really hard standard to live up to, but this is clearly God's will for his children, and he asks us to abide by this plan for our own good. Do you understand what I mean?"

Ann nodded mutely, astonished to hear her dad speaking so candidly about this topic. This was all familiar to her, but she and her father didn't have these kinds of conversations very often. Dad continued, "I know that when I dated girls in high school and college, the sexual temptation was almost unbearable. It was especially tough when your mom and I were engaged to be married. We wanted so much to give in to our desire for one another! But with God's grace we were able to wait until our wedding day, and we have confidence that you will be able to do the same, if you make a decision *now* to do so.

"This leads me to the real reason why I wanted to have a special evening with you tonight, Ann. I want to ask something very important of you. Do you understand what a covenant is?"

Ann nodded and replied, "It's a holy promise between people and God, that must never be broken."

"Exactly," Dad replied. "I would like you to enter into a covenant agreement with me and with God. Marriage itself is a special kind of covenant, but let's just call this a 'premarriage covenant.' I want to ask you to make a promise to yourself, to me, and to God, that you will pray for the man God has prepared for you, and that you will remain sexually pure until the day you marry him. I know this is asking a lot, probably even more than you realize right now, but don't you agree that it is one of the most important decisions you could ever make?"

"Yes, Dad," Ann agreed, thoughts swirling in her

mind. *A covenant. What a heavy thought. If I make this promise now, I'll have to live with it forever. But I know Dad's right. I want to do what God says is the best thing. I want to have a 'future and a hope' with the man I marry someday.*

"I can do it, Dad. I will agree to the covenant. I promise God, you, and myself that I'll pray for my husband every day from now on, and that I'll wait until I marry him to have sex. I know God's design for marriage is the best." She saw tears fill her dad's eyes as she smiled at him.

"I'm so proud of you, Ann. There will be days when this will be the hardest thing you've ever had to do, but I know you can keep the covenant. I knew you would agree with me that this is something important enough to do. Here, I brought you a present to celebrate." He handed her a small gold box tied with a silk ribbon, explaining, "This is a symbol of the covenant we have made together before God. I bought this as a reminder for you that God will help you to keep your commitment, and that Mom and I will always be praying for you."

As Ann took the lid off the box, she drew in her breath quickly—it was beautiful! Nestled in the cotton was a golden key on a delicate chain. "This represents the key to your heart, Ann. Wear this every day as a reminder of the covenant, and on your wedding day, take it off and give it to your husband, because your heart will belong to him then." Even Ann's eyes grew misty as Dad fastened the chain around her neck. She stood and gave him a big hug, and as they left the restaurant hand in hand, she whispered quietly, "I love you, Daddy."

Thanks, Dad, for having the courage to broach the subject of sexuality with me. I know it must have been uncomfortable for you, but it showed me that you truly cared. You enabled me to see that God's plan is the best way, and you helped me make the commitment to live a life of purity. I'm still wearing the golden key, Dad, praying and waiting for the man God has chosen for me. I hope he's a lot like you!

A Friend to All

It was one of those late-night knocks on the door. Struggling to get his robe fastened, Dad headed down the steps to see who was out at this hour. Opening the door, he came face to face with Cephas. Stammering with anger and embarrassment, Cephas began to explain: "It's my wife, Mr. Harvey. She's done kicked me out again."

"Oh, Cephas, I'm so sorry," Dad replied. "Come on in and we'll fix you up with something to eat and a place to sleep."

This wasn't the first time Cephas had arrived on our doorstep in trouble, nor would it be the last. Cephas seemed to have troubles aplenty. If it wasn't his wife, it was his son or some other wayward relative. More often, Cephas was short of funds, and Dad always helped him out. I remember once asking, "Dad, why do you put up with Cephas?"

"Why, he's my friend!" Dad answered with surprise. "I'd help you or your friends if they were in trouble, so of course I'll help Cephas."

Cephas was the local maintenance man who

worked at the hospital in our small southern town. His was a large black family with plenty of needs. Dad, along with many other families in our neighborhood, employed him to help with painting and other household projects. In their spare time he and Dad would go shrimping or pecan picking together. It didn't seem the least bit odd for Dad to call Cephas his friend.

Dad himself was a small-town lawyer who served in the state legislature. Later in life he was elected lieutenant governor. In his profession he came into contact with every conceivable type of person, and he treated them all with respect. He expected us to do the same. Even though we grew up in the segregated South—before civil rights and political correctness—we were taught to always treat folks with dignity. Racial slurs or unkind jokes simply weren't permitted—ever. Dad had no patience for discrimination.

We kids often joined Dad on the campaign trail. We'd stand at the gates of a small textile mill and greet the laborers as they changed shifts. Dad had an unusual ability to connect with each person. He might ask them a personal question like where they had gone to school, or how their family was doing. Often he and the person he was addressing would know someone in common. If the person had a problem, he'd pull a piece of paper out of his pocket and make a quick note to see how he could help them out. When we got home he'd be sure to pull out those folded notes and follow through on them. To Dad this wasn't just politicking; it was serving. He was the same person at home that he was in public.

During the years he was lieutenant governor, he was assigned a state policeman who provided security when he appeared in public. Jeremiah wasn't someone who merely served Dad; he became an extended family member. Graduations, weddings, family celebrations—Jeremiah was always there. Yes, he worked for Dad, but he quickly became Dad's friend as well.

When I was nineteen, I went to the Democratic National Convention with Dad. Meeting senators, presidential hopefuls, and especially movie stars was a real high for me. I was very impressed with the powerful, glittery folks. But Dad wasn't. He had just as much fun with a small-town delegate as he did with the high-profile power broker. With Dad, *position* in life wasn't nearly as important as the *person* created in the image of God.

Today, as I raise my own three kids, I am so thankful for my dad's example. Because my husband is the CEO of a large company, we have the opportunity to meet with various heads of state, visit at the White House, and entertain many high-profile people. Yet, our street-friend Albert, the recovering alcoholic with whom we worship on Sundays, and the desert nomads we met in Pakistan, where we sponsor a school, have also become true friends. I want my kids to catch their grandfather's perspective: that each person is valuable, no matter where God has placed them in life.

Thanks, Dad, for raising us with your visible example that a person's position in life doesn't matter nearly as much as the person. Your life demonstrated for us how to respect and to value each person just because God created them. I pray that our kids will walk in this legacy that you have given to each of us.

Lima Beans and Post-it Notes

❦

Trying to summon up the energy to get going for my early class, I sat on the edge of my bed and stared at the mess. Dirty clothes were piled in the corner, books were spread out on the floor, and old coffee cups topped with curious white mold were strewn about my small room. Then I glanced at the stack of sheet music on my desk. There were all the Italian lyrics I still had to memorize for my opera audition.

Feeling overwhelmed, I pulled my comforter more tightly around me and fought anxiety. *What if I didn't get the audition? What if I bombed in the rehearsal? What if I never made it in opera?*

Then I glanced up at the faded Post-it note. Stuck up on my wall in the midst of souvenir programs and playbills, it said simply, in manly script, "Remember your daddy loves you."

That's one thing I can count on, I mused as a smile crossed my face and I hopped out of bed. I was in graduate school at the Manhattan School of Music. Striving to make it in opera in New York City was a challenge. Competition was keen and my finances were tight. I sang in a church, I sang in a restaurant, and I auditioned for everything I could. Some days I got lucky breaks and got a job, other times I experienced the pain of rejection. It's a fickle world out there and I never knew exactly how the reviews would go. But one thing I knew for sure. My daddy loved me!

It was something I'd always known. When I was little Dad used to take me on father-daughter lunch dates. His favorite place was the K&W Cafeteria in our small town. We always piled our plates high with food, and we always had green lima beans. They were the specialty at the K&W and we loved them.

It wasn't unusual for another businessman to stop by our table while we were eating and say, "Who's this pretty little girl you have with you today, Sir?"

Dad would respond, "Why, it's my favorite daughter, Lucy." (He only had one daughter!) I, of course, would beam with pleasure. Dad's taking me out always made me feel special. He was a very busy man with a growing business, but he still made the effort to be with me.

Dad was of the "old school," in which many men weren't comfortable verbally expressing their feelings. So I knew he worked hard to say to me over and over in a teasing, gruff voice, "You know your daddy loves you?" It was a game we played, and he'd often sneak up behind me, throw his arms around me, and ask me that question. I never got tired of being asked.

Both Dad and I are very driven perfectionists. Folks would call us "Type A" people. It's hard for him to accept it when I don't do things well. Because we are alike in this area we could easily drive each other crazy—and we've done so on occasion. Even so, over the years Dad has worked hard to reassure me again and again that his love for me isn't based on my performance.

We also both have strong opinions, and we get into intense psychological and philosophical discussions. We often disagree. Still, Dad always says, "Well, I may not understand, but I love you anyway."

Recently he came to visit me and we had a date at our current favorite eatery, The Huddle House. Pancakes have replaced lima beans these days, but I'm still his "favorite daughter," and at twenty-six, I'm still proud of it.

Today, as I'm getting ready to leave my room, I look up and see stuck on the back of my door the latest Post-it he sent with some rent money. It said, "Honey, it was so good to see you this past week."

It sure was, Dad. Just keep sending me those Post-it notes!

Thanks, Dad, for those special times with you. Thanks for your Post-it collection that is growing in my tiny room. Thanks for giving me the reassurance that no matter what I do, say, or think, you love me.

Humble in Heart

❧

For many Christians, John Stott is considered the "C.S. Lewis of today." He's revered and renowned around the world for his Christian writings. But to me he's always been "Uncle John."*

Because my dad is an Episcopal minister, I've known "Uncle John" for many years through church circles and our family friendship. Growing up, I never thought of him as a famous writer and preacher. He was just a smart, kind, and fun older man that adults got especially excited about seeing. I knew he loved chocolate and birds as well as speaking and writing. It wasn't until I reached college that I realized just how much he has written and the impact he has had.

After graduating from college I was given the opportunity to work for Dr. Stott as a study assistant. My dad said that if I didn't take the job, he would! So off I went to England to become the tenth in a succession of Stott study assistants.

Many people ask me, "What's it like to work for

---

*We asked our son/brother, John Yates, to share this special story of his.

Dr. Stott? It must be amazing to be around such a great man." It's difficult to respond to questions like this, especially when I know how much he is embarrassed by praise. For me, working for Uncle John hasn't held any surprises. He is still the same kind, humble man I came to know as a child.

Not too long ago, Uncle John and I spent the afternoon cutting down weeds and clearing out a small creek bed in the fields surrounding his country home. I had the glorified job of operating the weedeater while he stood, covered in mud up to his knees, cleaning out vegetation and accumulated muck in the creek. It was a nasty job, and although fifty-three years my senior, Uncle John dove into it with an energy and enthusiasm for work that I was hard-pressed to match.

That same morning, long before the afternoon chore in the creekbed, Uncle John and I had prayed together as we always do before the start of the day. As he often does, he began his prayer by thanking God for the rising of the sun that acts as a constant reminder of his grace. He always thanks God for the simple things, the basic things in this life that God has given us, *those things that, without a spirit of constant thankfulness, slip out of the realm of God's awe-inspiring sovereignty and into the empty taken-for-grantedness of everyday life.*

Later that evening, after dinner, as is his habit, Uncle John washed the accumulated dishes from the day. He won't let the rest of us wash the breakfast or lunch dishes. He insists they be left for him until after dinner. He says it is his way of contributing to the meals, since he never cooks. This is true, but I think the other reason he insists on dish duty is because of the sheer joy he gets out of cleaning up the kitchen.

I spend a lot of time with Uncle John, and from early morning prayers to an afternoon in the mud, to washing dishes after dinner, he maintains a simple posture of humility before our Maker and before those around him. He is a willing servant, not just because he knows it is the right thing to do but because he truly enjoys serving others. For Uncle John, doing work and serving others are not things to be loathed, but rather are joyful opportunities through which our Creator is glorified. I have never met a more disciplined man, yet his discipline seems to be a completely natural result of his relationship with God. He doesn't spend the day on his knees, but that is the only physical posture that translates the attitude of his heart.

Uncle John has never had children of his own. In fact, he has never married. He has certainly had the opportunity, but somehow he knew he was called to other things. Even though he will never father a child in the flesh, he has more spiritual children than one can begin to count.

Thanks, Uncle John, for praying for me and reminding me to thank God for those things that I might otherwise easily forget. Thanks for working alongside me, sharing in those dirty tasks that you could ask me to do on my own. Thanks for demonstrating the truth that work, service, and discipline are part of our divine purpose and a source of immeasurable joy for the humble in heart.

Back Porch Perspective

⌘

In every life there are times when you just can't talk with your parents. Either they aren't available when you need a listening ear, or you are looking for an outside perspective because you've already *heard* theirs, or maybe you have something you'd simply rather discuss with someone else. Even those of us with wonderful parents need extra role models in our lives! In times like these, everybody needs an Allan or an Emily. This couple, though old enough to *be* our parents, are *not*. They have adopted my husband Will and me into their hearts and home and have become two of our closest friends. Emily is our faithful encourager and prayer warrior. Allan is our sounding board and source of godly wisdom and perspective.

When we visit Al and Em, as we affectionately call them, we greet each other with great warmth and spend a little while catching up on our lives, and then Will and Allan head straight for the back porch. They go out and close the door. Em and I are left to our own resources and we do just fine amusing ourselves. We both understand the importance of these back porch conversations.

Allan is retired from a very successful career in the business world, and he is truly gifted with wisdom. He is someone to whom Will can spill his thoughts and feelings with complete faith. Allan will listen and respond thoughtfully, without judging. Will is in full-time ministry, and often becomes burdened by church-related issues. It is really helpful to him to have someone with whom he can discuss these things who neither goes to our church nor works in ministry at all! It is a blessing that we live in different places and that Will and Allan have followed very different career paths. This gives Allan an objective and alternative outlook to offer Will. He is not personally involved, and he has no preconceptions or personal attachments, so he can help Will by looking at things from an "outside" perspective. This is such a gift!

Will and I rely heavily on our own families for wisdom and advice, but sometimes it is helpful to have someone on the outside to whom we can turn. There is a real freedom in this. I can remember several times when Will has had a troubling situation at church and has felt that because of the sensitive, personal nature of the situation, there was no one to whom he could turn for advice. At these times he has called Allan. Allan doesn't know the people involved and doesn't care who they are. He simply provides a listening ear and an outside perspective.

While Will and I were dating through college, Al

and Em often invited us to their home and encouraged us in our relationship. When Will decided to ask me to marry him, the first person he enlisted to help in setting up his plan for asking me was Allan! He knew Al could be counted on not to spill the beans, and that he would help with all the little details. Allan arranged for roses to be delivered to me, he made sure everything went according to Will's plans, and he and Em rejoiced with us when I said "Yes!"

After Will and I were engaged, we struggled, trying to decide between two great job offers in two very different situations and geographic locations. This was one of the first "big" decisions we had to make together, and it was hard! We discussed our options with our families, but in a sense they were "too close" to help us have perspective on the ramifications of the decision. After all, our decision would affect them directly! Al and Em helped us to make this decision. They simply knew the right questions to ask to enable us to see the answers more clearly for ourselves.

Thanks, Allan, for all those back porch conversations. We rely so much on your years of life experience. God has truly gifted you with wisdom. I know we can turn to you with our questions, and you will respond with perspective and insight.

The Real American Dream

I once had a college assignment to write about the "American Dream of Success," and what it meant to me. This was an easy topic for me, as both of my grandfathers have been clear examples of what it means to really pursue the "American Dream," although they both redefined this term from its common understanding. Growing into manhood during the Depression, both Pop and Doc, as I have always known them, were forced to redefine "success" in their own lives, and to pursue dreams that by today's standards would not be considered lofty. I have learned from them, however, that the dreams they chose to pursue were the ones that truly mattered in the end. Let me explain.

Pop graduated from college in the Roaring Twenties, and with $10,000 and a generous dose of confidence set out to make his fortune in the booming Florida real-estate market. Monetary success came quickly and his fortune grew—that is, until the day the bottom fell out of the market and he was left without enough money for bus fare home.

Humiliated but not defeated, Pop began to pursue a redefined version of success. He learned quickly that his own strength was not always enough. He had to work hard and trust God to provide for him. Pop worked as a clerk in a department store, eating simple lunches in the basement with the elevator operator because he couldn't afford the diner across the street. Pop refused to take handouts, instead relying on his own hard work to earn a meager living for himself and his growing family.

As the nation rose from depression to economic stability, Pop stuck by his newly defined version of success. It was his goal to honor God in all he did and to provide adequately, but not excessively, for his family. He continued working in the retail industry, crossing the cultural color barrier to lunch with the elevator operator, and putting his family's life and faith ahead of monetary gain.

Doc, during this same time, was learning similar lessons. A child born to wealth, he had always anticipated the finer things in life that his older siblings had received. However, when the Depression hit, there was nothing left in the family coffers for him. Doc worked his way through college and medical school, doing odd jobs and selling men's clothing. He dressed himself in the suits he earned as commission. He refused to borrow money, because he had seen debt's destruction ruin his parents. Instead, he paid cash up front for everything he needed and refused frivolity. In the summers, Doc worked in a church youth camp, where he learned the joy of serving God and caring for others. In his medical profession, he turned down offers for lucrative advances in order to work with student athletes at a university—a job that he loved, but that would never bring the material wealth so many others craved.

Both of these men lived lives that challenge me to redefine my understanding of the American Dream. Our culture claims that the dream is to rise to the top of the material ladder of success, to gain fortune and power. My grandfathers both learned that this is not the most important goal. Difficult lessons learned during the Depression years taught them the value of hard work, the importance of family and faith, and the fleeting nature of monetary wealth. They each made choices in their lives to put their families and their love of God ahead of opportunities to earn greater wealth. Pop mortgaged his home to help fund the building of a neighborhood church. Doc abhorred waste and taught his children (and grand-children!) the blessings of giving to others rather than hoarding for one's self.

The greatest lesson I have taken away from this is that these men were *wholly satisfied* with their choices. They pursued success in the eyes of the Lord by seeking to please him first. They gave generously to those in need, they provided for their families, but they were never selfish in their pursuits, and they were content! In a world that so often tries to persuade us that happiness comes only with comfort, and stability with material wealth, I have only to look to the generations before me for a reminder that the *best* American Dream I can pursue is one of deepening my faith, loving my family, and serving others.

Thanks, Pop and Doc, for pursuing the "American Dream" in such unusual ways! Your lives have modeled for me true success. You were both living witnesses of Matthew 6:19-21, where Jesus urges us, "Do not store up for yourselves treasures on earth, where moth and rust destroy ... but store up for yourselves treasures in heaven ... for where your treasure is, there your heart will be also."

Romans 8:28

❧

"**I** was five years old when I first realized that something about my dad might not be right," Mike explained. "I remember one night just before Christmas when Dad came home and the whole family disappeared. I didn't understand why they had all left. I stayed with my dad and soon understood why they had walked away. Dad was drunk, and Dad got mean when he was drunk. That night he hit me in the face with his fist for the first time. I didn't recognize it at the time, but this was the first step in a downward spiral."

Mike's dad was a typical alcoholic. He drank often and a lot. He went on drinking binges, abused his family, and was lustful both with alcohol and with other women. Mike's memories of his childhood are full of horror, with bad memories outweighing good.

"In fact," Mike explains, "I remember only one time that just the two of us spent time together. I was quite young and I was involved in baseball. Dad didn't come to many of my games. One day he seemed to have a temporary change of heart. We went out and bought about thirty baseballs, and we spent an entire afternoon together. He threw ball after ball to me in batting practice, and for a few hours we enjoyed each other's company. But that's the only happy time I can recall spending with my father. Maybe I remember the incident so vividly *because* it was such a rare moment. It made a lasting impression on me. As a father myself, I want to create *endless* memories like that for my children. Memories of *good* times spent with me."

Mike's parents divorced when he was twelve, and this began a new period in his young life. Without Dad around, life was more peaceful than it had been, even though it took everything the family could scrape together to survive. Mike and his siblings all worked, and their mother kept *three* jobs. They pooled their meager earnings just to make ends meet. In the meantime, his father literally lived on the streets. He had no permanent address and no permanent job. He never paid child support, and spent time in and out of jail. He remarried six times. "He never acted like a true father to me," Mike says, *"but I learned I had to love him anyway. He was a street bum, but he was my dad."*

While Mike's dad was living on the streets, Mike came to know Jesus in a personal way. He gained a new understanding of God as his heavenly Father.

His earthly father had certainly not been caring or loving. There was a dramatic change in Mike's life when he realized that God not only loved him as a precious child, *but he loved his dad in the same way.* This understanding enabled Mike to begin to love his father in a new way, in spite of the man's obvious failures.

"I realized that I had to pray for him. I had to honor and respect him *because he was my father*, even though there was no earthly reason even to acknowledge him." Mike began a conscious effort to reach out to his dad, and to try to care for him. He is still trying today, but has been rejected at every turn. In spite of this, Mike persists.

"Sometimes the bitterness and anger come back," Mike admits, "and I wonder why I bother with him at all. He never bothered with me! However, I know without a doubt that God has used this man in my life to accomplish his own purposes. The Bible commands us to honor our fathers and mothers, and so I keep trying. The one thing I can say that my dad taught me is how *not* to be as a father. Because of the childhood we had, all of us children in our family have bonded together to help each other overcome our past. We have *chosen* to make a fresh start in our generation.

"My wife and kids are the most important people

in my life, and it is my relentless goal to create for them the loving environment and happy memories that I never had. I want to be everything my father was not. The suffering I've gone through with my dad has not been in vain. It is clear that God has used it in my life. Second Corinthians 1:3, 4 tells us that God is our comfort. He sure has been in my life! And if I have received any comfort from God, then I am to share it with others who are suffering in the same way, and God has provided me with amazing opportunities to do this."

Mike is in full-time student ministry, and has a unique ability to reach the kids who are hurting the most, *because he knows their pain.*

"I guess my life is an example of Romans 8:28 (RSV), which promises that God works all things together for good for 'those who love him, who are called according to his purpose.' There is really nothing good in my relationship with my father. Even today, in spite of the fact that I try to care for him, he prefers the refuge of alcohol to a relationship with me.

"God has used this suffering in my life and he enables me to be the father to my children that I never had myself. He equips me for ministry through my pain. I have to honor my father in his brokenness, because he is still my father. He always will be. I'm thankful, though, that I have a heavenly Father who can fill up the hurting, empty spaces left in my life by my earthly father."

It is hard to say "Thanks, Dad." You have caused me so much pain. My heart is full of grief for the person that you have chosen to be. Yet, I love you because you are mine. Thank you for giving me life. Deep in my heart I can say that I am thankful for the suffering you have caused me, because I can see that God is using it for good. It still hurts, Dad, but I'm praying for you. I won't give up the hope that one day you will choose to acknowledge your heavenly Father who loves you, and also choose to be a father to me again.

I Know You Can!

Have you ever read the children's book, *The Little Engine That Could*? This is one of my old favorites, a story about perseverance in the face of obstacles. A tiny blue engine is called upon to help pull a train full of toys over a mountain to the boys and girls on the other side. All the other, more qualified trains who had been asked to help declined for various reasons, but the tiny, unlikely, inexperienced blue engine willingly said, "I'll try!" When the track uphill got steep and scary, her chant became "I think I can! I think I can!" and the little engine did!

A dad I know has a similar confidence in his daughter, Lynn. For her nineteenth birthday he wanted to remind Lynn that he believed in her, because she was struggling with some issues regarding her education and pursuit of a profession. He gave his grown daughter a copy of this favorite childhood book, with the following inscription:

Dear Lynn,

This book has lessons that can be of great value to you as you go through life. It was a favorite of mine when I was young, and now that I am older I have a deeper respect for its simple wisdom.

Most people start life as a happy "Good Little Engine" until the problems of life begin to affect them. The three engines who were asked to help and wouldn't all had serious character flaws that stood in their way: pride, impoliteness, arrogance, and a lack of true self-confidence. These engines could have easily gotten the job done, but were unwilling to be useful, or even to try.

The tiny blue engine (a lady, by the way), was polite, compassionate, and self-confident. She was willing to take a chance on failure but dwelt on the positive with her actions and attitude. She was not willing to let her size or other influences discourage her. Lynn, this tiny blue engine reminds me of you. The Lord has given you the ability to pursue a steady, consistent course to its conclusion; to have clearness of focus and discipline.

When the times get tough, remember this little engine and how she never gave up without trying. She kept her focus on the top of the mountain, and not on the load she was carrying. Remember that the Lord uses the unlikely to accomplish the impossible. Keep your focus on him. "I know you can, I know you can!" See you on the other side of the mountain.

I love you,
Daddy

This gift came to Lynn at a time in her life when she really needed encouragement to pursue her dreams, no matter how unlikely they seemed at the time. Today she is well on her way to accomplishing the things her father always knew she could achieve. Because of his encouragement and confidence in her, and his willingness to walk alongside her, cheering her on, Lynn has been able to take risks and to attempt the seemingly unattainable. She knew her dad believed she could accomplish anything.

Thanks, Dad, for using a familiar story to remind me
of a timeless truth. God uses us, when we think we are
an unlikely choice, to do the impossible! Thank you
for giving me this tangible reminder of how
much you believe in me. I'll see you
"on the other side of the mountain,"
where we can rejoice together in my success!

The Refiner's Fire

∽

When I was in high school, my dad was on the receiving end of an ugly lawsuit. Nothing like this had ever happened to our family before, and we didn't quite know how to deal with it. When it began, we sat down together and Dad explained what was going on. We didn't know quite what to expect, but since Dad was a minister at a prominent church, we were sure the news would be in all the newspapers in the weeks ahead. We were sure Dad's character would be maligned in the public eye. At the time, I understood that it would be a headache for him, but honestly, I was more concerned about how it would reflect on me. I thought people would be talking about it behind my back.

Dad was very busy in the months that followed. He left the house early and stayed at church until late at night. He was trying to do his job and at the same time meet with lawyers, track down information, and deal with all the details of a lawsuit. When he finally came home long after dark, he looked more and more tired every day. Until now, Dad had always seemed so strong to me. I thought he was invincible, able to handle anything that life might throw his way. Now here he was: tired, weak, and nearing the end of his rope.

One night during dinner, Dad gave us the weekly update on how the lawsuit was going. He faithfully explained the details the way he always did, but then he continued. He began to share how he was handling the struggle personally. He talked about how hard it was for him, how tired he was, how he felt like he was failing, and how he needed our prayers. Even though he was exhausted, he managed to carry on with all of his various responsibilities. He continued to make his daily prayer time a special priority. He bent with the struggle, but he was not broken. Like the Bible says, he was "hard-pressed on every side, but not crushed; perplexed, but not in despair; persecuted, but not abandoned" (2 Corinthians 4:8, 9). He never gave up.

Eventually, the case was dropped. Dad and everyone else involved were cleared, and our lives returned to a more normal pattern. Those months during the lawsuit had been hard. Lies and unkind words had been spread. Yet I knew that something significant had happened to Dad. Watching him over that time, I saw an amazing juxtaposition. Here was a man who was on his knees before God, yet somehow remained strong enough to stand tall in the confidence that God would be faithful to the end.

I've now had a few years to reflect on that period in our lives. I saw my father pushed further than I ever had seen before. I saw him tired and broken. Yet, I also saw his inner strength rise to the surface. His was a fortitude that rose out of a genuine humility and required a season of suffering to really show through. During this time Dad modeled for all of us how to walk the fine line between being weak and broken before God and holding your head up while walking on through the storm. From Dad, I have learned that out of the refiner's fire the purest gold is cast.

Thanks, Dad, for not being afraid of vulnerability.
Thank you for being honest about your struggles.
I thank you especially for your demonstration that a
man who is humble before God and submissive
to his will can make it through those dark nights
of the soul. You showed me that when we are
weak before God, he is strongest in our lives.

More Valuable Than Billable Hours

As Josh's team ran across the field to the dugout, he scanned the parking lot for a familiar sight. He knew his father's blue convertible would pull in any second, and Dad would head across to his favorite spot on the bleachers. This was a double-header day, and just knowing that Dad would be here made Josh feel excited and confident about the games he would play.

Josh's dad was a lawyer in one of Boston's top firms. He had a pretty impressive office from which Josh could see the whole city! Josh knew that his dad was considered a really important guy by everyone he worked with, and it made Josh proud. He also knew that his dad got paid by the hour for his work, and Josh had once accidentally overheard him telling someone how much he actually earned every sixty minutes! The number was so big it made Josh's head spin. He could never earn that much in a *year* on his paper route!

Josh didn't really care so much about the amount of money his dad earned. What he cared about was the fact that Dad came to every single baseball game Josh played—even when it was during working hours. Sometimes Dad brought his briefcase with him to the game, but when Josh's team started to play, the briefcase was snapped shut and all of Dad's attention was focused on Josh and his teammates. Dad knew when to cheer really loudly, like when Josh made a double play or hit a really good ball, and he knew when to keep quiet and just give the "thumbs-up" signal, like when Josh was getting ready to pitch to a tough opponent. Every time Josh looked up at the stands, his dad was there, cheering him on.

Josh's glance usually traveled from his father's smile to the big clock on top of the scoreboard. As the minutes of each game ticked by, Josh kept a mental tally of the money his dad was spending on him. It's not that Dad was giving Josh cash, but in a way, he gave his son a fortune every time he came to watch a game. Josh knew his dad could be making money every minute, but instead he kept his briefcase closed and watched his son play ball. Josh was clearly more important to his father than those billed hours.

Dad could be earning hundreds of dollars. Instead he's watching me! It makes me feel like I'm worth a fortune! Josh thought. Then he saw the familiar figure saunter over to the stands. Dad nodded in encouragement as Josh continued tossing warm-up balls.

Josh smiled back and thought to himself, *I must be the richest kid in the world this afternoon!*

Thanks, Dad, for so clearly demonstrating that
I was more important to you than making money!
So many people would have chosen billing hours over
watching endless baseball games—
but you chose me instead. I know that to you
I am far more valuable than any worldly gain.

What Makes a "Daddy"?

I have a young friend, Ashley, who has lived for most of her life with her mother and stepfather, Dan. She sees her biological father infrequently, usually under uncomfortable circumstances. Ashley has opened her heart to embrace her stepfather in a way that few young people are able to do, and she offers here her keen insight on what it really means to be a "daddy."

What is the differance between a father and a daddy? A "father" is there at the time of conseption, but the "daddy" is there for a baby's first steps or for a teen's first date.

My "daddy" is not my biological "father," but he is the one who has always been there for me. Chorus concerts, camping trips, birthdays, music resitals, my first crush and my first heartbreak, and now as I learn how to drive! He was there last Easter when we went on a nature walk—he carried me on his back through the mud so that my shoes wouldn't get dirty. (Well, they were new shoes!) This past Valentine's Day when I was

feeling sad about not having a boyfriend he bought me
a huge boukay of flowers and snuk them into my room
at 5:00 A.M. so they'd be sitting there when I got up for
school! Lots of times when I've been sick or hurt he gave
me a reashuring hug.

Dan has always been the shoulder I can cry on and
the lap I can climb up into and feel safe from dangers.
I thank God for my "daddy" and pray our relationship
will grow stronger with each new day.

Thanks, Dan, for choosing to become my "daddy."
You have been there for me in the little ways that are so
important—ways that my 'father' has not.
I will always cherish our relationship. You have taught
me what it really means to be a "daddy."
Remember that old saying, "Any man can be a father
but it takes someone special to be a daddy!"
You are that special someone in my life.

By the Dawn's Early Light

⌒

Each morning began the same way when I was in high school. The radio next to my head would blast out at 5:45 A.M., declaring something about "and the high today is expected to be in the low 40s...." Or sometimes it interrupted my sleep with the latest pop music chart-topper. With my heart racing from this rude awakening, I would slam the alarm off, sit up, and plant my feet on the floor. It always took me a moment of just sitting there to fully gain consciousness. Then, in the hazy semidarkness that comes with early mornings and not yet having my contact lenses in, I would make my way downstairs, grasping the handrail for dear life as I tried to make my sleepy legs perform. At the bottom of the stairs I'd turn left and head for the light—literally.

The one light that was always on when I woke in the mornings was the light at my dad's desk. He was completely reliable. No matter what else happened, when I woke up, Dad would already be sitting at his desk, sipping a cup of coffee, with his Bible and his prayer notebook open on his desk. Some days he'd be showered and clean-shaven; others, he'd be wrapped up in his old blue bathrobe, but he was *always* there.

Ever groggy at that rude hour of the day, I would stumble into Dad's study and crawl into his lap. By the time I reached high school this was easier said than done. My lanky frame didn't fit in Dad's lap quite as cozily as it once had. Still, I would perch on the edge of his chair next to him long enough to at least have a big hug before it got too crowded for the both of us.

Dad always asked the same question: "Sleep well, Honey?" and I generally replied, "Yes, but not nearly long enough!" This was especially true on a number of days when *my* desk light went out not too long before Dad's came on!

Dad would rub my back for a moment or so and ask me if there was anything special going on that day that he could pray for. Sometimes he showed me the things in his prayer notebook that he had already been praying about that morning. He always told me that he loved me, and concluded our morning ritual with the reminder, "I left the kettle warming for your coffee." Dad, unlike Mom, understood the need for an early morning caffeine jolt to get a tired high-schooler ready to face the day!

As I crawled back upstairs with a steaming mug to

snuggle back into bed for my own Bible-reading and prayer time, I was always encouraged by the knowledge that my dad had already done the same thing. He had prayed for me while I was still sleeping, just as he did every day! Just knowing that Dad was so consistent in his time alone with God encouraged me to be more so. I knew that Dad prayed specifically for many people and situations, and that God answered unfailingly. Every so often, Dad would pull out his old prayer notebooks and show us how God had answered his prayers for each of us children. Sometimes God provided a special friend, healed an illness, or supplied a job. My father was faithful in his prayers, and God has always been faithful in responding.

Even today, as an adult, I know that Dad is awake long before dawn, reading God's Word and talking to our heavenly Father. Sometimes when I am unmotivated by the alarm clock that still bursts into my dreams every day, it helps me to remember that Dad has already been awake for hours. If he can do it, I can do it.

Thanks, Dad, for living a life committed to prayer.
Your faithful example to me speaks more of your love
for the Lord than any words ever could. I know that
you pray for me and for others, and from the example of
your life I have seen how essential it is to live in daily
relationship with our heavenly Father. I know that if I
walked in your front door at dawn tomorrow, your
light would already be on, you would have already
prayed for me, and I could still crawl into
your lap for a quiet moment!

Money Talks

❧

"**G**uess what, guess what!" Catherine cried as she ran in the door of the kitchen, clutching the telephone.

"What? What is it?" Mom and Dad exclaimed in unison, dropping the dishes they were carrying with a clatter.

"I got the job! I'm going to be an assistant editor for the magazine I've been interviewing with! I did it! My first job!" Catherine was literally jumping up and down with excitement. It had been a nerve-wracking couple of months since college graduation. She'd been searching for jobs, interviewing, and trying to make a good impression. Now all that work was finally paying off. Hooray!

Mom and Dad overwhelmed Catherine with hugs and congratulations, exclaiming, "We knew you could do it! We're so proud of you! You're a real working woman now!"

Dinner conversation that night was filled with excitement. The whole family wanted to know every detail of the job that would mean a move to

Washington, D.C. for Catherine. Where was the office? What would she be doing? Would she meet famous people? And of course Dad, ever practical, wanted to know, "Are they going to be paying you enough to live on?"

"Well, I'm certainly not going to be rich, but I think I'll have enough for bread and water at least," Catherine replied with a smile. "Actually, I was hoping you could help me with that stuff, Daddy. You know—filling out all of the financial forms, planning a budget, and so on. I'm also going to have to buy a car. I'm going to need lots of your financial advice."

"I was hoping you'd ask!" Dad grinned. "It's about time we had a little father-daughter financial chat. How about after dinner?"

Catherine's dad had always been careful with money. She knew he used an elaborate budgeting system to run the family finances. She had been aware of this even as a young child, because she had often seen her dad working on "the budget" at the kitchen table. Dad had always taught the children that before they spent anything they should give a portion of their allowance or earnings to the church, and that they should also put some into their piggy banks to save.

As Catherine and her dad sat down at the kitchen table after dinner that night, they reminisced a little bit about the fun things their family had done in the past. They had been on some very special vacations together, and each one of the kids in the family had had the opportunity to spend time living and studying abroad.

"Catherine, I want you to realize that it's only through extremely careful planning that our family has been able to do these things," Dad reminded her. "When you were very little, Mom and I decided we wanted to be able to go on family vacations together as you kids grew up. We planned and saved for this for years before we actually went! None of these things just came about on their own. It takes goal setting and lots of financial discipline to do these kinds of things, but they *can* be done! You just have to plan and be patient."

As they began to look at Catherine's salary profile and what her expenses would be, she realized what a task it would be to allocate her dollars sensibly. "This is hard, Daddy," she admitted.

"I know it is, Catherine, but it's so important. If you don't plan exactly where your money is going, it has a way of disappearing before you even know it. That's how so many people end up in debt and can't get out. They just spend and spend without really thinking, and pretty soon their credit cards control their lives. We may never have had wealth, but I am proud to say that other than a mortgage on the house, your Mom and I have never gone into debt. Even during the times when I've been out of work, we've survived. We've done without many things we would have liked, but I'd much rather go without luxury than be enslaved to debt."

"You're right, Daddy. I really want to start off on the right foot in managing my money. I never felt like I did without anything growing up, and I know that it's because of your meticulous planning and careful spending. I'm willing to make sacrifices and to be disciplined. I just need a little guidance from you on how to do it!"

"Well, then, let's get started. First, we'll start with tithing. You'll want to give back to God 10 percent of your earnings...."

Thanks, Dad, for your wisdom in financial matters. I know that I have been well provided for because of your careful planning and saving. Thank you for your commitment to living frugally and in a godly manner. I have learned from your example, and I want to be responsible with what God has given me, too.

Sunday Night Syndrome

⚘

For a while she tried reading under the covers with her pencil-sized flashlight, but Nancy Drew's mysteries only got Mary so far toward sleep. They were entertaining, to be sure, but they didn't help sleep come any faster. She tried lying on her back with her eyes squinched shut as tightly as she could get them, counting imaginary sheep. Mary lost track somewhere around "one hundred forty-nine, one hundred fifty …" and her thoughts wandered back to school, the place she most wanted them to avoid. The more Mary tried to fall asleep and stop thinking about it, the more she worried about what fifth grade would bring this week. It wasn't that she didn't like school, but the *weekends* were definitely the best part of Mary's week.

On weekends, Mary could do exactly what she wanted, when she wanted, as long as Mom said it was OK, of course. She didn't have to worry about who to sit next to at lunch, or whether anyone would want to sit next to her at all. Instead she ate with her brother Pete at the little round table on the back porch. She didn't have to worry about getting picked or *not* getting picked for the kickball teams in gym class. She didn't have to do gym on the weekends. She could read books, play with her friends next door, and run and yell and holler as much as she wanted without being reminded to "Act like a lady, Mary" or "Use your inside voice, please" because she could be outdoors!

That reminded Mary: it was supposed to rain all week. She tossed and flopped onto her stomach in frustration, throwing back the covers. The class would have to stay inside for lunch and recess every day and talk quietly instead of playing. Oh, what a dreadful week it was going to be!

Groaning just loudly enough that maybe someone would hear it, Mary began to mentally list everything else that could possibly go wrong this week at school. So much could happen! If only it were Friday night instead of Sunday, then she'd be looking forward to the weekend instead of dreading school. In school, she might trip and drop her lunch tray on the way to her seat. She had seen a boy do that once last year, and the kids were still teasing him and calling him "klutz." She could forget her homework and Mrs. Horne might call her "unreliable and scatterbrained" in front of the whole class. She might even miss the bus tomorrow and have to walk to school and be late and miss homeroom and have to go to the principal's office and *everyone* knows what happens there! Worst of all, she might cry in front of everybody....

"Mary? Are you all right in there? I can hear you moaning all the way down the hall!"

Startled out of her nightmarish revelry, Mary turned to see her father's silhouette in the door of her room. "Daddy!"

"Do you want me to come sit with you for a while before you fall asleep, Sweetie?" he whispered.

"Please!" Mary replied urgently. "I'm having bad dreams about school and I haven't even fallen asleep yet! Help me feel better, Doctor Dad!" Mary's dad worked in a hospital making sick people well, and his magic touch often worked at home, too.

"Well, tell me what your symptoms are, young lady," he said in his deep "doctor" voice. "Chest pain? Heart palpitations? Difficulty breathing?"

"*Yes!* Everything! And I can't sleep either. I keep thinking about ... you know ... *things.*"

"Hmmm ... things," Dad repeated to himself, very scientifically. "What sort of *things*, exactly?"

"Well, *school* things. Bad things that could happen during the week. Like forgetting my lunch and having to borrow money from the mean lady in the front office, or getting sent to the principal, or ..."

"This sounds like a very familiar problem!"

Doctor Dad interrupted. "In fact, this is caused by a sickness that infects many young boys and girls late in the evening. In fact, I suffered from it myself as a boy," he chuckled. Hearing the laughter in Dad's voice made Mary begin to relax. She snuggled her head into the crook of his arm and asked, "So does this disease have a name, Dad? Is it serious?"

"Oh, very serious," Dad continued in his doctor voice. "So serious that it can cause total dismay in even the most reasonable of children. It can lead to worry, fear, nightmares, and even total lack of sleep!" Mary could tell he was teasing her now and she started to feel her fears slip away. "This dreaded disease does have a name. It's called Sunday Night Syndrome, because it only strikes on Sunday nights, usually after dark, while its victims are innocently lying in their beds, trying to sleep! It never happens on a Friday or a Saturday, or any other night of the week, and it is especially bad if the victim has any tests or quizzes coming up. It freezes your brain, makes your palms sweat and your heart race, and fills your mind with all sorts of horrible thoughts!"

Mary giggled and said, "Well, Doctor Dad, I seem to have a terrible case of this Sunday Night Syndrome. Can you prescribe a medicine for me?"

"No. No, I can't." Dad shook his head sadly. "Unfortunately there seems to be no proven medical remedy for this dreaded disease. There is, however, something that has been known to cure patients in the past, but it's not something you can buy at the drugstore."

"Well, what is it?" Mary insisted. "I'll never make it through the night with this disease!"

"Well ... I don't know. It's very risky." He hesitated. His voice dropped to a whisper. "It's called the *mmf rumf tmat.*"

"It's called the *what?*" Mary whispered back. "Cure me quickly, Doctor Dad!"

"It's called the '*tickle treatment!*'" he cried gleefully, and pounced on Mary's bare feet, tickling them mercilessly. She cried out with glee, "Oh, Doctor Dad, I'm cured!" and in between gales of laughter she gasped, "I'll never have that dreadful disease again! Thank you, Dad!"

Thanks, Dad, for listening to my fears. You understood how my young mind worked, and how gripping simple worries could be. You took my mind off of my "certain doom" and helped me see the humor in the situation, without belittling me in any way. You cured my Sunday Night Syndrome, and helped me laugh at myself in a constructive way!

A Birthday Tribute

*D*ear Dad,

Do you remember that big tree by our house in Great Falls? We sure do! That tree was in all the pictures we drew and stories we wrote as children. Many of our childhood memories center around that tree. It was a constant presence in our lives. In a similar way, we feel that everything you have given to us in your role as our father is a constant presence in our lives—a presence that will never stop shaping us. For your birthday, we, your son and daughter, want to share with you some favorite memories of our times together.

(From your son)

When I was a boy, I can remember fishing with you in the rain at River Bend. Dad, there you caught your first and last fish … your fishing career went downhill after that! I also remember the time you spent as my T-ball coach. I remember your steady presence at all of my basketball games. I could always count on your being there! Another great memory is of the times when Mom and Sis went out of town. You and I would stay up late at night drinking root beer and eating Swiss cheese and crackers with mustard as we watched The Rockford Files. It was kind of like a "guys' night out," and it made me feel so good to know that you loved being with me! The funny poems you always wrote on my birthday made me feel that I was your Number One Son. You have always been so accepting of me! Sometimes it seems like the small, simple things you did were the ones that influenced me the most.

(From your daughter)

When I was a girl, I remember how special I felt when I was with you, Dad! I treasured our "dates" to the 7-11 convenience store and Saturday morning swim practices, followed by breakfast at McDonald's. Some of my other favorite memories are of you tucking me in at night, going to football games at Christmas time, praying with you when I was nervous about tests at school, and your teaching me how to study. I could always count on you for chocolates on Valentine's Day and I loved hearing you tell me that you were "always in my corner." You said that if anyone ever asked if my dad loved me, I should be sure to say "yes!" I have always known that you accept me for who I am, and that you believe in me.

(From both of us)

Not only have you given us great memories, Dad, but you have also provided us with a strong foundation for life. You are like that tree in our neighborhood. Your roots go down deep, and you in turn have helped us grow roots of our own. The greatest gift you have given to us is your character. We made up a list of words we feel describe you: unselfish, accepting, stable, honest, loving, forgiving, hardworking, generous, perceptive, and sensitive to others! These qualities can flow from only one place—from making your family your top priority.

As long as we can remember, you have been teaching us about priorities in life. We know the list by heart now! First comes Christ because that is our most precious relationship. Christ always seemed to be included in your decisions and actions, Dad.

You also taught us about the priorities of marriage and family as we saw you care for Mom and for us. We have always known how important Mom is to you. Your love for her is very evident to us! You made integrity a priority as well, and we saw this illustrated in the way you handled situations at work and in your personal life. Dad, you have given us a desire to live lives firmly rooted in our priorities.

Just as that strong tree in our neighborhood represented stability, protection, vitality, consistency, and safety, you have been all of those things to us and more! Dad, you have been our greatest teacher and hero. We love you and thank you for all that you have given to us.

Happy Birthday! And thanks, Dad, for everything.

Thanks, Dad, for . . .

_____

_____

_____

_____

_____

_____

_____

_____

_____

_____

_____

**Other Books by Allison Yates Gaskins
and Susan Alexander Yates**

Thanks, Mom, for Everything. This companion book
is available from Servant Publications, 1997.
ISBN: 1-56955-017-4

*Tightening the Knot: Couple Tested Ideas to Keep Your
Marriage Strong,* Piñon Publishers, 1995.
ISBN: 0-89109-905-0

Other Books by Susan Alexander Yates

*And Then I Had Kids: Encouragement for Mothers
of Young Children,* Word Publishers, 1988.
ISBN: 0-84993-456-7

*What Really Matters at Home: Eight Crucial
Elements for Building Character in Your Family,*
coauthor, John W. Yates, Word Publishers, 1992.
ISBN: 0-84993-416-8

*A House Full of Friends: How to Like the Ones You
Love,* Focus on the Family Publishers, 1995.
ISBN: 1-56179-409-0

I was knocked ~~to the floor amid a cloud of colored~~
powder. I struggled beneath the weight that pinned me
to the floor and stretched for a pistol that was no longer
there.

"Looking for this?" Jackie said. I looked up into the barrel
of the big automatic.

"Shoot him, Jackie!" Slim shouted. "Shoot the dirty,
rotten blasphemer!"

"Jackie wouldn't shoot me," I said. "Not after all the
good times we shared."

"He's right," Jackie said. "Shooting him would be too
messy." She stepped away from the chamber and
gestured at it with the gun. "Why don't you climb
inside?"

I held up my hand. "I'd like to ask you one last question."

Jackie hesitated, then sighed impatiently. "Okay, let's
hear it."

"I was waiting for the right moment to ask you, but I
guess this is as good a time as any.... Jackie?"

"Yeah?"

"Will you marry me?"

She laughed and shook her head. "I'm too young to be a
widow."

JAKE STRAIT

DAY OF JUDGMENT

FRANK RICH

A GOLD EAGLE BOOK FROM
W★RLDWIDE®

TORONTO • NEW YORK • LONDON
AMSTERDAM • PARIS • SYDNEY • HAMBURG
STOCKHOLM • ATHENS • TOKYO • MILAN
MADRID • WARSAW • BUDAPEST • AUCKLAND

Second edition July 2007

ISBN-13: 978-0-373-63263-3
ISBN-10:   0-373-63263-0

DAY OF JUDGMENT

Printed in U.S.A.

DAY OF JUDGMENT

Something told me the three goons coming up the fire escape were looking for me. It could have been the way they dressed, the urgency with which they scrambled up the ladder, or maybe it was the submachine guns slung across their chests. Call it an educated guess.

I moved back from my office window. I thought about closing and locking it but was afraid they might break it in their eagerness to shoot me. I crept to the door, opened it quietly and slipped into the hall, leaving the door slightly ajar so I could peek inside. I drew my gyrapistol and waited.

"Don't move," said a voice behind me. My back muscles tensed, and I glanced over my shoulder. A short man in a brown rubber overcoat came up the stairs at the end of the hall, machine pistol in hand.

"You're looking for Strait, too, huh?" I gambled.

He appeared confused for a moment, then slapped his forehead. "Don't tell me you're working the same contract."

"Afraid so," I whispered, peering through the crack in the door. The trio of gunmen crawled through the window and slipped into my office with slow, careful steps, pointing their weapons into dim corners.

"Goddamn should have guessed," the short man whispered, coming up behind me. "With a bounty as big as this one, I'm surprised the place isn't crawling with bogeymen." He peered over my shoulder. "Is he in there?"

"Yeah," I whispered. "And it looks like he has some friends."

"Yeah?" he said. "How many?"

"Two."

"Well, listen. Maybe we can work a deal. Split the bounty. There's more than enough for the both of us."

"Okay," I said. "Fifty-fifty. Here's the plan. I boot open the door and we both go in, me high, you low. I take the two on the left, you take the goon on the right. Got it?"

"Got it." He moved beside me, crouched low and nodded.

I drove a heel into the door, and we jumped in. The two on my side stood together near the closet, their faces full of surprise. Explosions crowded the room, and a burst of gyrajets from my pistol chopped them to the floor with sledgehammer force. I spun to my right, but the third man was already down. He had enough holes to kill a dozen men, and my comrade was still hosing him down.

"I think he's dead," I shouted above the din.

His machine pistol ran out of ammunition, and the room screamed with a sudden silence. "I like to make sure they stay that way," he said wildly, wiping sweat from his eyes. "Whew! Nothing like a firefight to get the blood pumping. Which one is Strait?"

I closed the door, then pointed at the one he'd shot. "That's him."

He walked over and stood above the corpse. "So that's Jake Strait. He don't look half as tough as his reputation. Just goes to show." He took a miniature power saw from his overcoat and crouched over the body. It took him only a moment to cut off the right hand, the hand in which the dead man's ID chip was embedded. I sat on the edge of the desk and watched him. I'd done the same thing countless times before but I'd never watched someone else do it.

"Goddamn, ten thousand smackers, just like that," he said excitedly. "Well, five thousand, since we're splitting it. But that's still a lotta tubes of good giddy gin, if you get my meaning. My name is Victor Henly, by the way. I usually operate out of Barridales, but I'm always willing to go out of my way for a fat score. Hey, you ever think of going partners with somebody? We made a great team a minute ago. What's your tag, anyway?"

"Jake."

"Well, ain't that a coincidence. You know, this guy sure don't look much like his picture, does he?"

I leaned over the mutilated body and took a closer look. "No, he sure doesn't."

"Yeah, in the picture I saw he had lighter hair and it was kinda cut in a mohawk."

"Yeah," I agreed. "Kinda like mine."

"Yeah, more like yours. And he looked bigger in the picture, more muscular."

"Yeah, more like my build. And in the picture he looked a lot more dashing and handsome, like me."

"He did, didn't he? And in the picture he had a scar on each cheek, just…" His voice shut off and his shoulders hunched.

"Like me," I finished. He looked up and stared into the barrel of the gyrapistol. "Hi," I said.

"Oh, Jesus." His eyes dropped to the corpses on the floor. "Who're these poor saps, then?"

"Just some guys looking for a fat score. You know."

He raised his hands and slowly straightened up. "Hey, wait a minute, pal, it wasn't nothing personal, just doing my job. It's the Hayward Pimp Association that has the bounty on you."

"I know that. And of course it'd be my job to kill you."

He swallowed and stared at the gyra.

"But I'm going to let you live," I said, "so you can deliver a message for me. Tell the Hayward Pimp Association to call off the contract or I'm going to start liquidating their membership. Got it?"

"Yeah, I got it." He tried on a smile. "I'll tell those bastards to go to hell for you. I don't like killing fellow bogeymen anyway, know what I mean?"

"I know just what you mean. See you around."

He glanced down at the corpse beside him and lingered, torn between fear and greed. "What about the hand? Maybe this creep's got a death warrant out on him, maybe he's worth something."

I looked down at the detached hand sitting on the floor like a bloody tarantula. "Take it," I said.

Victor crouched and adroitly slipped the hand into a small plastic bag. He dropped the bag into his coat pocket, leaned toward the door, then hesitated again. He dropped mournful eyes on the two other bodies. "You know, the same logic applies to the other two. It wouldn't take me more than a minute, and it seems like a waste not to."

"There any warrants out on you?"

"I'm on my way," he said, sidestepping to the door with remarkable agility for a fat man. He closed the door gently, and I could hear him descending the steps briskly. I moved to the window to watch him exit. He climbed into a turn-of-the-century envirocruiser, then roared down Hayward.

I holstered the gyra, picked up the phone and punched in the three-digit reclamation service number.

"Reclamation!" a happy voice said.

"Three reclaimables," I said, then relayed my address. "I'll leave the door unlocked. Donate the reward to the Homeless War Orphans Hooked on Whack Relief Fund." I hung up and stared at the sprawled bodies bleeding on the carpet. I wanted to feel outrage about heavily armed thugs creeping up to my office to kill me on behalf of a vengeful and bitter gang of pimps, but I couldn't swing the emotion. It was just the way the things were in the City, like the rats and the radioactive rain; there wasn't any sense in getting worked up about it. I went to the door. I didn't want to be around when the reclamation boys came by to haul them to the protein vats.

I opened the door and nearly collided with the most clinically beautiful woman I'd ever seen while sober. We stood toe-to-toe, our noses intimately close, and I stared into bleached gray eyes as hard and pale as chips of concrete. As she backed off half a step, my eyes took the full tour. Her hair was organized into a platinum swirl, her skin as pale and smooth as porcelain, her conservative jump dress, stockings and shoes all a glaring white. She looked as if she were carved from a tall block of ice, and a conscious frigidity added to the effect. Her eyes ducked my stare.

"Pardon me," I said.

"No, pardon *me*." She moved her head to look past me into the office. "I'm looking for Mr. Strait."

"I might know where he is," I said, moving to block her view. "But we'll have to talk somewhere else."

Her head shifted. "I thought I saw…"

I crowded her back and closed the door behind me. "Saw what?" I asked, looking her in the eyes. "Ms…."

Her lips parted and her eyes dropped. "Miss Pan. I'm sorry, I must be imagining things."

I led her down the hall to the stairwell. "What do you want with Mr. Strait?"

"I need someone found."

We cleared the first landing. "Who are you looking for?"

"My sister. You know, it seems strange to conduct a business conversation while descending a stairwell."

"There's a bar across the street. We can talk there."

"I don't like bars," she said, the taps of her high heels catching up with me on the sidewalk.

I stopped and faced her. "We can talk right here if you like."

She glanced around at the hustlers and hoboes, the whores and hoods who populated Hayward Avenue. She clutched her white sequin purse to her breasts and peered across the street. "Is that it over there?" she asked. "St. Christopher's Lounge?"

I nodded and we crossed the street. We took a booth in the back, near the jukebox.

"How strange to name a bar after a saint," she said, sitting down.

"Not when you think about it. Would you like a drink?"

"I don't drink," she said, gazing around. "It's so terribly dark in here."

"Hides the decor."

"And everyone appears to be some sort of barfly or criminal."

"Those are the two largest local industries." I ordered a screwdriver from the anemic waitress. Miss Pan sat reticently, politely waiting for my drink to arrive. I noticed the room's murkiness didn't affect her appearance; in the dim light, she seemed to radiate an unassailable purity.

When my drink arrived, I put half of it down with a single swallow. I ignored Miss Pan's frown of distaste. "So," I said, "your sister's missing."

"I'd prefer to deal directly with Mr. Strait."

"You are."

She eyed me disparagingly. She'd obviously expected a snap-brim fedora and overcoat. "Please, sir, I haven't time for games."

"But I really am Jake Strait," I protested. "Inner-city avenger. Righter of wrongs. One hell of a swell guy."

"Then why did you lie to me?"

"I did not. I said I might know where I was. Here I am."

"You misled me."

"You can't be too careful in my line of work. You could have been a killer. Or a bill collector even."

She smiled politely, then lifted a 3-D photo from her purse and laid it on the table. I picked it up and held it to the light.

Except for her black hair and brown eyes, the woman in the photo could have been the twin of the woman sitting across from me. Her smile was mischievous, bordering on sinister, and her eyes seemed backlit by inner fires of questionable morality. She wore a long black lace gown, and a gang of silver occult symbols dangled from her neck.

"That's my sister Jackie," Miss Pan said. "She's been kidnapped."

I raised an eyebrow. "Really. By whom?"

"Those were *bodies* I saw in your office," she blurted suddenly. "Weren't they?"

"What has that got to do with your sister?"

"Those *were* bodies."

"We like to call them cadavers. I'm an amateur surgeon. I'm conducting experiments."

"I heard gunshots."

"All in the name of science."

She stared at me. "I wish you'd be honest."

I lit a vitacig and filled my lungs with nutrients. "Okay. To be honest, those men were vacuum-cleaner salesmen. The real pushy kind. I told them to leave, but…" I shrugged.

She put on an affronted frown. "I don't believe you."

"Would you believe they were assassins trying to kill me?"

"No."

"Then what's the sense of being honest?"

"Why would assassins be interested in killing you?"

"A criminal organization wants me dead for killing one of their members."

She covered her mouth with delicate fingers. "Should I be hiring you?"

"Why not? I'm not the one taking the eternal nap."

The tug-of-war going on inside her was reflected on her troubled face. I thought I was losing until she said, "I guess I have no choice."

"How do you mean?"

"Nothing." She touched a tiny crucifix hanging between her breasts and bowed her head, her huge gray eyes searching the table for words. She finally breathed deep and let the story tumble out. "My sister has been kidnapped and brainwashed by an evil cult. The Set of One. Have you heard of it?"

"I've heard the name. How'd your sister get mixed up with them?"

She shook her head. "Jackie was always the wild one. She experimented with the occult and death rock when she was younger, but our parents always kept her in check.

When they died six months ago…" She shrugged and let the sentence drift off. "I returned for my parent's funeral to find Jackie had fallen in with a bad crowd that belonged to the set. They'd come over and play that horrible music of theirs and use strange drugs, extort money from her. Then one day four months ago she and all her things were gone and…" She covered her eyes, and tears trickled from beneath her fingers.

I offered her a napkin but she refused it in lieu of a white handkerchief retrieved from her purse. She dabbed at her eyes and said, "Forgive me, I usually don't get so emotional."

"I understand. Miss Pan, have you considered that your sister may have left of her own free will? Joining a religious group isn't exactly against the laws of the World Party."

She looked up suddenly. "I know my sister, Mr. Strait. She's a little misguided, but she's not a fanatic about anything. She's either a prisoner or they've brainwashed her into staying. If you had seen them, you'd understand how evil and sinister they are. That's why you have to find and rescue her."

"You said she disappeared four months ago. Why have you waited so long to seek help?"

"I kept expecting her to come to her senses and come home. When she didn't, I knew she was being held against her will."

"Have you reported any of this to the SPF?"

She looked embarrassed. "No, I'd like to keep them out of it. And from what I gather, they have little or no power in the City. That's why I've turned to you."

I leaned back into the cushions of the booth. "Do you realize what a private enforcer does, Miss Pan?"

"I assume it means you enforce the law when the Party's Security and Protection Force cannot."

"In a general sense. More specifically I kill criminals wanted by the SPF. For the reward."

She gasped and stared at me with new, frightened eyes. "You mean you're a *bogeyman?*"

"You knew I was a private enforcer."

"Yes, but I didn't realize they were the same thing. I thought you were like a private eye."

"Those are our roots. But we're more akin to hit men than gumshoes these days."

"What happened?"

"The world got meaner. We adjusted."

She stared blankly. "A bogeyman. I never realized."

"It's pretty common knowledge."

"I've been away. I've lived in a convent since I was fifteen."

I lit another vitacig. "Yeah? Upset your parents?"

"I was a nun."

That explained her flagrant piousness. "Why'd you quit?"

She looked at the table. "Have you ever seen an angel, Mr. Strait?"

I shook my head as she looked at me with those concrete chips. Whenever our eyes locked, I had to restrain myself from leaning toward her.

"Neither have I," she said, her eyes returning to the table. "When my parents died, I left the convent to look after Jackie. But it was too late to save her."

We sat in silence for a moment. She stroked her lower lip with an index finger and stared into space. I was beginning to detect a depth to her that defied her virginal image, a hint of subconscious sultriness her outward frigidity couldn't entirely conceal.

"A hired killer," she said speculatively.

"It's not the only thing I do."

"But it's the main thing."

"Yes."

"I don't know if I want to hire a killer."

"Believe it or not, Miss Pan, killer and idiot are not synonymous. I know my way around the City. If you want me to look for her, I will. If you have moral objections, go find someone else. I can tell you right now, though, you're going to have a hard time finding a white knight in this part of town."

"Oh, really? What happened to them?"

"They were killed by the people they were supposed to protect."

"I'll hire if you can guarantee me no one will get hurt."

"I can't make any guarantees. Kidnapping is a violent trade. There may be some violence involved in getting Jackie back—you have to accept that. If you can't, maybe you don't want her back as much as you think."

Her head jerked up. "No, I want her back. I really do. I just don't want anyone's death on my conscience."

"Just because I'm on a case doesn't mean I'm going to walk out in the street and start shooting people. If I do shoot anyone, they had it coming."

"Like the men in your office."

"Right. But don't get me wrong. Heck, most days I don't kill *anyone* before lunch." She appeared shocked, and I comforted her with a smile. "That's a joke." She didn't say anything. "I *mean* well," I said.

She stared at me with those big silver tear makers, and I started to lean. Her lips parted and her eyes softened, then she caught herself. She dropped her hands to the purse in her lap and frowned at them. Her repressed sultriness was like a body that wouldn't stay buried; it kept popping up at the most embarrassing moments. "All right, Mr. Strait. What are your rates?"

"Three hundred a day plus expenses. The first week is paid in advance."

"That's quite expensive."

"I won't be wasting your time."

"I believe you won't." She reached into her purse and came out with a big wad of credits.

"I didn't realize the sisterhood paid so well," I said.

"My parents left Jackie and me a substantial inheritance."

She left me twenty-one bills, her sister's picture and a number I could reach her at. "I may be out of town for a while, though."

"I'll leave a message if you're not in."

She nodded and got up, then seemed to remember something. "There's one more thing I should tell you, Mr. Strait."

"What's that?"

"My parents did not die of natural causes. They were murdered. The party responsible was never caught."

I looked up at her. There were questions I wanted to ask but I instinctively knew they would only complicate matters. Even the most innocuous mouse of a case could turn into a gnashing multiheaded monster if you prodded it enough. I liked myself enough to keep my cases straightforward and simple. "I'll keep that in mind," I said.

She nodded, then walked away. My eyes followed her to the door. She didn't walk like a nun.

I ordered another screwdriver to celebrate my surviving the morning and another to mark the beginning of a new case. The fourth congratulated my good luck, the fifth saluted the dead men in my office, the sixth was for my headache, and I couldn't think of a good reason for the seventh. By the time the eighth rolled around, I didn't need any cheap excuses.

I left the bar feeling in total control of my destiny, my power assured, undaunted by any eventuality, good or ill. It was what I liked best about alcohol; it fed you the big lie when you were in a state to believe it. I stumbled to my car and drove to the ghetto of Colfax, home of riots, rampant crime and my rent-free squat.

2

I stepped off the elevator and noticed three goons in overcoats and fedoras lurking around my apartment door. These goons I knew.

"The donut shop's down the street, boys," I said, unlocking my many locks.

A tall, skeletal man worked the skin stretched over his skull-like face into a sneer. "Where you been, Strait? We've missed you."

"I flew down to the Bahamas to expand my butterfly collection," I said, slurring only a little.

"Maybe you should have stayed there. I hear the Hayward Pimp Association is looking for you."

"Yes, I've had a word with them. They missed me, too." As I went inside, the trio followed.

"I always figured you lived in a dump like this," the skeleton said.

I peeked into the bedroom to see if Monique was around. She wasn't. I dropped into a plaid armchair and lit a vitacig. "What do you want, Degas?"

SPF Inspector Degas sat on the arm of a red vinyl sofa, the centerpiece of my daringly eclectic living room set, and his pals spread out, poking around for casual clues. Degas removed his hat, revealing close-cropped, prematurely gray hair. He set the hat carefully on his knee and began picking lint from its crown. "You hit a husband-wife terrorist team two months ago in a City bookstore," he said. "A Mr. and Mrs. Cassady."

"Since when does the Party's Security and Protection Force have an interest in things criminal?" I noticed there was a folded note on the coffee table in front of me. The word "Jake" was underlined and circled in Monique's florid scribble. "I thought your interests ran more toward political offenses."

"Do you remember the hit or not?"

"Sounds familiar," I said, picking up the note.

"Let me refresh your memory. During a brief shootout you killed the husband and spared the wounded wife."

"She was pregnant," I said, unfolding the note. "I told reclamation to take her to the hospital."

"That's right. She was held in a Party hospital's detention ward for three days before she managed to find something sharp, to slash her jugular."

"Did the infant survive?"

Dear Jake, the note began.

"Why do you care?"

"I'm sentimental."

Even as I write this I don't know if I'm doing the right thing.

"They were able to save it."

"Well, perhaps there's a God after all."

I'm leaving you. Don't think that I never loved you, because I did, even if you did murder my father. Really. Love, Monique.

I carefully refolded the note, making sure the creases were perfectly straight, went to the door and threw it open. "Thanks for the update, Inspector. You may leave now."

"I'm not through yet."

"This is a SPF no-go area, spif. I could raise the hue and cry, and you and your playmates would be lynched before dinnertime."

Degas put a hand inside his coat and came up with a comunit the size of a cigarette lighter. "I say the word, and Party rotors reduce this building to smoking rubble."

I reflected for a moment, then closed the door and returned to the armchair. "All right," I said. "You can stay. But if you think I'm putting you up for the night, you're crazy."

Degas moved his lips just enough to fake a passable smile, then continued. "Mrs. Cassady revealed some rather remarkable things while in our care."

"Yeah? What'd you squeeze out of her?"

"Something about a data chip of information on her husband's person."

"That a fact?"

"We managed to contact reclamation before they dumped Joshua Cassady into a protein vat. We conducted a complete body scan, a scan so thorough even a microchip wouldn't escape detection."

"Let me guess. You didn't find the chip."

Degas glanced at his boys, who stood on either side of him. "Didn't I tell you guys Strait was sharp?" He looked back at me. "That's right. But we were at a disadvantage. Not all of Joshua's body made it into reclamation's hands. A piece of him was missing."

"A hand, perhaps?"

"That's right. His scanhand. Of course, it is customary for a bogeyman to take the scanhand as proof of his deed, so he can collect his bounty from the SPF."

"As is right and just."

"Our data banks, however, contain no record of you ever turning in that hand. Which is strange, since there was quite a lucrative reward involved, in the neighborhood of two-thousand credits."

I shrugged. "Maybe I'm not motivated by financial reward."

"That's not the Strait I know."

"Perhaps I've changed."

"Perhaps you're a liar." Degas smiled his thin, skeletal smile. "Where's the hand?"

"I paid a restaurant tab with it."

"Don't play games with me, Strait."

"Honest to God. Check with the wait staff at the Shamrock Café in Borders. They'll tell you."

Degas whispered to the datacorder on his wrist, then addressed me. "We also have witnesses at the scene of the hit who say you had a little talk with the wounded Mrs. Cassady before you left. What did you talk about?"

I shrugged. "This and that."

"Did she mention a religion or any names?"

"Not that I recall."

"What did she say?"

"She told me to kill her."

"Why didn't you?"

"I don't take orders from criminals."

Degas picked one final speck of lint off his hat, then rose. "You're not telling us everything. That could come back on you."

"A karmic backlash?"

He put on his hat, taking a moment to place it at the proper cant and tilt, then walked to the door. His goons walked backward, covering his retreat. "I could take you down to SPF central and twist it out of you," Degas said, opening the door.

"You wouldn't get out of this building alive."

"Perhaps not. But neither would you."

I shrugged. "Sounds like a bad deal all around."

"We'll be talking again."

"Sure," I said, getting up. "Bring a bottle and some prettier girls along, and we'll have a party."

I locked the door on angry faces, sat down and reread the note. As a trained detective, I figured I'd be able to detect subtle clues that would reveal the note as an elaborate hoax. Ten minutes of intense deciphering revealed no hidden codes.

I went to the bedroom, opened the closet and confronted the brooding void where Monique's many vestments once hung. *No, no hoax.*

I prowled around the apartment, taking account of what was missing. She'd taken everything she had claim to, however vague. She'd even taken the picture of us sitting together on the Oldsmobile, holding hands and grinning like naive newlyweds. She'd left no residue whatsoever. *Nothing to burn.*

I stood in the middle of the living room, thinking disquiet thoughts. "I hate this place," I told the furniture. "I never liked it. Never will."

I retreated to the kitchen. I could feel something big moving toward me and I instinctively understood it was the tidal wave of her leaving. It wouldn't roll over me just yet. The idea had just hit the outer defenses, and hope was still entrenched in my heart, a desperate fighter and a hard bastard to kill. Like a faithful dog, it would guard the body of its dead master long after common sense told it to give up. Oh, but when it did wise up, Mr. Screaming Agony would be leaning on the doorbell.

I went to the cupboard beneath the sink and dug out a

grime-coated bottle of mescal. It had appeared there during some long-lost weekend, and I'd ignored it for months, unwilling to confront what dark premonition made me bring home something so consummately vile. Now I understood.

I sat at the kitchen table and twisted off the dusty cap. The terrible odor hit my nose like a spiked fist, and I jammed the bottle into my mouth before I lost my nerve. I took a long pull, gagged, then took another to wash back the vomit crawling up my throat. Straight from the well— that was always the best way, I couldn't allow myself to be limited or restrained by the capacity of cup or glass; there could be no slacking tonight.

3

Morning arrived on the back of a horrific hangover, my skull too fragile and tight for the swollen and throbbing flesh inside. I had paid the terrible price and now I could accept she was gone. I blamed that cruel pimp Fate; he was always screwing me. I even entertained the notion that she'd been a figment of my imagination. There was certainly no physical proof, just some dim memories and in the end memories always turned out to be cheap and gaudy whores.

I went through the breakfast ritual with awkward inattention. I rehydrated a mound of egg-and-potato-flavored soy and washed it down with strong cups of kelp coffee. The morning news flashed over the table monitor, but I was too concerned about my own woes to browse through everybody else's. I wanted to get on the kidnapped-sister case, but there was the small matter of one of the City's more powerful crime syndicates disliking me enough to want me dead. It made me nervous, and I found it hard to concentrate on other matters.

I poured another cup of kelp coffee and looked up the HPA's main office on the monitor. I switched the monitor to the telephone mode and gave them a call.

"Hayward Pimp Association," a businesslike female voice said, the monitor's screen remaining rudely blank.

"I'd like to talk to the head pimp," I said.

"Mr. Hayes is in conference," she said. "Can I take a message?"

"No, thanks. Who can I talk to about a hit contract?"

"You want the public relations office. I'll put you through."

There was a click, a brief ringing, then another click. "Public relations," a low male voice said.

"I'd like to check the status of a hit contract."

"Who's it on?"

"Jake Strait."

"Hold on." I could hear key clicks in the background. "Okay. Jake Strait, death contract, ten-thousand-credit bounty payable upon proof of demise. Would you like his stats?"

"I know them. Put me back through to the main line."

"Hayward Pimp Association," the female voice said.

"I'd like to leave a message for Mr. Hayes."

"Yes?"

"Tell him Jake Strait called concerning a contract and that I will enact on my promise of retribution should he not adjust his position concerning my welfare."

"'Straight' as in 'straight as an arrow'?"

"No. 'Strait' as in 'dire straits.'"

"Got it. Would you like to leave a number?"

"No, thanks," I said, and cut the connection. I went to the closet, put on a rugged black-and-gray envirosuit, then packed a bag with the things I'd need to help change Mr. Hayes's mind.

An hour later I crouched atop the six-story building across the street from the Silver Spoon Café, favorite hang-out of Hayward pimps. I sighted down the enviroscope of the Phillips speed rifle, bracing its barrel against the parapet. Pimps came and went at a leisurely pace, making for easy targets. I waited for a particular one.

Sonny "Stick" Hesse strutted out of the Silver Spoon and struck a pose on the curb, lighting a cigarette with quick, choppy gestures. I thumbed the magnification button on the enviroscope, and Stick's televised image went to close-up. I watched smoke shoot out of his nostrils in twin streams, clouding his cruel face. Stick didn't get his name from his narrow frame. He got it from the way he punished and occasionally killed whichever of his whores he imagined had gone astray. He whipped them with a pimp stick, a stretched-out metal hanger.

I clicked the acquisition stud on the handgrip. The enviroscope shot out an infrared beam and adjusted for distance, wind, temperature and barometric pressure. I thumbed the magnification again until Stick's face filled the scope. I put the red dot of the beam between his eyes and squeezed the trigger.

A minirocket zipped down the infrared beam and hit Stick's head, splattering the whores around him with gore and skull fragments. Stick's body, with nothing to show from the jaw up, teetered in confusion, then tipped over. The rifle was back in its case and my feet were on the sidewalk before the screaming stopped.

I drove to a part of town that didn't know my face, ate an early dinner in a Turkish restaurant, then spent the day in a coffee shop whose main business seemed to consist of seeing how many customers they could piss off. I browsed through the array of underground newspapers on hand and waited for the grapevine to do its work. When night fell, I wheeled around town until my lids got heavy then parked in front of an all-night Laundromat. Falling asleep was a cinch once I got used to the emergency-brake lever digging into my ribs.

In the morning I called the HPA from the Laundromat's public phone.

"Public relations," the low voice said.

"I want to check on the status of a contract. Jake Strait."

Keys clicked. "You're in luck. The bounty just doubled to twenty thousand." There was a suspicious pause. "May I ask who is calling?"

I hung up and looked at the housewives lined up on a wooden bench like despondent crows. They stared into the spinning bellies of the laundry machines, by all appearances hypnotized by the hum and motion. I sat next to a middle-aged Latino woman and tried not to think about the new price on my head.

"Just like life," I said, watching the socks and T-shirts tumble. "Tossed around by a cruelly indifferent machine, round and round, getting the soul and humanity sucked right out of you." I looked at her. "What do you think?"

The Latino woman frowned deeply, eyeing me suspiciously. She instinctively understood a man without laundry dropping non sequiturs in a Laundromat was not a man to be trusted. *"No comprende,"* she muttered.

"Yeah, me neither." I got up. "Well, back to work."

THE SILVERSTEIN BROTHERS operated their brothel out of an old business tower. They kept their operation and girls slightly upscale to draw in the suburban crowd, married men with more appetite than conscience. I happened to know the Silversteins ran an efficient blackmail operation.

After renting a motel room and changing clothes, I slunk into the Silverstein Tower's lobby-lounge dressed like a well-off exec looking for some discreet and tasteful action. I took a stool at the bar and ordered a beer. The big, friendly bartender delivered my drink with such a complete lack of animosity I was immediately put on guard. Keeping an eye on him, I surveyed the talent.

The lighting and price of beer were both low enough to depreciate any standards one might have had upon entrance. I dished out longing looks all around, and eventually a bobbed brunette with an eye patch and an interesting gap between her front teeth pushed off from the bar and strolled my way. She was perhaps thirty, past her prime as a hooker. There was a fallen arrogance in her walk, shadows of a vanity lost. She fired off a demure smile at five meters, then went straight for the jugular.

"Looking for a date?" she demanded.

I looked around with bewilderment, as if I'd walked into the wrong place. "You mean like dinner and a movie?"

"We can skip that part. What I meant to say is, are you looking for a good time?"

I sighed and shrugged. "Good time, bad time, who really knows what they're looking for?"

She gave me a puzzled look. "How's that?"

I toyed nervously with the wedding band I'd slipped on before coming in. "Yes, I am. A discreet and tasteful good time."

"That's all we got around here," she said, back on track. She latched on to my forearm and pulled. "C'mon, you big lug."

"But I haven't finished my beer," I protested, locking my ankles around the legs of the bar stool.

"There's better things than beer," she said, detaching me from the bar stool with an emphatic jerk. Maintaining a firm grip on my arm, she steered me toward two big men idling near an elevator. "The rooms are upstairs," she explained.

"You don't think much of the civility of small talk, do you?"

"Small talk is a social cancer we can do without. Besides, my shift is almost over."

The bouncers looked me up and down, then demanded three hundred credits for her and fifty for the room. I affected the sheepish grin of the straying husband and handed over four hundred credits. With an open arrogance they shortchanged me twenty credits, their sneering faces daring me to do something about it. I shoved the change in my pocket as if eager to complete the financial aspect of the deal. My date exaggerated a yawn, of which the bouncers took more than casual notice, and she and I got on the elevator.

As the car started upward, I rolled the ring around my finger manically, oozing angst and guilt.

She looked down at my hands. "That thing burning you?"

I acted surprised, then smiled wanly. "Like it was red-hot."

"Got a wife, huh?" she said sympathetically.

"And seven kids."

"Seven? You seem young for seven kids."

"Most are adopted," I said, fast on my feet. "Homeless war orphans." I tried wringing the guilt from my hands.

She put her arms around me and gave me a motherly hug. "It's okay, honey. Everyone needs a break from the family rut. You're not doing anything bad."

I looked at my reflection in the polished chrome of the elevator button panel and winked at myself. "Really?"

"Of course. And no one is going to know except you and me. It'll be our little secret."

The elevator doors hummed open, and I stepped out of

her arms. She led me to room 2214 and opened the door.
The decor was Las Vegas swank, circa 1975. Banks of
smoky, diamond-shaped mirrors occupied whole walls,
gaudily painted plaster lions and tigers growled from beneath decadently ornate pseudomarble Roman tables, and
there were tassels everywhere, on the rugs, the tapestries,
the grotesque lamp shades.

Velcro snapped and my date's clothes went from skin to
floor with one efficient motion. She lay back on the red
satin bedspread, spread her legs and started making impatient sounds. After a moment of my eyeing her glumly, she
sat up. "C'mon," she sighed, slapping the bed. "Have a
seat."

I sat down and lolled my head. "This is the first time
I've ever done this. I guess I'm a little scared."

"It's okay," she said, putting an arm around me. "Everybody cheats now and then."

I stared at her. "Oh, I've cheated before. I've just never
slept with a one-eyed person."

She looked affronted, then laughed it off. "It had to
happen sooner or later, baby."

"My Henrietta, she isn't a bad wife. It's just that she's,
well, *unresponsive* in certain ways, to certain needs."

"I know," she said, unbuttoning my shirt. "And no one
can blame you for wanting to have a little fun. It's like my
daddy used to say, there's no reason a hog should have to
eat from the same trough all the time."

"That's *beautiful*. Jesus, I'm spilling my guts to you and
I don't even know your name."

"It's Jeanne. Jeanne from Bihimi." She giggled. "Let me
help you with that belt."

"You're from Bihimi?"

"No, but it rhymes. Don't you get it?"

I told her I did, and with Jeanne's help I got undressed. She pulled me to the middle of the bed like a tiger dragging a carcass and went to work on me.

I admired anyone who approached their work with a professional attitude and I couldn't find a single fault with Jeanne's performance. Instead of following the whore's maxim of getting it over with as quickly as possible, she seemed intent on making it last. We changed positions a dozen times, and she always made certain I faced a particular smoked mirror above the headboard. I made certain of adjusting my head so they'd get my good side. When the sweat began to run, I found myself caught up in the action and tried not to let the tacky surroundings and distant audience diminish the ambience. I focused my energies, and we made one last brutal, capture-the-hill-at-all-costs charge in the missionary position. I collapsed into her arms, reveling in the warmth and wetness of our sweat.

"Henrietta doesn't know what she's missing," she whispered hoarsely.

"Can I come back again?" I asked hopefully.

She looked up at me, and for an instant regret clouded the mercenary coldness of her eye. "Sure," she said flatly, slipping from beneath me. "Why don't you jump in the shower and I'll join you in a minute."

"Okay," I said, and went to the shower, a big goofy grin on my face.

Jeanne didn't join me in the shower, but I hadn't expected her to. Toweling off, I stepped out of the bathroom to find the room occupied. But not by Jeanne from Bihimi.

"The bosses wants to talk with you," a burly, middle-aged thug told me. I recognized him as one of the unethical bouncers from downstairs.

"With me?" I squeaked. "What could they want with me?"

He shrugged.

"Mind if I get dressed?"

He shrugged again. "Suit yourself."

I laughed at his cleverness. "I bet you get a lot of laughs with that one."

He shrugged again.

After I'd suited myself, we took a ride to the penthouse suite. The elevator opened into a lavish office of white-oak panelling, potted palms and crystal chandeliers. Behind matching gold-gilded, mirror-finished chrome desks sat the Silverstein twins, Ciro and Ronni.

"Did you check him for heat?" Ronni asked the muscle.

"I checked his clothing while he was in the shower."

"You've been bad," Ciro, the shorter and hairier of the two, pointed out.

"How so?" I countered.

He turned around the monitor on his desk so I could see it. It was me and Jeanne wrestling on the bed.

"I don't know," I said after a moment of viewing. "I think I did pretty good."

Ronni sighed and rolled his eyes. "Every other one is a wiseass these days. Where's the remorse and guilt anymore? It used to be a man broke down and goddamn *cried* with grief and terror when confronted with evidence of him shagging some bimbo while the wifey was at home baking cookies for the kiddies. What's the world coming to?"

"The bottom line," Ciro said, "is unless we get a check from you each month for twenty percent of your gross income, and we'll find out how much you pull down, we'll be forced to make available an unlimited number of video-chip copies to your friends and family."

"I don't know," I whined. "Twenty percent is a lot. How would I explain it to my wife?"

"Tell her it's a new kind of insurance premium," Ronni suggested. "Marriage insurance."

"What if I say no?"

"Then you might consider it life insurance."

I stroked my chin thoughtfully. "Can I have some time to think it over?"

"Sure," Ciro said, looking at his watch. "You got thirty seconds." They steepled their fingers and put on fragile smiles, the kind likely to collapse if you said the wrong thing. I smiled back and thought it over. The bodyguard stood to my left, arms folded. I shifted my weight a little and visualized a plan of action, running the violence through my head again and again.

"Time's up," Ronni said. "Are you gonna walk outta here poorer and wiser or disgraced and deader?"

"How about if I walk outta here rich and wise both?"

They laughed in sync. "How you gonna manage that?" Ronni asked.

"Like this," I said, driving my heel into the side of the thug's knee. His leg gave at the joint, and he collapsed to the carpet, howling. I dropped a knee into his larynx to shut him up, then pulled the revolver from his shoulder holster in time to catch Ciro lifting an automatic from his desk. The gun in my hand barked once, and Ciro's shoulder exploded, spilling the pistol from his hand.

I moved toward them, pointing the revolver. "Good night, gentlemen."

"Hold on!" Ronni yelled. "You can have the video!"

"Naw, you keep it," I said.

"What do ya want, then?"

"Your lives."

Realization clicked in Ciro's eyes. "He's that rogue bogeyman creep Marcus told us to watch out for."

"That's me." I pointed the pistol at Ronni's head.

"Hold on, for crissakes," Ronni cried, waving at the gun. "I ain't ready to die yet!"

"Yeah?" I said. "Why not?"

"I don't know, you kinda caught me short. If you woulda killed me out of the blue, that would have been all right, but now you got my interest up."

"When are you gonna be ready, then?"

"I don't know, man, it's not one of those things you can just predict."

"Okay," I said. "We can talk for a while." I sat on the edge of Ronni's desk. "So what made you guys want to be pimps anyway?"

"Gotta make a livin' somehow," Ronni said.

"There's better ways than pimping."

"Yeah," Ciro said dryly. "We could be killers like you."

"Why you wanna antagonize the man?" Ronni said, glaring at his brother. "Why you always gotta screw things up?"

"Why's he wanna kill us is what I'd like to know," Ciro said.

"Yeah," Ronni said. "Why you wanna kill us?"

"Ah, man, don't ask me," I said. "I'm just Fate's triggerman."

"Who's this Fate guy?" Ronni asked, hope jumping into his eyes. "Maybe we can work a deal."

"*Fate,* you idiot," Ciro said to his brother. "He means like destiny. It's a pun." He looked at me. "Ain't he dense? It's a pun, right?"

"Sort of," I said.

"See?" Ciro said to Ronni. "It was a pun."

The conversation fizzled, and I raised the pistol again.

"Hold on!" Ronni said. "How can you talk to us like we're just a coupla guys, then casually feed us bullets?"

"You know, it used to bother me." I shrugged. "But now it's easy. I guess you get used to anything."

"Go ahead and shoot," Ciro said. "My shoulder's killing me anyway."

"Oh, nice," Ronni said. "Tell the man to shoot us. That's fine for you to say, you're all wounded and probably gonna die anyway."

"That's right," Ciro said. "And you're going right along with me." He laughed meanly. "And you were always bragging about how you'd outlive me. Watching your frigging cholesterol and exercising all the time. Lotta good it's gonna do you now."

"It ain't quantity, it's quality. I've lived a full life, I got a big house, a beautiful wife...."

"Yeah, some kinda wife," Ciro interrupted. "Ugly as a cancer wart, but I guess that never stopped me from putting it to her. I was never gonna tell you but...but what the hell. I've been shagging your wife every Sunday for the past fifteen years. While you was out playing golf, I'd be plugging her right on your living room floor."

"Liar!" Ronni cried. "Stella would never cheat on me!"

"Oh, wise up. Didn't you ever wonder why she always had rug burns on her ass?"

"That's a hereditary rash!" Ronni screamed, lunging for his brother's throat. "I'll kill you, you lying son of a bitch!"

I pulled the trigger twice, and Ciro and Ronni exited the world as they'd entered, together and screaming.

I spent the next three days in the cheap motel room I'd rented, watching TV and doing push-ups. I wanted to give the HPA time to think hard about the way things were going. On the morning of the third day, I packed up and gave the HPA a call from the motel lobby.

"What's Strait worth now?" I asked public relations.

"Thirty thousand."

"Well, that's just great." I hung up. It seemed the HPA was a stickler on principle. It was time for a personal visit.

4

I looked up at the building. For a gang of pimps, the HPA had rather Victorian tastes. The mauve-and-aqua three-story town house serving as their main office was located in the kind of neighborhood that attracted reclusive dowagers with too many cats. The paint was fresh, the lawn and hedges recently trimmed, the guards at the door tastefully attired.

I'd sat in my parked car since noon, watching the front of the building. I didn't know what Marcus Hayes looked like, but the big cruiser sitting in the president's parking space hadn't moved all day. Clerical types came and went until five o'clock rolled around and then they mostly went. Yet the big cruiser remained. Evening arrived, and except for a new shift of guards, the only sign of life was a light burning on the top floor.

I went for a walk around the building. On its east side I found what I was looking for. A sturdy drainpipe snaked up the shingles, passing near a third-story balcony. I stepped over the white picket fence that guarded the yard and went to the base of the pipe. When I pulled on it, it creaked only a little. I hoisted myself up, bracing my feet on the wall. All the Victorian protrusions made for easy going, and in a matter of seconds I was crouched on the third-floor balcony.

The sliding glass door was unlocked, so I let myself into a dark hallway. Long tapestries of medieval design hung from the walnut-paneled walls, illuminated by light flooding from beneath a door at the end of the hall. I drew my pistol and crept toward the light.

I opened the door and stepped inside. A huge cherrywood desk sat in the middle of the room. A small brass lamp atop the desk was the only source of light. A large black man sat behind the desk, his shaved head bent low over the papers he scratched with a quill pen. His eyes glanced up, went to the gun in my hand, then back to the papers.

I sat in a dainty chair uncomfortable enough to be antique and watched him. He finished the paper he was working on, put the pen back in its well and looked at me with an unfathomable expression.

I smiled. "Hello."

He took off his wire-rimmed spectacles and rubbed his bloodshot eyes. "You going to shoot me?" he asked in a deep voice, his accent somewhere between Harvard and Harlem.

"Maybe," I said. "I'm Jake Strait."

He thought for a moment, then nodded. "Thought you might be coming around. How'd you get in?"

"Your security isn't very good. I think the HPA has come to rely too much on the mythical power of its name for protection. That's dangerous." I leaned back in the chair. "I've come to talk business."

The pimp half smiled. "You've been busy, bogeyman."

"I'm a workaholic."

He nodded. "You've done a good job at making the HPA look bad. Why, a dozen of my members called me today, concerned about their safety. What am I supposed to tell them?"

I shrugged. "You know how it is. I hated to be so heavy-handed about it, but I was having a hard time making a point."

"That being?"

"Well," I said, leaning forward and bringing heavy hand and pistol language into play. "I think it was sort of a cry for help. I was subconsciously projecting the fear and aggression that arises from having an important and vital part of one's life threatened. The breathing part, for example."

"Oh," he said, rubbing his chin thoughtfully, "that fear-of-death thing."

"Yeah, that thing." I leaned back in the chair. "Man, you really understand me."

"I can get behind what you're saying," he said, folding his hands on the desk. "But what do you want from *me?*"

"I want to offer you a deal."

His eyes slitted. "What kind of deal?"

"You call off the contract, and I let you and the rest of your association live."

He chuckled. "Now, how would that make the HPA look if I let you off like that? You've killed some of our most prestigious clients."

"What if I said I was sorry?"

He stared at me for a moment, then said, "What would the street think if we accepted just an apology, however heartfelt?"

"They'd think you noble."

"The street doesn't understand that word."

"Yes, but the street also has a short memory. I don't think you'd suffer much PR damage in the long run."

He laughed. "Seeing how you got the gun, I'd be stupid to say no, wouldn't I?"

"Yes, you would."

"As soon as you left, I could have a memory lapse and forget about the whole agreement."

"I'd come back for you."

"You might not be able to get near me next time."

"I got in here once, I can do it again."

"I could increase my security, hire some more body-guards."

"Yeah, you could live in a shell for a while, but sooner or later a little daylight would show and I'd get you. I don't think you want to live like that. Always glancing over your shoulder, fearing shadows like a scared old lady."

He smiled, nodding slowly. "Yes. But you have to give me something in return for your pardon."

"I already did. Your life."

He looked at me with his crocodile eyes and laughed. "Okay, Mr. Bogeyman, you got me. I'll spread the word you atoned for your sins. Made a deal with the devil."

I regarded Hayes, not knowing if I could trust the devil or not. Something told me I could. "All right," I said, standing up. "My life for yours."

"Yes, that's right," Hayes said, then laughed as if he'd said something funny. "Whether you think so or not, Mr. Bogeyman, you owe me one."

"Only as much as you want to believe," I said, and went out the way I'd come in.

I spent the night in my apartment, sleeping with my faith in the devil.

5

I spent the morning at the table monitor, drinking kelp and sifting through library files, news reports and data banks for information concerning the Set of One. I learned the set had popped up only four years ago from origins unknown and had spread rapidly, setting up resurrection missions and conversion centers in most of the world's major cities. They had a massive advertising budget, raising most of their capital through telemarketing and liquidation of their converts' worldly possessions. The set's spiritual guidebook, *The Word of One,* had inched its way up the underground bestseller list during the past three years and had just recently broken into the top ten.

For all their ad campaigns and blatant propaganda, there was little information about what the set actually stood for, aside from worshiping a god called One. In fact, the only straightforward and frank thing about the set was its corporate logo, a boldly phallic red arrow thrusting upward, passing through a pink cloud of suspect contour.

The only address listed in the City directory under the Set of One was a resurrection mission on Bukowski, right in the middle of the mission district. With this in mind, I passed on the day's shower and shave, dressed out of the hamper, and opened a bottle of cheap bourbon.

I stood in front of a full-length mirror next to the coat-rack and made certain I looked the part. My suit jacket was wrinkled and soiled, my pants baggy and stained, my shoes scuffed and worn. I disheveled my hair with my fingers and rubbed vitacig ash on my face to complement two days' worth of growth. I looked like a man who'd hit the skids just recently but was not dallying on his way to the bottom.

"A fine-looking wino," I told the mirror. "All we're missing is that essential aroma." I grabbed the fifth of bourbon by its scrawny plastic neck and twisted off its top. I doused the front of my jacket with cheap booze, then rinsed some around my mouth. The thing was, before I could spit the bourbon out I'd accidentally swallowed it. I tried again, and the same thing happened. What the hell, I thought, taking a pull of the bottle. I'd go all the way, I'd actually *drink* the bottle as a real wino would. A dedicated private enforcer was always willing to go that extra distance to ensure the completeness of his disguise.

Five minutes later and I was strolling down Hayward toward its intersection with Bukowski, the liquor in my walk no lie.

Besides serving as a magnet for the destitute, the long stretch of Bukowski Boulevard termed the mission district also embodied the City's damned soul, the thriving nucleus of spiritual activity. This was not surprising, considering the highly religious nature of most winos. I walked among the video preachers and street-corner messiahs, past the confession machines in which you could dial in your sins, feed in the appropriate number of coins and be forgiven by a computer-generated voice, all approved by the mad-man in Rome. I experienced the horror of a religion that had become morally bankrupt, an arcade-style vacuum of greed, a cheap circus event that sold prayers and salvation for cold hard cash.

Soon I was passing the rescue missions, distinguished by blank-eyed old ladies in the uniforms of the Lord ringing bells, calling in the hungry and heathen alike. I found the Set of One Resurrection Mission between a flophouse and a hockshop. Aside from its skin of fervent red paint and the frantically winking red neon phallic symbol on its front, the set mission looked much like the rest of the ilk. I decided I'd stake it out from across the street for a while.

"You, sir!" a mechanical voice squawked in my ear. "You look like a sinner! Come shake the healing hand of Jesus!"

I turned to face a life-size plastic-and-steel mock-up of Christ set in a concrete base on the sidewalk. "Only a quarter cred a shake!" the speaker in the messiah's belly said. When I backed away from the machine, it shut up. I moved close, and it started up again. Heat sensor, I thought. I pushed a quarter cred into the slot in its chest, and the right hand shot up. I got a firm grip, and the mechanical fingers closed on my hand. Holy water squirted from a nozzle between its chrome teeth, neon eyes flashed, and the speaker cried out, "You are healed!"

"At long last," I said, and tried to pull my hand free. The machine's grip tightened.

"Five credits, and I'll let you go, sinner!" Christ announced. The hand began to squeeze like an iron vise, and I found the plastic. Jesus laughed and let me go, squawking, "Better luck next time, sinner!"

I backed away from the malicious machine, bumping into a molded-plastic kiosk bearing a sign that read, Zach's One Hundred Ways To Paradise. Over A Hundred Faiths To Choose From, Complete With Full Starter Kits Containing All Essential Literature And Paraphernalia. A slumming middle-aged exec parried with the intense-faced, pony-tailed hipster manning the counter.

"I want a religion that provides good social order but isn't heavy-handed about my personal life," the exec said. "No confessions or self-flagellation. And lots of holidays."

The hipster cross-indexed on a computer, chewing the stub of an unlit hashish cigar. "How about Xipe Totec, the flayed god of agriculture and penitential self-torture? I'm having a special on him."

"I'll bet you are."

"Well, there's Erzulie, the Haitian goddess of love, beauty, flowers, jewels, dancing and fine clothes."

"She sounds like an expensive whore."

"How about Holda, a righteous Germanic deity?"

"What's her line?"

"She's the goddess of fertility and hearth."

"I don't know, she sounds kind of stuffy. I want one with a more festive nature."

"Like Bacchus?"

"Yeah, but nothing that trendy. I want someone new and fresh."

"You could devote yourself to Ueuecoyotl, the Aztec god of sex, irresponsible gaiety and socially unacceptable impulses," the hipster said. "He's very lenient with the rules, has sixty-seven religious holidays per annum and one hell of a year-end festival. We're talking two solid weeks of serious, guilt-free partying."

The exec wrinkled his brow. "He sounds like a good time, but what about this god's personality? I mean, is he laid-back? I mean, *really* laid-back?"

"Friend, if he was any more laid-back he'd be laying down."

"Ueuecoyotl, huh? Okay, I'll take a chance. What's the outlay?"

"Fifty credits gets you the *Whispering Coyote's Secrets of Life* guidebook, a packet of holy incense, a half gram of sacred mescaline, a glow-in-the-dark coyote statuette and a full one-year membership in the Ueuecoyotl Sect."

"I'll take it."

The faith vendor took the exec's plastic, and the convert hurried home with his new god. I approached the kiosk.

"You heard about a god called One?" I asked.

The man looked at me, then lowered his eyes to a newspaper spread across the counter. "Yeah, I heard of him. But I'm not selling his line."

"Why not?"

"He doesn't franchise out. In fact, I understand he doesn't like competition, if you know what I mean."

"One of those jealous kinda gods, eh?"

"Yeah, one of those." He ran a hand through his long bangs, exposing a tragically high widow's peak. "You know, I can't understand why people go for the mean, hateful ones. They must think the harder the job, the better the pension, but it doesn't always work out that way. I could set you up with a god with a hell of a lot better attitude for a handful of change."

"No, thanks," I said. "Tell me, though, which god do you believe in?"

"Me? Shit, man, I think one god is too many. I'm just trying to make an honest buck."

"That's what I thought." I moved down the sidewalk until I mingled with a loose crowd gathered around a young hoodlum sporting gang fashions, laying out a sermon. I stood on the fringe of the group, shifting my gaze between the speaker and the set mission.

"Christ is comin'," the young hood said, "and the mother is mad. We done screwed him up once, nailing his ass to a cross, and this time he ain't gonna talk no hep about forgiveness. Hell, no, Christ gonna do a drive-by on the whole planet, and if you ain't wearin' his colors you're going *down*, my man, down to the hot barrio. So if I was you, I'd be joinin' up with the Jesus posse and get on with the baptismal initiation before he slides back in, 'cause his machine gun got *soul-killin'* bullets and he's lookin' to throw down with your own devil-lovin' sinna self. So you betta get right and sign up with the Combined Christian Militia 'fore it's too late to save your raggy sinna ass."

"Yeah, he's coming all right," a youth wearing an Allah's Assassins jacket heckled from the crowd. "And you better believe Muhammad'll be laying for his ass."

"Goddamn heathen-ass!" the preacher shouted back. "Christ gonna whup up on Muhammad so ruthless, Allah'll wish he never gave up his camel-herding job."

The exchange menaced along, and I watched a steady stream of winos filing into the set mission. It must have been close to dinnertime. I detached myself from the crowd and crossed the street.

A prim young man wearing thick glasses and a two-credit smile shook my hand at the door. "What's your name?" he asked exuberantly.

"Sammy," I lied.

"I'm Ted," he said, pointing at the name tag pinned to his lapel: Hi, I'm Ted And I'm Going To Show You The One Path To Paradise. He got busy with a marker, and in no time at all I had a stick-on name tag that read Hi, I'm Sammy And I Have Found The One Path To Paradise.

"Now you're on the right path," Ted said, beaming as if I were a dull child making reasonable progress with my potty training.

"Praise the Lord," I said mechanically.

Ted flinched, and his beaming face dissolved into the kind of mean stare the righteous reserve for infidels. "You can go to the arcades down the street if you want to grovel to that old myth," he said firmly. "We are not enslaved to the old gods here."

"Yeah?" I said. "Which deity runs this joint, then?"

He spared me a smile. "A *new* god. A better god." His face took on a pious yet proud cast as he gazed over my shoulder for good effect, making him go slightly cross-eyed. I left him to his regal pose and took a seat at one of many long rows of tables.

I'd touched bottom enough times to know what the inside of a mission looked like. The set's version seemed more sold on the service side of the job. Instead of having the winos stand in line, sweet young angels of mercy moved among the tables, delivering trays of bread and stew, pouring pitchers of weak coffee and punch. Many a derelict tried to meet an angel's eyes, intent on reviving some forgotten vanity, but the young ladies seemed only to have eyes for One. I turned to the stew. It was the same thin, prayed-over gruel you could find in any mission in the district, yet, like many forms of liquor, the taste seemed to improve as you went along.

I looked over my company as I ate—the same tragic faces common to any inner city in any part of the world. The same red-rimmed eyes dulled by drug and drink, the same greasy hair and beards masking the same dull and hopeless expressions, the same pungent stink, the same un-healed sores on bodies fallen to ruin.

"Boy, there's nothing like set stew," a wino tagged Leo said next to me. "Everyone knows that."

The others at the table nodded vigorously, mumbling agreement through full mouths.

"How long's this place been open?" I asked Leo.

"Four months, and it's already the most popular place in the district," he said. "And it ain't just the stew, brother, it's the message. They lay down a righteous sermon here, anyone can tell you that. Not like those other goddamn places where they make you sing and pray like you was in Sunday school. They treat you with respect here, bring the food right to you, you don't have to stand in goddamn line like a herd of swine." He winked and chuckled. "And everyone knows they got the best-looking girlies in the district!"

The other winos chuckled and rolled their rheumy eyes as if they were all in love with the young servers.

Ted began tapping on a mike on a podium at the head of the tables. "I have an announcement to make," he said with breathless excitement. "We have a special treat in store for you today. Instead of the usual interactive study, a very special and very lovely person has agreed to sing for us!"

"There she is," Leo murmured excitedly as the lights dimmed. "The Magic Girl."

The Magic Girl walked to the podium like a panther, smiling at everyone and no one. She lifted the mike, stepped into a blue spotlight and Jackie Pan began to sing.

She sang with the voice of an angel who had spent time in hell. She began in a pristine tenor, carrying the high notes like an opera diva, then sank into a bluesy giddy-lounge bass that rolled along with a rumbling gothic beat and what sounded like someone tinking on tin cans. Her pronunciation was clear, but I couldn't make out any of the words.

"What language is that?" I asked.

"The language of love." Leo swooned.

Midway through the song, Jackie began strolling about the room at a languid pace. All eyes followed her, and a feeling of contentment fell across the huddled crowd. They forgot their thin gruel and miserable lives as they traded in their mundane sorrows for a fleeting sense of joy that transcended the moment. I washed along with the tide, caught up in the same fanciful lie as the rest. I knew it was a false and temporary idol we worshiped, but in the face of such loveliness, truth didn't seem important. I was certain Jackie's darkly glittering eyes fell on me a dozen times. They would wander the room, then return to me like a faithful lover.

"She's not from this goddamn town," Leo whispered. "She can't be, everyone knows that."

He's right, I thought. The City could not produce such perfection of beauty any more than the barren wastes of Antarctica could spawn a rose.

A violent shiver traveled up my spine. Was *I* thinking those sentimental thoughts? They seemed alien and unfamiliar, as if someone had stuck them in my head. I stared at the faces around me. In the near darkness, all the pathetic masks of assured doom had twisted into expressions of boundless hope and joy, and I was shocked to discover I felt the same mad elation, a mindless exhilaration that I could not explain.

The lighting shifted, and a blue glow turned faces into skulls as hands dropped on my shoulders. I twisted around and fell headlong into the deep brown eyes of Jackie, and suddenly she and I were alone in the crowded hall. For the life of a single breath, we shared an unspeakable intimacy, then she moved on, not missing a note. She was ten meters away before I started breathing again. Her return to the mike stand coincided with the end of the song.

The crowd clapped and howled. Jackie bowed graciously and started toward a side door. Ted, obviously in love, blocked her exit long enough to gush praise and grovel, cupping her hands, swaying before her like a willow in a gusty wind. She smiled and nodded graciously without looking at him. She looked over his shoulder, and I was nearly positive she looked directly at me. Her eyes reached across the crowded room and sank hooks into what had to be my very soul and dragged me into their distant depths. After a dizzy moment she pulled away from Ted and vanished. I started to stand up. I had to follow her, to the ends of the earth if necessary.

"Look at ol' Sammy there," Leo said, laughing. "He's ready to trail her right out the door. But don't feel bad, ol' son, everyone in the place feels the same. Thing is, she's an angel, and we mortals ain't allowed to touch them heavenly creatures. Everyone knows that."

A sudden dizzy fear fell on me and sat me back down. *He's right,* I thought. *I don't deserve her. She couldn't possibly be interested in a bum like me.*

"Maybe you're right," I mumbled.

"'Course I'm right. I been up and down the long, twisty road many a time, and I know a true-to-life angel when I goggle one. If she ain't an angel, I got my doubts about heaven."

I had a hard time following the old wino's rap. A buzzing disquiet had fallen across the room; the angel had flown the coop, and all the grace and civility in the room went with her. Anguished wails and fights broke out as the mob vented its frustration at being left stranded in horrific reality. There was a tremor inside me; I could feel my worldview shifting in its moors. I tried to get a grip on exactly what was going down in the big hollow inside me when Ted grabbed the mike.

"Wasn't she wonderful!" he wailed. "Wasn't she the most! The best! Stupendous! Majestic! Premium!" He slobbered wild-eyed exaltations until he broke down in a fit of rapturous weeping, joined by the more-excitable members of the crowd. When the tears stopped, his voice sank into a mechanical monotone. "Those of you who need spiritual guidance can find it at our prayer tables on the north side of the room. Everyone else, go in peace and come again."

Most of the winos stampeded to a long row of cloth-draped tables manned by a platoon of serious-faced disciples of the set, all wearing black robes and large black sunglasses.

I lingered at the table for a moment, then got in line. One by one the winos ahead of me sat across from a spiritual adviser, placing their hands flat on the table. The adviser would speak to the person quietly, then hand him or her a copy of *The Word of One* and a small plastic card, either white or green. The winos departed with awed expressions and hope in their eyes. It was the glazed look of the dervish.

My turn came and I sat down, placing my hands flat on the table as instructed. The adviser's black, slicked-back hair glistened under the fluorescents as he bowed slightly forward.

"Whose cross you bearing, brother?" he asked routinely.

"My own," I said.

"Yeah? What's your faith?"

"I believe I'm going to hell, so that must make me a Christian."

His head jerked up slightly. "What a terrible thing to believe."

"Man's gotta believe in something."

"I suppose one would," he said, shifting uncomfortably. "Yes, I sense you live a life of pain, of death. Your existence revolves around killing."

"Remarkable," I said.

"And I sense that you were a man of war once, a special kind of soldier. You are perhaps now confused about where you fit in the world, now that the wars are over."

I studied the adviser's sunglasses. Instead of hooking around the ears, the thick arms disappeared into his hair, canting toward the back of his neck. When I looked closely at the skin around the opaque lenses, I could see the flicker of shifting light and color.

"But the wars aren't over," I said, working the toe of my boot under the cloth that hung from the table to the floor. "They never ended."

"One knows," he said. "One knows of the pain of men." He smiled grimly. "Even of bogeymen."

I dropped my eyes. "I once was. But I've given up on that. I've been trying to find a new path. Unfortunately I found the bottle instead." I explored the recess of the table with my boot. After a moment it nudged what felt like a heavy power cable. *Ah-ha,* I thought.

"You won't find any answers in the bottle," he said sagely. "Only questions."

"I can't help it," I said, launching shamelessly into a fit of sobbing. I bowed my head until my forehead touched the table. Through the contact point of my skull I could detect the faint vibration of a scanner. "It's a battle I lose nightly."

"Yes, I can see you've had a few," the counselor said. "But it's never too late to change. Perhaps we could even find a good, positive use for your training and talents."

"Yes," I said, jerking my head up, making my face wild with hope. "Perhaps I *could* change."

The adviser's fingers tapped on a black plastic box on the table, and a red card popped out. He handed it and a plastic-back copy of *The Word of One* to me. "There's an address on the card. Go there tomorrow and give them the card. They'll help you discover the One path to contentment and purpose."

"Thank you," I said. "Why do I get a red card?"

"What?"

"Everybody else got white or green. I was just wondering why mine's red."

He worked up a patronizing smile. "Why, because you're special, of course."

I returned to my office a little unsteadily. The bourbon had taken its time waylaying me, but I could now feel its mean weight riding high on my back. I stuck a finger down my throat and vomited into my kelp-coffee cup before passing out in my chair.

6

I awoke at noon, my head full of vaguely menacing dreams. After washing my face, I scraped the cup of thickened vomit into the bowl-shaped receptacle of my modern-detective substance analyzer and sealed the top. I pushed the Analyze button, and the machine began to grind and shake fitfully. I slapped its aluminum casing until it settled into a grinding whir. Sitting on the edge of the desk, I lit a vitacig and waited. After a moment the analyzer beeped, then transferred its findings to the computer. A percentage pie appeared on the monitor, and among the breakdown of stomach acids, bourbon and set stew was the word "Zorgaine."

"Encyclopedia," I told the computer, and the monitor flashed to the encyclopedia menu. "Define Zorgaine." I spelled it out.

Zorgaine: a synthetic psychedelic compound used to induce a state of suggestibility and euphoria, developed in 1998 by ChemiCal Laboratories as an aid to training animals. Though relatively harmless in mild doses, long-term exposure to Zorgaine can lead to addiction.

So that's what keeps the winos coming back, I thought, and why the hooch had hit me so hard. It also explained why I'd failed to do my job. I was under the fiendish influence of a high-tech love potion.

I considered staking out the mission, but Ted had made it sound as if Jackie didn't play that gig much. I took the red card out of my pocket and examined it. There was a street address on one side and a magnetic strip on the other. I put on a black motorcycle jacket and went out, feeling all the world as if I were falling into a funnel.

The address was a nondescript three-story brick building in the borough of Riverdale. The discreet brass plaque on the steel door said, Visionary Placement Service. The door was unlocked so I went in.

An attractive secretary with a surgically enhanced smile sat behind a desk. A waiting area was crowded with plastic chairs pointed at a monitor bolted to the wall. Silky tones whispered from hidden speakers. I appeared to be the first customer of the day.

"Can I help you?" the secretary asked, grinning. Permanent-grin surgery was de rigueur among the corporate-secretary set, but it always struck me as a little eerie. I doubted she got invited to many funerals.

I handed her the red card. "I was told to come here."

"Certainly," she said, feeding the card into a slot in her desktop computer. "Would you run your hand under the scanner, please?" I did so and she regarded her monitor. "Very good, Mr. Strait," she said, beaming as she pushed a button on her intercom. "Now, if you'll have a seat, a counselor will be with you in just a moment."

I sat on the edge of her desk. "How long have you worked here, sugar?"

I could see her facial muscles tugging down on the fake smile. "My name isn't 'Sugar,' Mr. Strait."

"Call me Jakie Baby. So what's up with this outfit, Marcy?"

"My name is not Marcy."

"Tell me what it is, and maybe I'll stop getting it wrong."

"I'm not supposed to give out my name," she said with an added coldness designed to offset her inviting grin. "If you'd please take a seat…"

"How can I take a seat with you leering at me like that?"

"I can't help it!"

"Yeah, they *all* say that." I sniffed the air like a randy dog. "What *is* that sexy perfume you're wearing? Say, is that Eau de Sex Frenzy? That's my goddamn all-time favorite, I swear it. Say, I got a grand idea. How about you and me having a little slow dance, right here in front of the desk?" I jumped up and opened my arms wide. "Whaddya say, hot mama?"

"I can't!" she cried. "I'm married!"

"That's all right, baby, I'll bet there's plenty room for a new hog at *your* trough. Now c'mon," I said, reaching for her. "Let's *lambada!*"

She shot back from the desk on her swivel chair and smacked into the wall. "I'll go see what's taking the counselor so long," she blurted, and fled the room.

"I'll be waiting," I called after her, stepping behind the desk to view the computer monitor. A 3-D image of my head rotated over my name, vital statistics and a rather slanted view of my history. Below my condensed life story was some cryptic data:

Contact Point: Recruitment Center Seven
Recruitment Code: A-9
Occupation: Homicide

Personality: Unstable, vicious, possibly
schizophrenic.
Evaluation: If he can be converted, a professional of
his experience would be of great help to the set.
However, due to the nature of his trade and personality, he is probably unsalvageable.

Below that, in urgently blinking red letters, was the
clincher:

Special: Override above. This subject is to be recruited at all costs. If subject shows an unwillingness
to join, detain and summon HQ. J.P.

I heard footsteps so I danced back around the desk, employing a dance step that incorporated a lot of grunting and
impassioned crotch thrusting.

The secretary stopped a safe distance away. "It'll be a
few more moments. In the meantime you can fill out this
questionnaire." She dropped a clipboard-size plastic data
board on the desk, then backed away.

A question was already blinking impatiently on the data
board's gray screen. "Is this for your purposes or the counselor's?" I asked.

"Oh, no." She grinned, shaking her head. "Not for me."

She wouldn't return to her seat until I moved into the
waiting area, so I picked up the board and sulked over to
the plastic chairs.

The questionnaire seemed to be loosely based on the
Andover-Dietrich Mental Deviation Series used to determine just how twisted you really were. I removed the attached light-pen and went to work. After poking in my

name, age and gender, the questions became more ambiguous and suspect.

1. A close friend confesses his intention of murdering his coworkers. Do you:

a. Ignore him.

b. Try to talk him out of it.

c. Encourage him.

What are friends for? I thought. I poked *c* and went on to question two.

2. Voices convince me to do things I wouldn't normally do. Do you find this statement:

a. False.

b. True some of the time.

c. True much of the time.

It was usually my landlord's voice at the end of the month. I marked *c*.

3. You are captured by a tribe of cannibals. After starving you for a week, you are offered a meal of boiled human flesh. Do you:

a. Angrily refuse.

b. Explain you are not hungry.

c. Eat the meal.

Politeness above all, I reflected and marked *c*.

The next four questions drew *c*s, as well, so, swift to identify a trend, I marked the rest of the exam with *c*s without bothering to read the questions.

I put the data board aside and looked at the secretary. She had returned to her desk and was watching me carefully, as if I might lunge at the drop of a hat.

The TV monitor on the wall pointed down at me, offering a Flash TV segment. Lightning-fast images, coming and going at speeds almost too quick to identify, flickered across the screen, bombarding my mind with a numbing array of symbols, sex, violence, faces, shapes and colors.

"Mr. Strait?"

I flinched in my seat and looked around.

"The counselor will see you now," the secretary said carefully. "Down the hall, third door on the right."

I stood up, shaking blurred thoughts out of my head. I looked at my chrono. The Flash program had imprisoned my mind for over thirty minutes. On the way to the hall I stopped in front of the desk and gave the secretary baleful eyes. "We gonna dance when I come out?"

She shook her head slowly, her eyes dangerous. "Oh, no."

"Ah, well," I said, and limped down the hall.

I opened the door to the small pink room. Behind a small plastic desk sat Ted from the mission.

"Well," he said, rising and smiling. "Mr. Strait, good to see you again."

I shook his extended hand and sat in the straight-back chair in front of the desk. "This your day job?"

"Yes, right," he said vaguely, relieving me of the data board. He slipped out its disk and popped it into a disk drive. "Let's see what we have here," he said, and stared into the monitor. I watched various expressions flower and die on his face. He finished with a startled look.

"So, Doc," I said with a grin. "Am I nuts?"

He glanced at me and frowned. "These machines malfunction all the time." He popped the disk out, thumbed it back in, then checked the monitor again. His expression became more tense.

"Anything unusual?" I asked mildly.

He straightened his spine and resurrected his smile. "Well, that series is somewhat outdated. Why don't we run another little test by you and see what we come up with? How does that sound?"

I shrugged and slouched lower in the chair. "Whatever you say, daddy-o."

He frowned and attacked a keyboard with darting fingers. "Let's do a little word association, shall we? I'll say a word, and you tell me the first thing that comes to mind. Understand?"

"Ferret," I said.

"What?"

"Ferret. I associate the word ferret with the word understand."

He smiled thinly. "No. That wasn't part of the test. I was merely asking if you understood the premise of the test."

"I thought you were trying to trick me."

He smiled reassuringly. "No, no tricks here, Mr. Strait. Let's start, then." He paused significantly then said, "Tractor."

"Otter."

He looked up at me. "Okay," he said, tapping keys quickly. "Tribe."

"Mink."

"Mountain."

"Weasel."

"Blue mountain!"

"Blue weasel!"

Ted closed his eyes, and I noticed his right hand was clenched into a trembling fist. "Mr. Strait, how can you get the word *weasel* from *mountain?*"

"You told me to say the first thing that came to mind. I was thinking of the blue mountain weasels of Bangladesh."

"Mr. Strait, there are no mountains in Bangladesh."

"Maybe not by your standards. But to a weasel a mere *knoll* seems like Mount Everest."

He sighed, then began what appeared to be a deep-breathing relaxation exercise, his lips moving to some inaudible mantra. A moment later we began again.

"Cracker," he said.

"Linebacker," I responded.

"Breast."

"Bird nest."

"Chair!"

"Double dare!"

"Ram!"

"Flimflam!"

His fist smacked the desk sharply, and he yelled at me. "This is not a means of testing your rhyming ability, Mr. Strait!"

"Crooked!"

"Stop!"

"Go!"

"No!"

"Yes!"

His eyes clenched shut, and he rocked in his chair, both fists thumping the desk at a steady tempo. He repeated what sounded like *rumbaman* over and over.

I lit a vitacig and waited until he finished. "How'd I do?" I asked.

Without opening his eyes, he steepled his fingers and launched unenthusiastically into his recruitment pitch. "The Set of One is a very large and multifaceted organization, with a great many opportunities for bright and right-thinking individuals. We do have certain criteria, of course, but we provide special training to lift you to those standards." His eyes flickered open, and a frail smile crept to his lips. "How does that sound?"

"Sounds like you want to brainwash me," I said.

"Not so," he said, closing his eyes. "We will merely expose you to basic truths so you can approach your job with the proper perspective and bearing."

"And what job is that?"

His eyes opened again. "Whatever job the set chooses is right for you."

"Listen," I said, leaning forward, trying to hold his eyes. "I'm a killer. That's what I'm good at. I wouldn't mind working for your organization—I'm a little tired of free-lancing. But I'm not going to go through any identity-stripping courses where they make me chant silly words and act out my wildest fantasies in front of people I just met and don't particularly like."

He frowned. "I'm afraid indoctrination classes are essential to your joining the Set of One."

I stood up. "I guess I'll be going, then."

"No!" he said, jumping from his seat. "Don't leave. We can offer you a lot. This could be the best career move you ever made."

Standing, I studied him. His lips moved frantically and silently; he seemed to be trying to chant me back into my seat. "Okay," I said, sitting down. I leaned back in the chair and put my feet up on his desk. "But I want concessions. Lots of concessions."

He scowled at the boots on his immaculate desk top. "What kind of concessions?"

"Who was the woman that sang at the mission?"

His eyes shot from the boots to my face. "What?"

I snuffed out the butt of my vitacig on his desk top and lit another. He scowled as the smoke snaked to the ceiling.

"The songbird," I said. "The dame with the flashing eyes and raven mane."

His eyes lit up with jealousy. "What about her?"

"I want to negotiate my contract with her."

He squinted suspiciously. "Why her?"

I shrugged. "She's easier to look at than you."

He laughed harshly. "What makes you think you can come in here and demand an audience with the assistant to the director?"

"I possess skills the set desperately needs," I said. We stared at each other, he the protective father, me the infidel with perhaps diabolic designs on his beloved daughter. But we both knew what the flashing memo under my stats read. "I go through her or no deal."

"I can try to get you an appointment," he finally squeezed out, breathless after an intense moment of horrific inner struggle.

"Groovy." I stood up and dropped a business card on his desk. "If I don't get a call by eight, I'll tell the director I walked because of you."

He glared at me with impotent anger, seething hostility.

I turned around at the door. "If she's so high up in the chain of command, what's she doing singing to winos?"

"Everyone contributes at every level," he ground out. "That's the way the set works."

I nodded and left.

Eating dinner at a nearby café, I tried to get a handle on the set's great interest in recruiting me. There could have been a shortage of experienced killers in their organization, or maybe it was something else, something I didn't really want to know about. The case seemed to be progressing extraordinarily well, and I felt it foolish and bad luck to wonder why. In my line of work, trouble had its own way of finding your door. There was no need to go seek it out.

7

I arrived at my office to find Heidi waiting primly before my door. She was clasping a small porcelain purse to the middle of an off-white jump dress that hung just below her knees. A sheer gray scarf enveloped her hair, and hoops of ivory dangled from each ear.

"Have you waited long?" I asked.

"Not very long."

I unlocked my office and ushered her inside. I went to the desk and she went to the window.

"I thought you were going to leave town for a while," I said.

"I changed my mind."

"Any particular reason you're here?"

"I wanted to check on your progress."

"You could have called."

"All I got was your answering machine."

I nodded.

"So, how is the case progressing?" she asked.

"I saw your sister," I said.

She turned around. "What?"

"She sang at a rescue mission."

"A rescue mission?" she echoed, sounding shocked and pleased at once. "Why didn't you rescue her?"

"I was distracted."

"Yes," she said, a little spite in her voice. "She's very distracting."

"The Set of One isn't a small-time, slipshod cult," I said. "It's a huge organization more like a corporation than a sect. They recruit out of missions using drugs and hand-scanners, toward what end I'm not certain. They're extremely organized, but their dogma is blurry."

She untied her scarf, and her platinum locks tumbled down. "Are they too organized for you to rescue her?"

"No, it'll just be a little more difficult than I anticipated. I'm going to have to infiltrate their organization. With any luck I'll have an appointment with Jackie tomorrow."

"You'll rescue her then?"

I shrugged. "Possibly. Depends on the circumstances."

She looked down at the scarf she carefully folded. "Are you going to kill anyone?"

"If I have to."

"If you do, please don't tell me about it. I don't want to know."

My eyes traced Heidi's heart-quickening curves, silhouetted in the pale of the dying sun, to her snowy hair, glowing like a halo around a face of shadow. "'The word more painful than the wound,'" I said.

"What's that?"

"Part of a poem. Miss Pan, have you thought about what you're going to do with Jackie once I get her out?"

She looked at me blankly. "What do you mean?"

"I mean I didn't see any thugs guarding the doors at the mission. In fact, it appears she's part of the management—assistant to the director, no less. She might not be too happy about being rescued."

She studied me. "You believe that and you're still willing to attempt a rescue?"

"Of course."

"Why?"

"You're paying me."

"She could offer you more."

"Yeah, but then I'd feel bad about screwing you over."

She smiled coldly and stared at the floor. "Yes, we're all whores to our consciences, aren't we?"

"You drop a hard line for a nun."

"An ex-nun, remember?"

"There's something about you that makes me forget."

She turned to the window. "Do you know why I came to your office last week?"

"Sure."

"Why?"

"The same reason most women come into my life. God sends them down to torment me."

She smiled slightly. "You have it all figured out, huh?"

"It was only a matter of time. Too much coincidence. No one has my kind of bad luck unless there's a big mover behind it."

She unlatched her porcelain purse and produced a dog-eared paperback, its cover too worn and faded to make out. She opened the book to a marked page. "But down these mean streets a man must go," she read, "who is not himself mean, who is neither tarnished nor afraid."

I knew the quote. It was from an essay by Raymond Chandler about his romantically idealized private investigator, Philip Marlowe. "Sounds like a primer on how to get mugged," I said. "Where did you get that book?"

"It was my father's." She laughed sadly. "He always said crime fiction was his one bad habit. When my sister disappeared, I didn't know where to turn. Then I remembered him reading that passage to me when I was a little girl. I knew then I needed a Marlowe."

"A man of fiction."

"A man of principle."

"Marlowe wouldn't survive in today's world. His bulky moralities would get him killed."

"I mistook you for a man of principle."

"Principles are deadweight I cannot afford to carry."

"They'd slow you down that much?"

"Enough to get killed."

She nodded, then turned to stare down at Hayward, the sunlight making her eyes as pale as silver moons. I joined her at the window. A squad of militiamen passed below, young boys wild-eyed and jumpy, dangerous with the knowledge that the world wouldn't give them anything they didn't take. Across the street a grossly overweight fade ran a lively drug trade in front of the St. Chris, selling squeeze to junkies who came and went like deranged bees hungry for toxic pollen. Survivors of the previous generation, wolves turned sheep, hustled past the knots of mean youth, eyes straight ahead and blind, hurrying to get behind locked doors before night fell.

Heidi sighed. "So much strife, hatred and fear. Where did it all go wrong?"

"It's been wrong from the start," I said. "Man has always been evil. It just took him a while to reach his full potential."

She frowned. "*That's* what's wrong. We lost our compassion for our fellow man."

"Fellow man?" I laughed, watching the animals prowling below. "Yeah, I've met *that* bastard. He doesn't deserve any compassion."

She ran a white-gloved finger down the windowpane. "How many of your fellow men have you killed, Mr. Strait?"

"Why do you want to know?"

She lifted the finger and stared at the black stain on the tip. "With horror always comes a certain morbid fascination. I don't know if you're a good man driven to kill or a killer faulted with goodness."

"That's a heavy judgment to make about someone you don't know."

"I know you don't believe in morality."

"What makes you say that?"

"Because you kill so easily. Because you're a bogey-man."

"Maybe that means I believe too much in morality. Enough to sacrifice my soul for the greater good."

"You think you're on the side of good?"

"In a vague sense."

"Then why do you think you've sacrificed your soul?"

I shrugged. "Because the system is rigged that way. When you start dealing in human lives, you gotta doubt your chances of going anywhere but hell, regardless of whose side you're on. The dice are heavily loaded against you."

"Was it worth the sacrifice?"

I considered the question. "I don't know. I feel right about it, but I can't see any effect. I'll probably spend all my years wondering."

"I don't believe in heaven or hell," she said smugly. "I think the whole afterlife concept is simple egotism." I noticed she was staring at the bloodstains on the carpet. "Are those pimps still hunting you?" she asked.

"No. I convinced them otherwise."

"Really? How?"

"I made a deal with the devil."

"I don't believe in the devil, either. I think man alone is wicked enough to account for all the evil in the world. Do you have any more cigarettes?"

I passed her one from the pack in my breast pocket and flicked my lighter. She leaned the vitacig to the blue flame, inhaled deeply, then broke into a fit of coughing.

"I didn't know you smoked," I said.

"I'm trying to learn." She took another deep drag and wiped at her watering eyes. "Do you find my sister attractive, Mr. Strait?"

I eyed her with suspicion. "She has a certain allure," I admitted.

"Yes," she said, nodding. "Men find bad girls very alluring, don't they? But then isn't that where character and sensuality lie, in the dark half? I'll bet you find nice, normal girls very bland and uninteresting." Her eyes confronted me. "Don't you?"

The question was too loaded to touch, so I kept my mouth shut.

"I rented a place in the City today," she said after a moment. "In a poor neighborhood."

"Why?"

"I want to know what it's like to be deprived, to be disadvantaged." She squinted through the blue haze of smoke, making a face. "Apartment 2601 of Complan B in Barridales."

"Renting poverty, Sister?"

"I want to know what's on the other side. Oh, what's the use?" She stabbed the vitacig out on the windowsill, waved at the lingering smoke and coughed. "I can't smoke those horrible things." Perched on the windowsill, she stared at the floor. "I guess I'm just not very good at being bad."

"Maybe you're trying too hard, Miss Pan."

She looked up from the floor with little-girl eyes. "You can call me Heidi."

"I like Miss Pan better."

She shot an affronted look at me and marched to the door. She jerked it open but caught herself before she could slam it behind her. Silver eyes cast back at me. "Don't let my sister hurt you, Mr. Strait."

"Is she that dangerous?"

"In more ways than you think. Goodbye, Mr. Strait." She closed the door.

The phone rang a minute later. In terse, angry sentences, Ted communicated that First Assistant Jackie Pan would meet me at 1660 Korangar Boulevard, Suite 4300 at 9:00 a.m. tomorrow. Then he hung up.

I got out my complimentary copy of *The Word of One.* Below the loud title sat a brilliant red sun on a dark horizon. It could have been rising or setting. I turned to the first page and began reading.

The first sickly, smog-choked rays of dawn were at my window when I turned the last page. I put the book down and covered my face. My head ached and my eyes felt as if they'd been clawed from their sockets with rusty forks, rolled in rock salt, then jammed back in with white-hot ice tongs.

But what a super book, I thought. A really good read, full of great ideas. I was so excited I wanted to pass the word, scream to the world what a marvelous religion the set was. But at the same time I couldn't remember what the hell the whole fat book was about.

I went to the bathroom, threw cold water in my face for

five minutes, then returned to the desk. My ideas about spreading the word faded, and I stared out the window and wondered how to rescue Jackie Pan from the evil grip of a powerful religion.

When the sun had crawled to its eight-o'clock position hours later, the answer still eluded me.

8

Korangar Boulevard ran smack through the City's business district. Sixteen-sixty Korangar was occupied by a monstrously wide barrel-shaped mirror-and-concrete tower. There was no sign or symbol on the building indicating who operated within, but that kind of thing went along with the unlisted phone number.

I walked through the revolving front door without any conscious knowledge of a plan. Since I had no idea what sort of environment I had entered, my plan was merely to react to and flow around obstacles as they presented themselves, attacking at the point of least resistance until I achieved my goal. In modern detective manuals it was called the mercury flex-reactive system. In practice it was better known as the time-honored ass-in-the-wind technique.

The lobby was decorated with potted rubber plants and flickering neon lights. A chrome security station towered in the middle of the lobby, oppressing an otherwise lighthearted air of sophisticated tackiness. I knew it was a security station because it said so in big red neon letters across its front. I tried to slip by but the uniformed guards behind the counter seemed intent on checking me for weapons and bad intentions. The revelation of my shoulder holster and gyrapistol excited them to the point of taking me to a back room for the personal touch. The neon decor didn't stop in the lobby. Interrogation Room was snaked out in flickering blue neon across the rear wall of the small cubicle.

"Is this the interrogation room?" I asked as one ape pointed an electronic Weapon Weasel at me while the other covered me with his pistol.

"It's going to be the emergency room if you don't put a sock in it," the one holding the gun said.

"Jesus Christ!" the guard with the hand-held weapon detector cried. "This guy's loaded with heat!" The Weasel homed in on various parts of my body, squealing at metal and dense plastic. "He's got another gat in his sock," he reported, coming up with a small .25 automatic. "And there's another in his goddamn pocket. And, Jesus, do you believe it? He's got another one in the back of his belt." He leaned back and glared at me. "What are you, some kinda goddamn traveling gun salesman?"

"That's right," I said. "And I sell *below* wholesale."

"Oh, I see," the one covering me said. "A wise guy." His free hand shot out and connected with my cheekbone, snapping my head sideways. Things got a little hazy for a second, but I didn't go down. "There's more where that came from," he assured me.

I could feel a bruise rising over my cheekbone, and I bit my tongue to keep it quiet. *Flow around the obstacles,* I told myself, *like a bead of mercury.*

A moment later his pal finished the search, gathering his finds on a table. He took a step back and glowered. "What the hell kind of guy are you? What kind of sick bastard walks around with five guns and two knives on his person?"

"I like to be prepared," I replied.

"Prepared for what?"

I shrugged. "Whatever."

"I don't like that answer. Put your hand under the scanner."

The one who'd frisked me stared at the screen as I ran my hand under the head of the scanner. "Look out," he said suddenly, jumping back a step and drawing his pistol. "He's a goddamn bogeyman!"

The other one tensed, wrapping both hands around his pistol. "Should I shoot him, Mike?" he croaked in a high voice. "Should I shoot the bastard?"

"Who've you come for, bogeyboy?" Mike demanded.

"I have an appointment with the assistant to the director. Miss Pan."

"Yeah, right," he said, lifting the receiver from a red neon wall phone with his free hand, not taking eyes or pistol off me.

"You're just begging for a lesson, aren't ya?" his partner snarled, smiling sadistically and balling up a fist. "Well, you're gonna get one."

"Hold it," Mike said, hanging up the phone. He gave me an apologetic smile but didn't holster his pistol. "Sorry for the inconvenience, Mr. Strait. You can go straight up to Suite 4300. We'll hold your weapons until you return."

His partner's jaw dropped, and he began stuttering to Mike. He didn't seem to want to let me go scot-free, without a lesson.

"Relax, chum," I said on the way to the door. "We'll have a chance to chat later." I left the room and found the elevator under a big yellow neon sign that said Elevator.

I got on with a gaggle of ambitious young execs, their eyes full of lust for unlimited power and gleaming late-model sports cars. The elevator shot upward as one of the execs, sporting a monocle and a trendy molded-clay haircut, went on at length about a new loft complex only certified water-heads wouldn't bust a gut trying to sink every credit of their savings into.

"What kind of goddamn religion is this?" I said, interrupting his fevered pitch. "Whatever happened to spiritual growth through vows of poverty and goat herding?"

The doors opened, and several of the execs sneered at me as they got off. "Poverty is for assholes," the monocled gent informed me as he stepped off.

"So are monocles, mud head," I fired back wittily as the doors hissed shut.

The elevator continued upward, and I thought hard about my next move. I'd flowed around the first obstacle but not without cost. Getting Jackie out unarmed seemed about as likely as walking the length of Hayward without being accosted by a junkie demanding spare change. The doors opened on the forty-third floor before I could work up a good plan.

The office of the assistant to the director was across the hall. I opened the door and entered. I sat in a chair constructed of wrought iron and coiled black hemp and faced an unmanned mahogany desk with gargoyles carved into its broad face and stout legs. Tribal masks, spears, swords, knives and other weaponlike knickknacks crowded the wall, and a door-size plaque of the set's phallic symbol was set in the wall behind the desk. It pointed up to the single pane of black mirror that served as the ceiling. The overall effect was so menacing I was able to wrestle down the powerful urge to rifle through the desk.

The plaque hissed into the wall long enough for Jackie to slink in. She lowered herself into the swivel chair behind the desk with a sensual ease, fluid as a snake. The black, broad-shouldered, narrow-waisted exec suit she wore failed to detract from her overwhelming aura of femininity. Perhaps it even intensified the effect.

She leaned her chin on bridged fingers and smoldered at me. But I didn't notice her intimate smoky stare, the elegant curve of her brow, the way her red lipstick accentuated her full, sensuous lips. I was too focused to be distracted by trivialities that might endanger my life. *I'm too much of a goddamn hard-core professional to make that kind of mistake,* I assured myself.

"You wanted to see me?" she asked, as steamy as her sister was frigid.

"Yes," I said, gingerly touching the bruise on my cheek, wondering if it added to or detracted from my good looks. "But I was hoping we could meet in your office instead of the torture chamber."

"Are you here to insult my decor or negotiate?"

"I'm talented enough to do both. Do you remember me?"

"Should I?"

I frowned. "As a matter of fact, you should. I was at the mission. You put your hands on my shoulders. You stared at me yearningly from across the room."

She laughed. "I'm afraid I can't recall. But I'll bet most of the men at the mission will swear I'm in love with them. What did you think of my performance, by the way?"

I sat back, somewhat miffed. "You're a real crowd pleaser. But then you had a little help."

"I don't know what you mean."

"Everyone in the place was tripping."

She smiled slightly and examined her long black nails. "And what do you think of an organization that employs such tactics?"

I waved a hand. "Hypocrisy and moral corruption don't bother me. They've become such an inherent part of human nature I don't even notice them anymore."

"You're a very cynical man."

"Most killers are. What does a religion want with killers anyway?"

"What makes you think we want killers?"

"Because I'm here, J.P. That's how you sign your memos, isn't it? But I guess the real question is, why me? In a city full of killers, why humble *moi?*"

"You came to us."

"It's more than that."

Jackie smiled. "When your name came up in the recruitment pool, we did some research—it's a perfunctory thing. It turns out you're a minor street legend. You're the one who hit Marta and Joshua Cassady."

"You knew them?"

She laughed. "They worked for us."

"Small world. So you employ terrorists, too."

"I meant *worked* in the past tense. We let them go because of their rather questionable methods."

"I'd call blowing up churches and assassinating clergymen more than questionable."

"So would we. That's why we let them go." She picked up a stiletto-shaped letter opener and tested the flexibility of the blade. "Our sources tell us you are one the finest…technicians in your field. We try to recruit only the best."

"Who are you planning to kill?"

"Not kill," a voice said behind me. "Purify!"

I turned around as a tall man strode into the room with the presence and self-importance of a knight carrying a gilded banner. He circled my chair and grabbed my hand.

"So you're Jake Strait. I've heard so much about you. Your data sheet reads like an adventure novel." He shook my hand athletically and grinned like a wolf from behind huge round glasses. He wore a loose black suit over a solid build that contradicted the scholarly cast of his features. He looked like a tenured Oxford English professor who pumped iron and gobbled steroids between readings of Chaucer.

"Who the hell are you?" I asked.

"You are in the presence of Alexander Martin Sinn," Jackie revealed, "the founder and director of the Set of One. One of the highest-ranked prophets in the world."

Sinn grinned modestly. "She flatters me, but I guess that's her job. Are you interested in joining our management team?"

"Jackie and I were just touching on the subject."

"Excellent. What do you think?"

"She's a little vague about the job description."

"Oh, I see. Well, come with me and I'll do my best to fill in the details." He took my elbow and tried to steer me to the door, but I held back, caught at the crossroads. *What are my chances,* I wondered. *Of breaking his neck, throwing her over my shoulder and fighting my way out of here bare-handed?* Jackie addressed me with big black eyes, and I set my feet, muscles tensing, brain slipping to the utterly ruthless murder groove.

"Go with Sinn," Jackie said suddenly. "We'll talk later."

I hesitated and the tension and kill energy flushed out of me, leaving me drained and defeated. "See you then," I mumbled, letting Sinn usher me out the door. I cast one last wistful glance back at Jackie and found her dark eyes watching me closely.

Sinn made amiable small talk as he led me down a

wide, sparkling hall that ran the width of the tower. We passed polished oak doors bearing brass plates inscribed with cryptic names: Imprint Extraction Room, Indoctrination Processing Bureau, Phoenix Program, Mass Persuasion Center, and stranger, more enigmatic titles.

"What do you think of our religion so far?" Sinn asked.

"It reminds me more of a corporation than a church," I said.

"It should. That's the way I set it up. But then most religions are corporations. I just built mine without all the hypocrisy and superstitious mumbo jumbo." We passed into a spacious reception room at the end of the hall, the desk manned by a hulking male secretary.

"Hold all visitors and communications," Sinn said, and ushered me through a large mahogany door that simply said, Alexander Sinn, Prophet. The prophet's office was airy and delicate. Frail ferns idled against pinkish white marble walls, soft beige shag cushioned the floor, and vases of wispy pink feathers rested atop marble stands carved with smirking cherubs. The glass-topped, white marble desk appeared too delicate to support a box of paper clips, and the room as a whole whispered elegance in a regal if effete voice.

Sinn led me behind the desk to a private elevator between two tall, narrow windows. He inserted a card into the gilded slot, and the doors slid open soundlessly. The interior was as elegant as the room, with marble walls and gold fittings. When the doors shut, Sinn pressed the middle of three unmarked buttons. We rode up two floors in a curious silence.

The doors opened, and Sinn gestured for me to go first. I started to step out, then lunged back. Dropping into a fighting stance, I squared off with Sinn, getting an angle on his jugular. Outside the elevator was a two-story drop.

Sinn looked at me and laughed. "It's all right." He stepped outside and appeared to hover in midair. "It's tempered glass." He tapped his heel. "Perfectly safe."

The area around his feet showed the slightest bit of light distortion. I reached out with a foot and touched something solid. I brought the other foot out and stood in the middle of nothing.

"It's a little hard to get used to at first," Sinn said, setting a slow pace along the edge of the wall. "I would have told you, but it's a test I like to give my potential managers. To see how they react."

"How'd I do?" I asked, walking beside him, each footstep a broad leap of faith.

"You proved you are above all a creature of instinct. Your reflexes are quite remarkable. When presented with potential danger, you immediately fell into the animal attack posture. Why, by the look in your eye, I imagine you were thinking about ripping out my throat."

"Nothing as crude as that," I said, noticing wherever there was a fluorescent directly overhead, the transparent floor shined a little, enough for me to fill in the gaps. We were apparently treading a circular observation hall that ringed the round tower. The hall's transparent inner wall and floor overlooked a great many transparent-ceilinged rooms two stories below, reminding me of a sectioned beehive.

"I call this the God Hall," Sinn said with a sweep of his arm. "Below our feet are my most important offices, the thriving nucleus of the set, and through this one-way glass I monitor its activity and health."

"Every boss's dream," I said, looking down. Clerks hustled in the offices below like mice, their backs slightly hunched. Occasionally they threw furtive glances upward, perhaps sensing their master's eyes. "So let's hear the pitch."

Sinn nodded, linking his hands behind his back and standing erect. "We are a young religion, Mr. Strait," he began, "and a very ambitious one, not content with the status quo. We can see the state of the world around us, and we want to do something about it. In that way we are different from the old faiths. We will not turn a blind eye to the vileness of the human race, we see the evil and we are willing to take bold and direct action to root out and destroy it. And when I say action, I'm not talking about aggressive charity drives."

"What are you talking about?"

"I'm talking about the good in mankind making a stand against the tide of evil before it's too late. I'm talking about employing the ruthless tactics of the criminal and about taking the war to the streets. The prey will become the hunters, and the hunters will become the prey."

"You're going into the bogey business."

"Exactly! I hope you don't mind."

"There's plenty of room for competition." We strolled over a hive of cubical rooms crowded with medical equipment and technicians. In the center of each room sat what appeared to be an incubation chamber mounted on a heavy base. Inside most of the transparent chambers lay still human forms.

"We were hoping you would see it that way," Sinn said. "We started our Martyr Program months ago, but we've run into some snags. Though our soldiers' commitment and faith is beyond question, they are relatively inexperienced in the ways of war. And that's what it is, a war, a campaign against evil. They need a teacher and a leader."

"And that's where I come in."

"Precisely! Your qualifications make you the perfect candidate for the job. We'd be asking you to perform the same mission you've pursued so diligently for so many years. The destruction of the bad guys, the elimination of evil from society. But instead of toiling alone against the horde of fiends, one man against the sea, you can lead an army of believers, backed by a powerful and efficient organization. You can strike a hundred blows instead of just one, go after the really big crooks instead of their minions, lop off the head instead of just chopping at the tail. How does that sound?"

"Sounds like you want me to lead your death squads in a bloody purge."

Sinn smiled wanly. "You don't like to dress things up, do you? Okay, you've painted it as you wish. I'm sorry you won't accept."

We passed over Jackie's office, located directly below another elevator. Jackie studied the monitor at her desk, tapping occasionally at a keyboard. "I didn't say I wouldn't accept."

Sinn laughed. "What a strange engine you are. You've called my melon a turd and still want to eat it?"

"It doesn't matter what you call it, shit still tastes like shit. I've come to develop a taste for it."

He laughed again. "I like you, Mr. Strait. You're a man who puts it on the line. One can trust a man such as that."

We halted over a crowded seminar room. The blindfolded audience, wearing only diapers and plastic weasel snouts, flapped their arms and howled at the insistence of a burly instructor. He goose-stepped among them with a cattle prod and can of whipped cream. We watched the instructor touch one of the initiates with the prod. The man collapsed to the floor writhing with pain and received a mouthful of whipped cream for his trouble.

"Why exactly does One want to kill criminals?" I asked.

Sinn smiled wolfishly. "Why do you care, just as long as he does? The men and materials he will give you are real—as real as a pistol in your hand." He clenched a hand into a fist.

I looked down at the seminar room. "No indoctrination classes?"

"No," he said, following my stare with a small smile. "Those are for the maladjusted. I like you just as you are. I wouldn't think of changing a thing. I don't find fault in your nature, Mr. Strait. Amorality is excellent armor." He laid his left hand on my shoulder. "I've studied your file very closely. I know what forces drive and haunt you—I know the frustrations that boil in your stomach like black acid. I want to give you the power to take control of your destiny, the power to change the world around you for the better." He held out his right hand to me. "Take my hand, bogeyman, and I'll pull you in."

I looked into eyes burning with the heat and power of a volcano. "All right, Sinn," I said, taking his hand. "I'll be your killer."

"Excellent, excellent!" Sinn beamed, slapping me on the back. "When can you start?"

"Tomorrow, if you like."

"Splendid!"

"However," I said, "there's still some things I'd like to talk over with Miss Pan."

He gave me a sly smile. "I hope you don't intend on stealing my Jackie away from me, young man."

I headed off surprise before it reached my face and transformed grimace into grin. "Wouldn't think of it, sir."

"Well, then," he said, slapping a fatherly arm around my shoulders. "Let's both go down and talk with Jackie."

Sinn rolled out niceties and enticements all the way to Jackie's office. When we got there, the office was empty.

"Now where has she gone?" Sinn said, then snapped his fingers. "Oh, that's right. She's scheduled to sing at our resurrection mission at noon. Maybe you can catch her before she goes on."

I looked at my chrono. It was a quarter past eleven. "Perhaps I can," I said. "I'll be seeing you."

"What time can I expect you tomorrow?"

"How does 8:00 a.m. sound?"

"Sounds great." He took my hand and shook it vigorously. "Welcome aboard, commander. All you ever wanted, right here."

"Yes," I said. "Thank you."

I stopped at the security desk in the lobby on the way out. The gorilla who punctuated his courtesy lessons with left jabs stepped out of the booth and rounded on me with a slight bow to his head. He had the look of someone who has had a stern reprimand. He held out a black velvet sack clanking with hardware.

"Here's your stuff," he said grudgingly. "I didn't know you were a friend of Assistant Pan's. I guess I owe you an apology."

I took the sack with my right hand and judged its weight. It felt about right. "It's okay," I said with a smile.

"Good," he said, and his eyes cleared of false remorse. "I guess we're even then."

"Sure," I said, swinging the sack in a roundhouse arc. The mean weight of the weapons collided with the side of his skull, and he went as limp as a wet tea bag, slumping against the front of the booth, crushing the neon sign. His buddy Mike looked down from his perch, jaw agape.

"Even steven," I said and walked outside.

9

I parked across the street from the Set of One Resurrection Mission. I rearmed myself, then took up station on the hood of the Olds. I checked my chrono. If her performances were consistent, she'd be out in ten minutes.

"Shake the healing hand of Jesus!" a familiar voice squawked.

I looked back at the leering plastic-and-neon Jesus. "Still dropping that tired line?" I sneered.

Chrome teeth chattered under the mangy nylon beard and neon eyes flashed. "C'mon, sinner! Take a chance! Only a quarter cred a shake!"

"Screw you," I said, giving it the finger.

"Are you *scared*, sinner? Do you fear the awesome might of the Savior? Are you *afraid* of salvation, sinner?"

"All right," I snarled, sliding off the hood. I squared off with the machine and dropped a quarter cred in its slot. "Let's go, chump."

The arm came up, and I got a deep, dominant grip, the kind a good arm wrestler tries for. Christ spit holy water in my face, and the mechanical hand began closing. I tightened my grip on the rubber and steel, but not a lot.

"Deposit five credits, and the healing hand of Jesus will set you free!" Jesus said. The machine's viselike grip squeezed, and I clenched my fingers, matching power with power.

"Seven creds and I'll let you go," the voice box grated, and the mechanical hand bore down with horrific strength. I bunched my forearm muscles and squeezed harder. My fingers went death white, and my knuckles began popping one by one under the incredible pressure.

"Eight creds, and I'll let you go, sinner!"

"Screw you," I snarled, ignoring the cold pain. I could feel tendons stretching tauter and tauter, and the steel hand tightened like a slow-turning vise. My hand went numb, my arm began to shake, and I focused my entire being on my grip, visualizing my fingers closing around soft clay, closing, closing….

There was a snap of a cable breaking, then a metallic *clack!* The messiah's fingers crumbled beneath mine, and the machine jerked its crippled appendage away. The arm began flailing up and down feverishly, lights flashing, hydraulics squealing. "Sinner!" it squawked. "Sinner! Sinner! Sinner!"

"Who's laughing now?" I cried, backing away from the machine gone amok, holding my numb hand and laughing triumphantly.

"You won," a voice said behind me.

I spun around and faced Jackie. Her long black hair was swept up into a crown of red glass, exposing a long, sensuous neck. An ankle-length black dress and cape with flared collar completed the fairy-tale image, regal and surreal against an improbable backdrop of decadence and hypocrisy. Like her sister, she seemed removed from the ugliness surrounding her, yet, unlike Heidi, she also seemed inextricably part of it.

"He wouldn't let me go," I said, massaging my hand.

"But you're free now," she pointed out with a licentious grin.

"Don't get abstract with me," I warned. "Reality is screwy enough."

She bowed her head apologetically. "What are you doing here?"

"I was looking for something," I said, wondering how much of a struggle she'd put up if I rescued her right then.

She put on another lewd and allusive smile. "Did you find it?"

"You look at me like that one more time, and I'm going to scream."

She dropped her eyes but kept the smile, moving a half step closer, so close I could smell the fragrance of her hair, feel the heat of her skin, see the speckles of darkest brown in her downcast black eyes. "I've half an hour until I go on."

My mouth went dry as my mind raced with lusty visions. *Half an hour. A resourceful and charming man could go far in half an hour.*

"We could go have a drink," Jackie said. "I know a nice place near the set tower."

"Yes," I said, feeling as if I might swoon. "A drink. Good idea. We'll have a drink first."

We took my car to a swanky wine bar set in the lobby of a glittering new tower, all steel and mood glass. We sat at a table by a window so we could watch the late-working businessmen march between the money mills of greed.

"What are you having, Mr. Strait?" Jackie asked.

"A screwdriver. Double."

She signaled a waiter. "A double screwdriver. Make that two."

She lit a cigarette. "How was your talk with Sinn?"

"Fine," I said. Two security men dressed as execs lounged near the door, and another leaned against the bar. They looked soft, lethargic.

Jackie stared through curling smoke. "And how did you find his offer?"

"Very attractive."

She nodded. The drinks arrived and we drank in silence.

"You look as if you're standing on the edge of a cliff," she said after a few minutes.

"That's where I live."

She nodded. "Well," she said, frowning, after a moment. "Are you going to tell me or not?"

"You're going to be late for your performance," I said, finishing my drink.

"I'll stand them up. They'll survive." The waiter came around and Jackie ordered another round.

"Ted might not."

"Yes, Ted." She sighed. "He's a dedicated servant of One."

"No," I said. "I think his god is right here on earth."

"You mean me."

"Yes."

She looked into her drink. "I wonder what he sees in me."

"He sees the unattainable, the lovely things he cannot have, the angel he cannot hold. The more he realizes he can't have you, the more he craves you."

She reached across the table and took my hands, sending a jolt through my heart. Her eyes crept up to mine, and she smiled demurely. "What do you see in me, Jake?"

I stared without shame, and it hurt me to look at her because I knew wanting her meant needing her, and that was the road to horrific grief. I could almost feel my heart cringing away. "You are the romantic lie and the leading on," I said. "You are false endearments spoken in hoarse whispers while making love. You are everything that repels a good heart, a bridge a smart man would not build."

"Are you a smart man, Jake?"

"No."

"Do you want me?"

"Yes."

"Because I'm unattainable?"

"I never wanted anything I couldn't take."

Her smile bloomed. "So you want me because you think you can have me."

"Yes."

I thought I saw a challenge surface in her eyes and I met it head-on. She didn't blink or break her stare, and I sensed she was focusing on the bridge of my nose, a salesman's trick. I wasn't sure what she was selling but I was prepared to buy all stock on hand at any price. I felt suddenly exposed and vulnerable, as if stripped naked. *Uh-oh,* said a little voice inside me.

She turned to the window, her expression cleared, and all the swirling passion of the moment blew away like the smoke it was. *Son of a bitch,* I thought.

"You know," she said, releasing my hands, "we were very distressed when you hit the Cassadys. We were afraid you had decided to focus your considerable powers of destruction on us."

I leaned back and lit a vitacig, feeling mean and spiteful. "I was just doing my job. They deserved to die."

She laughed. "But you didn't kill the woman, Marta."

"I assume you know why."

"Yes. But you killed her husband. Took his hand."

"That's how it works."

"But you didn't turn it in for the reward."

I studied her closely. "How would you know?"

"We have operatives in the SPF."

Realization washed over me like an icy wave. "It was your data chip."

She kept a smile pasted on, but I could see it was an effort. "What happened to Cassady's hand?"

I stared at her for a moment, then laughed. Reality shifted five degrees to the right, and suddenly everything appeared in a meaner shade of gray. "That's why you had a flyer out on me," I said, "researched me so thoroughly, offered me so much. You wanted me to tell you where the hand was."

"Where is it?" The smile vanished, cold hunger in its place.

"I gave it away."

Her laugh sounded like ice cubes rattling down a steel pipe. "Now why would a man of your poor financial standing give away something worth two thousand credits?"

"I had a change of heart. I got a new job."

"Yes, you did a bit of revolution work in Denver. Practically burned the city down in the process."

I shrugged. "It was that kind of gig." I stubbed out my vitacig, slowly lit another, then leaned back and squinted at her, trying to sum it all up. I no longer felt vulnerable or exposed; I was now comfortable in the armor her deceptions had lent me. "What was on the chip that made it so valuable to you?"

She leaned back and looked out the window. "Information about our organization, very damaging information if it were to fall into the wrong hands. Like the hands of the SPF."

"How did Cassady get hold of this information?"

"Cassady was a key early member of the set. He was to fill the position we've offered you. Unknown to us, he was slowly accruing sensitive data about the set as a means to blackmail."

"I see. So he was working a deal with the SPF, who viewed you as a potential threat."

"Yes. He planned on playing it from both ends. Extorting money from us and selling information to the Party. You can imagine our trepidation when he skipped out on us."

"Skipped out? I thought you booted him."

"We were about to excommunicate him when he disappeared with the chip. Then you popped into the picture. You killed Cassady and took the chip before we could find him. You were a random element no one had anticipated."

"Hold on," I said. "If the Cassadys were working with the Party, why'd the SPF have a death warrant out on them?"

"I don't know. Maybe Joshua wasn't handing over the information as fast or as cheaply as the SPF wanted. If Joshua died, they probably figured his body and the chip would show up at reclamation. Reclamation would alert the SPF, and they'd get all their information for a couple thousand credits."

"That's how they like to operate all right," I said, taking a drink. "Well, you're safe. The hand and chip were probably incinerated in a trash furnace months ago. Of course, you don't have to believe me."

She looked into my eyes. "Oh, but I do."

"Why did you wait for the long shot of my coming to you? My number's in the book."

"Believe me, we tried to find you. We traced you to

Denver, then alerted our chief operative out there. You somehow managed to kill him."

I laughed. "Don't tell me Babbit was on *your* payroll, too."

She appeared bewildered, then shrugged. "When we found out the HPA had a bounty on you, we guessed you wouldn't be stupid enough to come back to the City."

"I guess I showed you."

"I guess you did. You can imagine our surprise when a Jake Strait showed up in our recruitment data bank."

"That explains the red card. And your memo."

"Yes." She leaned across the table and took my right hand, more firmly this time. "But don't think any of this affects your position with us. Nothing has changed in that respect. Sinn is extremely excited about you. He thinks you're the one essential ingredient the set is lacking." She squeezed my fingers and leaned closer. "Let's just say we were looking for a nugget and found a gold mine."

Outside, execs marched by, leaning into important strides, desperate and impatient to be somewhere else. I pulled my hand away and finished my drink. Two paths stretched before me, both dangerous, both twisting and sinister. One seemed a little smoother than the other, and I lurched forward, ashamed of how easy it was. "Listen, Jackie," I said quietly. "I'm going to level with you. It wasn't just dumb luck that I showed up at the mission."

She dropped a burrowing look on me. "It wasn't?"

"No. I was looking for you."

"Me? Why?"

"Your sister sent me to find you. She thought the set kidnapped you."

Shock dropped her jaw and froze her expression. Just

when I thought she was struck speechless, Jackie threw back her head and laughed. "Heidi sent you? To rescue me?" She laughed some more, wiping tears from her eyes. "Forgive me, but that is so like her. My wonderful protector, my perfect conscience. That evil bitch." She took a long drink and shook her head. "She's so intent on my living a normal, boring life, so devoted to keeping her poor misguided little sister in line. The truth is she lives through me. She's so prudish, so closed minded. She enjoys watching me going astray, because she's so afraid to, so afraid of disappointing dear Mommy and Daddy."

"She cares for you."

"Like hell she does. She hangs on my neck like a parasite. My only worth to her is as someone to shake a finger at and scorn, a purpose for her hollow life. She can't stand to see me succeed—she's destroyed every relationship, every dream, every chance of lifting myself out of the pristine hell my parents built around me, always there to kick me back into the mud. But not this time—I won't let her."

Once she got it all out she seemed to deflate. She stared at the hand slowly stirring her drink. "If she hired you to rescue me, why haven't you?"

I shrugged. "She said you were imprisoned against your will, brainwashed, slave to some sinister organization. That's obviously not the case. She doesn't know you *are* the organization."

Jackie smiled seductively. "Is that the only reason?"

I blinked at her. "Of course."

"Are you certain?"

"Certainly."

Jackie nodded. "At what point did you cease being my dashing rescuer?"

I dangled a vitacig in my mouth and lit it. "Oh, about two minutes ago."

"Are you sure you're off the case?"

"If I was going to rescue you, I would have kept quiet and chinned you on the way back to the mission."

"How romantic."

I shrugged. "You know how it is."

"I suppose your interest in joining the set was just part of your rescue plan."

"Started out that way."

She stared at me. "You're considering Sinn's offer?"

"I accepted it."

She looked away. "And what will you tell Heidi?"

"The same thing I told you. That you're here of your own free will."

"She already knew that. Maybe you shouldn't tell her."

"Why not?"

"She might become violent."

"What?"

She looked carefully at her nails. "Dear sweet Heidi is not the pure angel she appears."

"Really?"

"Really. She has a dark side, a side as evil and ugly as the blackest pit of hell."

"I find that hard to believe."

"Perhaps some day I'll tell some stories about dear Miss Frump that just might change your mind."

"Tell me."

"You wouldn't believe me."

"I don't know. I believe a lot of things I'm not supposed to."

She shook her head. "No, you wouldn't. Perhaps later you will."

"All right," I said. I finished my drink and stood up.

She leaned across the table and took my hand. "Must you go?"

"I have no choice." I cocked my head. "Don't you hear them?"

She frowned. "Hear what?"

"The hounds. It's *me* they're after. And there's only one way to lose them."

She pulled her hand back. "And what is that?"

"Burn the bridge before they can cross. You of all people should know that."

10

I drove around the City, aimlessly charging down back alleys and side streets, sweating badly. I was running from the hounds baying in the distance, getting closer. I would have to face them sooner or later but I wasn't ready, not just yet. I careered out of a side street and fishtailed onto Hayward, stomping on the accelerator, faster and faster to the absolute limit. I had to put some distance between me and the hounds, buy a little time to think.

A junkie staggered into the headlights, and I swerved wildly, sideswiping a row of parked cars and careening to a halt against the curb of St. Christopher's Lounge. I hunched over the wheel for a moment, catching my breath, then lurched out of the stalled machine, ducking into the St. Chris.

I took a stool next to a gray barfly, ordered a beer from Amal, the one-eared bartender, and tried to get a grip on the mad emotion coursing through my veins.

"You look as if the devil's close behind you, my odd friend," Amal said as he delivered my second screwdriver.

I laughed and it sounded like a stranger's delirious titter. "You got it all wrong, pal. I've finally *lost* that bastard."

"And now you're wondering who's going to take his place?"

"Not at all. Just one more bridge to burn, and none of those bastards will ever catch me." I pushed my empty glass toward Amal and caught a look at myself in the smoky mirrors behind the bar. I looked like a wiped-out door-to-door salesman who'd tried to beat the company record with the help of too many amphetamines.

Amal passed over a fresh screwdriver. "Contract eating at your conscience, bogeyboy?"

"No, no more of that. I work for a new god now. He *wants* me to kill the bad guys."

The old barfly stirred next to me. "Oh, yes!" he croaked. "Everyone turns to new gods to solve old problems."

"The old gods seem to have dropped the ball," I countered. "Maybe it's time for a new batter to step up."

The old man stared at me in the mirror, then mumbled, "Jehovah wasn't such a bad god. He was a little harsh in Old Testament times, but he was young then. He mellowed after a while." He tipped his glass and sank half of his highball. "Then we nailed his son to a couple of planks. I think that really hurt and horrified him. Since then I don't think he's cared very much, he just stopped paying attention. Then science got a stranglehold on him. Man came up with his own answers to life's riddles. That's why the world is so cynical and faithless. We know too much to believe in anything."

"Knowing all the answers doesn't mean we can solve all the problems," I said.

A commotion broke out near the door as four angry-eyed Hayward hoods with blunt instruments charged inside. "Who owns the big shitmobile parked outside?" the brawny leader demanded. "Who's the bastard that sideswiped my cruiser?"

He addressed no one in particular, and no one offered an answer.

"All right," the leader said. "Clam up, then. The bastard can't stay in here all night, and we'll be waiting *outside*." They backed out the door.

"Made some new friends, I see," Amal commented.

I waved a hand dismissively. "Comes with being one of karma's busier henchmen." I ordered more drinks with wild abandon, fueling the delirium. When Amal brought my tenth drink around, he looked concerned.

"Maybe you better take it easy on the hooch, Jake. I'm going to have to alert my wholesalers if you keep it up. Don't you think misery is drowned by now?"

I grabbed the glass from him. "I'm not drowning misery. I'm floating a ship of hope. I finally get to win."

"Win what?"

"Everything. All of it."

"All of what?"

I frowned. "Listen, all I ever wanted was to do something about all the...*shit* I see every day. It goes on all around me, all the time, all the human meanness and horror. I just wanted to make a dent, hold the line somewhere. Now I finally get a chance to, regardless of what it costs my soul."

Amal stared at me incomprehensibly.

"Okay," I said, "let me bring it down to your level. Of all the creeps in the world, who do you hate the most?"

Amal rolled his eyes back. "Rude drunks."

"Suppose you suddenly had the power to make all the rude drunks disappear. Would you?"

"Hell, no. Rude drunks make up ninety percent of my clientele—I'd go out of business. And besides," he said, reaching across the bar to pat my shoulder, "I'd miss you, Jake."

I glared at him. "Don't you have some drinks to pour?"

Amal shrugged and moved down the bar. I finished my drink and went outside. The traffic vigilantes had taken up position on the hood of my car, arms folded with determination. "Sure you don't know who the driver is?" the leader demanded.

"Okay, you got me." I sighed. "It's the one-eared man behind the bar."

The leader leaned off the car and squinted at me. "You sure?"

"Sure I'm sure. The bastard was bragging about it, laughing at your misfortune. Letting out little squeals of pleasure."

"The dirty bastard!"

"You better hurry, though. He was about to slip out the back when I left. I advise you to divide your forces and send someone around the rear."

They thanked me, split into pairs and stormed the bar.

I slipped into the Olds and wheeled into traffic. I caught their faces in the rearview as they rushed back out, waving their baseball bats excitedly. I leaned an arm out the window and waved back.

After a few blocks I realized the right front fender of the Olds was rubbing against the tire, so I pulled over in a parking lot to fix it. I muscled the crushed metal away from the rubber then looked up at a big neon sign that said, Have A Drinky At Winky's Liquors. A big, smiling neon clown, whom I assumed to be Winky, winked and pointed at a liquor store across the lot.

Why not? I thought. I went inside and bought a bottle of company. I sat in the parking lot and drank until my head went numb and I could hear the distant baying of hounds again. The more I drank, the louder they became, and I knew it was time to face their master.

I RANG THE DOORBELL, then discovered the bottle of cutter hanging in my left hand. I thought about hiding it behind my back, then figured, what the hell, what was a bottle among friends?

The door opened, and Heidi stood before me wearing a short gray jump dress and a frown of consternation. "Jake. You're drunk."

I tipped the bottle and took a long, defiant pull. "How can you tell?"

She made an effort to lever more disapproval into her frown, then turned away as if I weren't there. She went to the kitchen alcove of the big shabby Complan apartment and picked up a butcher knife big enough to mistake for a small sword. I hesitated in the doorway, and she began hacking at something on the counter.

"I'm having a late dinner," she said quietly. "Would you like to join me?"

"Sure," I said. I closed the door and moved into the kitchen, stopping just out of slashing range.

"Look at all the wonderful vegetables I found," she said.

I looked at the spread of real carrots, onions and potatoes she diced on the scarred cutting board built into the kitchen counter. "You must have paid a fortune for them."

Heidi shrugged. "Money is not one of my worries." The butcher knife thunked rhythmically against the board. The monstrous blade seemed too large and awkward for chopping vegetables, but Heidi seemed very adept with it. She finished dicing and scooped the chopped vegetables into a steamer.

"I walked around the neighborhood today," she said distantly, wiping her hands on a towel. "I saw this one-legged man. He was very drunk and lying in the gutter. His plastic leg had come off, and he was trying to strap it back on but he couldn't because he was so drunk. Eventually he just gave up and lay back in the filth and grime, laughing. I found it so strange."

"You shouldn't," I said. "In the gutter that wino's as happy as any rich man in his mansion, maybe more so. It's one of human nature's greatest enigmas. Some lose their bank account and leap from high windows. Others spend their lives in the gutter and never despair enough to let go."

"I feel so sorry for them."

"They don't want your pity. Or deserve it."

"Why not?"

"Because if they were born in your place, they'd act the same as you. So why pity anyone?"

"I just wish they all could live in nice apartments and have good jobs."

"Penthouse or gutter, it's all the same in the end."

She lifted the steamer's lid and poked at the vegetables with a fork. "I wish you wouldn't act so hard. I wonder what you would be like if you escaped the terrible prison of poverty and violence you're trapped in."

I smirked. "I'd be escaping the power that gives me the means to escape. It's hardship that provides the strength to run or stay. It's the soft prison that's the hardest to break out of, your prison of contentment and complacency."

"You poor man. You live in a paradox."

"Yeah, but the rent's cheap."

She rolled the mildly steamed vegetables onto two plates and carried them to a table in the dining alcove. She set two places and we sat down. She picked up a fork and began eating.

"No prayer, Sister?"

She shook her head. "It never seems to help."

We ate quietly and the silence ballooned until I could almost hear its thin skin ticking, stretching to the breaking point. I was thinking about making inane small talk just to let off some pressure when Heidi dropped the bomb.

"You're on her side now, aren't you, Jake?" she said without looking up from her plate.

"Why do you say that?" I said, annoyed that she had so little faith in me.

"It's so obvious. Is that why you're drunk? Because you didn't have the guts to tell me sober?"

"You don't understand."

"Oh, I understand," she said, stabbing meanly at her carrots. "She swayed you. I should have guessed. She always gets her way."

"It wasn't supposed to be a contest. I was supposed to rescue a prisoner from a dangerous cult. It didn't shape up that way. She's more warden than prisoner. Maybe you knew that."

"You said you didn't care. You said you would feel bad about screwing me over."

"I do feel bad. But they offered me something I couldn't turn down. It's as simple as that."

"Oh, really? And what was that something, Jake? Money? Power? Sex? Or was it heaven? Did the promise of paradise win you over?"

"Which would you prefer to hear?"

"The truth, if it isn't asking too much."

I found it hard telling the truth; the words had to be forced out. "They want me to lead their militia. We're going to attack the criminal subculture, clean up the—"

"So it's the power to kill that swayed you," she snapped.

"To be honest, I would have preferred the promise of salvation made you betray me."

"It's the next-best thing," I said, my voice rising angrily. "Don't you see the leap of grace I'm making? I have the power to stop all the terrible shit, to beat it back, to win!"

She laughed sadistically. "You really think you can win?"

"I can goddamn try!" I retorted angrily. "And that's better than watching from a window and wondering where it all went wrong."

She put down her fork, touched her lips with a napkin and rose. She went to the kitchen counter and picked up the butcher knife in an overhand, stabbing grip. Her hooded eyes flickered to me, and before the chill finished passing up my spine, she turned around and moved stiffly to a big red clay flower box on a table beside a window. She began stabbing the rich, black soil of the flower box.

"You poor man," she said after a long moment of silence. She doled out the words like medicine to a man who didn't deserve to be cured. "I guess I can't fault you. She offered you the one thing you crave the most. To blame you would be tantamount to condemning a drowning man for grabbing a life preserver."

"Does it matter who threw it to me?"

"That's your business."

I went to the window. I fished a wad of credits out of my pocket and tossed it among the gang of flowers in small plastic containers surrounding the clay pot. She glanced at the credit.

"What's that?"

"My fee. I didn't do my job so I have no claim to it."

"You can keep it," she said, turning the soil of the box with quick, efficient twists of her wrist. "You need it more than I do."

"That's never a reason to give anything to anybody."

She laughed. "So, you are not completely without principle."

"Nothing's all black or white."

She put the butcher knife down and began squeezing the sides of a container, working the soil from the plastic. She shook out the clump of root-entwined earth and lowered it into a hollow in the soil of the flower box, her hands moving efficiently, mechanically. I dumbly watched her labor, breathing the rich scent of the black soil, drunk enough not to feel obliged to speak. I wanted to leave, but there still seemed to be something that needed to be said, and I wanted to make sure I was standing on the right end of the bridge when I dropped the match.

"So, Jake," Heidi said casually. "Have you slept with my sister yet?"

She began squeezing a container encasing a tulip. "You sound as if it's eventual," I said, black hope in my heart.

"I know my sister."

"Apparently not as well as you think."

"Does that mean no?"

"That's right."

She moved the tulip to its new neighborhood and tamped earth around it with the knife. "Have you ever slept with an ex-nun?"

We stood in silence as she tamped soil and I searched for the hidden hook.

"I can't say I have."

"I've never slept with a killer."

"Maybe we're both missing something."

"Maybe we are." She put down the knife, wiped her hands carefully on a towel, turned around and fell into my arms. She trembled against my chest for a moment, like a swimmer pulled from frigid waters, then tilted her face to mine.

Her lips were at first hard and inseparable, her body tense and unyielding. I applied a gentle heat, softly kissing her face, neck and shoulders, slowly melting layer after layer of ice until her lips became as soft as warm butter and inner fires ignited then exploded with raw passion. Our embrace became animal and frenzied, our kisses hungry and desperate, wanting more, demanding, squeezing, biting, an unstoppable runaway train of desire racing to the end of the line at breakneck speed.

I picked her up and found her bedroom. I put her down and she danced away, striking a calculated pose at the foot of the bed, spine erect, chin up, eyes bright. Her right hand began inching up the front of her body, rising and falling with every curve and hollow until it reached the top of the long zipper that ran from her throat to the high hemline of her jump dress. With a soft growl of parting metal, the hand began sliding slowly, languidly downward, like a spider on a thread of silk.

"Don't hurt me, Daddy," she said softly, her eyes half-closed. "Please don't hurt me."

"I won't," I promised, the words falling out of my mouth like ignored strangers.

Her eyes closed, her chest heaved, and the zipper climbed the steep, carnal rise of her full, firm breasts. It peaked, pausing for the most salacious of moments, then started down, parting rough gray cloth, exposing smooth white skin. I was unable to remove my eyes from the zipper. It traveled the flat plane of her stomach, soft ivory in its wake, exposing the delicate concave of her navel, descending lower and lower still.

"I can trust you, can't I, Daddy?" she murmured as the

zipper stopped moving centimeters above the last, maddening contour, the wellspring of lust and desire.

I stared at the zipper, willing it to finish its magnificent journey. "Of course you can."

"How much?"

I hesitated a bare second. "Why, however much you need."

Time crawled by, and I almost died on the terrible rack of silence. *This is what hell is,* I thought, *this moment, right now, for eternity.*

"Okay," she finally said, and, like all the angels coming down from heaven to pull me from a lake of fire, I heard a lone *tick* of separating steel teeth, then another. The ticks beat on me like slow hammers, driving me deeper and deeper into a pit of hunger and lust until, after what seemed an eternity of famine, steel teeth parted over a darker hue and stopped.

"Promise me," she murmured.

"Anything."

"Promise me you won't help her," she said softly, her eyes as cold and hungry as a shark's. "Promise me you won't go to Jackie, Daddy."

Lust hit a high wall. "You know I can't do that."

With the flourish and hiss of a falling ax, the zipper shot back up to her throat. "Then get the hell out of my bedroom."

I hesitated, and for a single, bastard moment I was prepared to sacrifice everything for a single act of naked lust; I would tell her anything she wanted to hear. The moment passed like a black cloud over a parched desert then was gone. I felt tense and tight, and a meanness crawled onto my back and settled there heavily, like a creaking cross.

"All right," I said, and the match dropped. "I'm sorry I couldn't be of help. With the case, I mean."

She stared at me, her eyes grey ice. "Not as sorry as you're going to be, Daddy. You're going to get yours."

"Sooner or later. Goodbye, Miss Pan." I backed into the living room and let myself out.

I wasn't halfway to my car when a familiar feeling levered me into a local dive, a dim hole full of the off-work crowd. Burned-out and bitter door-to-door salesmen and factory workers lined the bar, shoulders hunched, heads pointed at their drinks, numbed by the ugly odds of success. I took my glass to a corner table, since I had no desire to drink with them. I didn't believe in the lives they led, the cruel lie they perpetuated.

I watched them throw back shots of liquor until their skulls went numb, then nurse beers until the empty words began to spill out of their grim mouths. First a trickle, then a stream, then a torrent of horror as the dams broke inside them. Sooner or later they would roll over like crocodiles, exposing their sickly white diseased bellies, and if you listened close enough, you could hear the grinding machinations of their souls, jagged gears and levers slimed with black oil. Theirs were the bitter voices of those who instinctively understood they were men born without destinies, that the world offered them no greater meaning than to live, die and be forgotten.

I hate them and they are just like me, I thought. I finished my drink and left.

I hunched against a vicious, stabbing wind. By the time I made my car, I was chilled to the marrow and felt as if I wouldn't sleep in a hundred thousand years. I drove around town, hoping the act would lend some solace, the humming of the tires on the road some rhythm of regularity. By the time the sun poked its dull head over the horizon, the wheel was still in my hands and sleep was still miles away.

11

"The Martyr Program occupies floors forty-one and forty-two," Jackie explained from behind her desk. "Forty-one is divided into an urban mock-up and exercise area, and forty-two houses the living and dining facilities."

"Where's Sinn?" I asked, rubbing my eyes, so tired even the rope-and-iron chair seemed comfortable.

"He's busy at the moment. You don't look well. Something keep you up late?"

I ignored her question. "Why do you house the martyr's in the tower?"

"Sinn likes the idea of having his soldiers near him at all times."

"Sinn lives in the tower?"

"Yes, in the penthouse. We've quarters for you, too." She rose. "Come on, I'll show you."

I followed her to the main elevator, and we descended one level to the forty-second floor. A wide-open bay greeted us, stacked with steel, uncomfortable-looking bunk beds and rows of metal lockers.

"Gosh, it's just wonderful," I said. "Which bunk is mine?"

"This is the martyrs' living quarters, silly," she said, laughing. "The commander's quarters is down here." We walked between the perfectly spaced and tightly made beds toward a door in the far wall, our shoes echoing across the meticulously polished floor.

"Glad you're not spoiling them," I said.

"I think you'll find the martyrs a highly disciplined unit," Jackie said. We stopped in front of the door, and I admired the polished brass plaque set in its middle. Commander's Quarters, it read in Gothic letters above a smiling skull. I nodded with approval, and she slid a black plastic keycard into a slot beside the door. The door hissed open, and Jackie handed me the card. "This is yours now."

I took the card and we entered.

My new apartment teetered on that thin line between stately and garish, with enough extra luxury thrown in to make me tingle with self-indulgence. In the middle sat a robot bed, capable of doing everything short of bearing my children. It faced an entertainment center loaded with video and audio equipment. Beside the bed sprawled a state-of-the-art workout machine, decadent with meters of gleaming chrome and black velvet upholstery. Near the door sat a sleek black-and-chrome command console only the tragically misinformed would term a desk, stacked with an array of advanced computer equipment. Animated landscape frames hung on every wall, shifting with form and color, and I could see a balcony amok with tropical plants beyond a tinted window that occupied most of the far wall. By the window, lurking like an agent of darkness, sat one of the most dangerous machines known to man: an autobar.

"Lucky there's a lock on the door," I said. "If the troops got a look at this, there'd be a riot."

"You find it acceptable?"

I strolled to the gleaming exercise machine. "I guess it'll do. This thing talk?"

"Of course. It's the Party's newest model. Hello, Melvin."

The machine hummed to life, and blinking lights located throughout the system winked on. "Hello, master!" the machine squealed in an eager-to-please tenor. "What sort of workout would you prefer today?"

"Melvin?" I said doubtfully, prowling around the machine. "I don't know, even the name sounds suspect."

"May I help you with your program selection?" Melvin offered.

"Go to sleep, Melvin," I said.

"Yes, *sir!*" Melvin squeaked, then blinked out.

"See?" I said. "I turned him off, and he didn't even threaten me."

"You have experience with interactive bioequipment?" Jackie asked.

"I have one at home."

"We could arrange to have it moved here if you like."

"Oh, no need for that." I sat on the edge of the command console and gazed at the best feature of the room.

"Why do you keep looking at me like that?" Jackie asked.

"Like what?"

"Like we have…shared intimacy."

I searched her eyes. What I saw did not dissuade me. "Perhaps it's a premonition."

The monitor on the command console chimed, and we turned to find Sinn's smiling face filling the screen. "How do you find your new home, Commander?"

"Shockingly decadent. Where's my late-model sports car?"

"Parked in the underground garage."

"I approve. And my luxury rotor with chrome fittings and built-in autobar?"

"On the roof, of course."

"Great." I looked at Jackie. "It isn't easy being a smart-ass around here, is it?"

"One delivers," Sinn said. "If you're finished up there, the men are waiting to meet you."

"Be right down," I said, and Sinn blinked off the screen. I slapped the console, and Jackie sat down beside me. "Is there really a chrome-fitted rotor on the roof?"

She nodded. "It's keyed to your door card."

I looked at the card in my hand and shifted on the console, sliding closer to Jackie. "Well, I guess now that I'm a high-powered exec with a swanky apartment and expensive machines you'll be hanging on me like a twenty-credit suit."

She smiled and leaned a hand against my encroaching chest. "The troops are waiting, tiger."

I tested the resoluteness of her restraining hand, then stood up. "Ah, yes, the troops."

She touched a button on the console, and the near wall opened, exposing a closet lined with pressed black uniforms. She took one and handed it to me. "You'll want to change before you head down. You'll find the martyrs in the exercise area on forty-one." She went to the door.

"Aren't you going to help me dress?" I said, trying to put my head through a pant leg. "This uniform seems exceedingly complex."

"I wish I could stay and help," she said, "but as assistant director I have many duties to perform."

"When do I get an assistant?"

"You'll find your assistant downstairs. Bye."

Jackie exited, so I took my head out of the pant leg and changed. The uniform was well made and formfitting, with snazzy pockets everywhere. A platinum lightning bolt on each epaulet signified my high rank, the small red skull embroidered over my heart proclaimed my allegiance, and I imagined the pointy chrome tips on my spit-shined jackboots demonstrated my willingness to defy good taste and decency. For five minutes I practiced confidence-shattering glares and ego-whipping scowls in a full-length mirrors. Then I went down to meet the troops.

I marched out of the elevator into a cavernous gym with a twenty-meter-high ceiling. In the open space between exercise equipment and stacked wrestling mats stood over a hundred men arrayed in four ranks, as still and erect as tin soldiers. They wore tailored black uniforms similar to mine, and their hair was cropped close to the skull. A chubby, prematurely balding man marched from the fore of the formation, snapping to a halt in front of Sinn and me.

"I suppose this is my goddamn assistant," I said.

Sinn gave me a bemused look, and the chubby man shouted, "Troops ready for inspection, Commander!"

Sinn gripped the man's shoulder and turned to me. "Slim here is your second in command. Up to now he has been in charge of the Martyr Program."

"Pleasure to meet you, Commander," Slim cried, practically slobbering with joy. "I gladly and respectfully relinquish control to your inspired leadership."

"Thanks," I said, taking his hand. "No hard feelings?"

"Oh, no, sir," he effused, pumping my hand enthusiastically. I noticed at the end of all his sentences there was a kowtowing lilt.

"Good," I said. "Then I won't have to kill you."

He frowned with confusion. "Sir?"

I smiled very slightly. "Just a joke."

"Oh, I see." He laughed mechanically.

"Well," Sinn said, "I'll leave you military men to your business. Commander, I'd like an evaluation report when you're finished. I'll be in my office."

"See you then," I said. Sinn departed, and Slim and I looked the men over. The formation seemed to consist of the cream of the crop of young hoods, confused run-aways, converted junkies and reformed winos. Just get-ting them off the streets had probably done a lot toward lowering the crime rate. While the majority appeared to be in their late teens and early twenties, there were nu-merous older, slack-jawed men mixed in, the breed of shifty-eyed perverts usually found in rubber overcoats and porn palaces.

"How much training have these horrible creatures had?" I asked.

"Well, we have a wide range here," Slim reported. "A few have actual combat experience from the corporate wars and the Party mop-up, much as yourself, Commander. Like Sailor there—he was in the Party Navy for a while."

An older, muscular man with weak eyes and a lecher-ous grin at the head of the first rank nodded. "That's right," he said, "I saw some serious shit down in—"

"Shut the fuck up," I snapped, then addressed Slim. "What about the rest?"

"Well," Slim said nervously, "some have gang and mi-litia experience but most, quite frankly, are fresh recruits. All have had a crash course in basic military training, in-cluding weapons orientation, drill, hand-to-hand combat and urban warfare."

"Who taught them?" I asked.

Slim smiled at his feet. "I did, sir."

"And who taught you?"

"Well," he said with guilt-gilded pride, "I am more than

a little ashamed to say that before I got right with One I directed a Protestant redemption team."

"You mean you led a death squad."

Slim grimaced. "Some would call it that."

"You want to speak straight with me, Assistant. What else can you tell me about these low men?"

"Well, they're all graduates of Set of One indoctrination, of course."

"Of course. What does that consist of?"

He looked at me with abject disbelief. "You didn't go through indoctrination?"

"I got a note from my doctor," I explained. "I'm allergic to whipped cream and high voltage."

He frowned deeply, creasing his forehead. "Well, the basic five-day course consists of personality stripping, emotion dissolution, inner discipline, conscience-clamping techniques, sleep deprivation, humili—"

"I get the gist," I cut in. "What sort of physical-fitness program have you had them on?"

"The best," he said, smiling brightly. "And more than a little tough, I can tell you. We do dinarobotics, tenseraerobics and a modified form of hypertonics I developed myself."

"And I suppose you got them out disco dancing on the weekends," I accused.

"Huh?"

"That's what I thought. Well, it looks like I have my work cut out. Follow me."

With Slim in tow, I moved to the head of the front rank, stopping in front of Sailor. The chevrons of a squad leader glittered from his collar, and he gave me the smarmy, ain't-we-seen-it-all grin veterans like to pass around after a few drinks. He held out an easy hand and said, "Howsa boy, Skipper?"

I kept my face blank until his smile melted and his hand retreated. After a moment of ducking my stare, he began shooting glances to his buddy Slim.

Slim cleared his throat and tried on a smile. "Ol' Sailor here was—"

"I heard it," I snarled, leaning close to Sailor's face. "I don't like your type, Sailor. Not at all."

His face flushed with fear and loathing, and I left him with it. I moved down the line, stopping briefly in front of each soldier. They stood ramrod straight, but their fearful eyes followed me very closely. Their muscles coiled like springs, as if they were certain I would lunge for their throats at the least opportunity. A young, innocent-faced Oriental in the middle of the first rank, standing out like a mouse among weasels, seemed particularly certain.

I glanced at his name tag. "You looking at *me,* Nu?"

"No, sir!" he shouted.

"What were you looking at, then?"

"Nothing, sir!"

"Are you calling me 'nothing'?"

"No, sir!"

"Then what in the hell were you looking at?"

"I don't know, sir!"

"Where you from?"

"The burbs, sir!"

"Runaway?"

"Yes, sir!"

"What are you doing in this formation?"

"I got tired of being pushed around, sir!"

"You got tired of being pushed around so you decided to join up and kill some people to get even, is that it, Nu?"

He sputtered and croaked, too scared to lie. "Yes, sir."

"Good enough," I said, and moved down the line. I finished tormenting the first rank, then moved to the second. A rangy black stood at its head. He and Slim exchanged secret smiles. I looked from one to the other. "Something going on between you two?"

Slim blushed. "No, sir!"

"Are you buddies?"

"Squad leader Brown and I served in the same militia unit."

"Oh," I said. "Death squad chums." I looked over Brown's shoulder at the Third Squad leader. He was a big, winking brute of a man. "What about him? Is he your buddy, too?"

"Well, Soutie and I went through advanced indoctrination together. During the bonding phase we—"

"And I suppose the Fourth Squad leader is your longlost cousin from Monticello."

"Well, no, Rolf is my—"

"Put a clamp on it," I snapped, causing Slim to cringe. I stepped to the right of the ranks. "All right, martyrs, let's play a little game. When I give the command, I want the man at the head of each rank, that's *you,* squad leaders, to run as fast as he can to the end of the squad. As soon as he goes, everyone moves a step to the left, and the next martyr in line shoots to the end. Kind of like musical chairs. Ready, *go!*"

The squad leaders rambled down the ranks, quickly followed by the next in line. After the first dozen men in each rank had moved to the end and I figured I had skimmed off Slim's cronies, I yelled, "Halt!"

I stepped back and looked over the new order. Fresh and timid faces stood in the squad-leader positions, including a very nervous-looking Nu. "Well," I said. "We have winners. You men at the head of each squad are now the squad leaders. Just like a Horatio Alger story."

"But—" Slim began.

"Shut the fuck up." I started down the third rank then stopped in my tracks. Slim ran into me and I turned on him. "Why aren't there any females in my formation?"

Slim chuckled conspiratorially. "No girlies allowed in this club, sir."

I glared at him, shaking my head dangerously. "Man, I swear to god, if you don't stop screwing up I'm going to rip your goddamn lungs out. From this moment on females will not be barred from becoming martyrs. If they pass the criteria, they're in."

"But—"

"Shut up," I said, and began moving down the fourth rank. By the time I reached the end of the rank, I'd managed to work myself into a fine frenzy.

"It's obvious to me that none of you are motivated," I said in a deep, ominous voice, moving to the front of the formation. "Therefore, I will forcibly *instill* you with motivation. Who knows what the quickest path to motivation is?"

They looked at each other, bewildered.

"Prayer?" Slim said behind me.

"Nope."

"Week-long intensive motivation-modification courses?" Nu offered.

"Nope."

"Cattle prods and pressurized dairy products?" another voice ventured.

"Wrong, wrong, wrong," I bellowed. "The quickest path to motivation is the *push-up*. Front-leaning rest position, move!"

It took them roughly two minutes to figure out I wanted them in the push-up position. I smiled down at them. "Get

back up," I said in a kind voice. "Go on, get back up."
When they found their feet, I threw a fit.

"Listen to me, you bastards! When I tell you to drop, I
want you to drop like goddamn ten-thousand-pound shit-
hammers fell out of the sky and slammed into your pointy
heads! You will lunge forward, your feet will fly out like
pistons, and your hands will hit the ground before your
boots do! Do I make myself clear?"

"Yes, sir," they mumbled.

"I can't hear you!"

"Yes, sir!"

"I still can't hear you!"

"Yes, sir!"

"Drop!"

They leapt to the ground as if they'd been sapped from
behind.

"That's better," I said. "Start knocking 'em out."

They began pumping out push-ups at various speeds,
some with more enthusiasm than others. "Get your butts
down and heads up," I shouted. "If someone walked by,
they'd think you were humping basketballs. Who gave
you permission to laugh?"

"This is exactly what they need," a voice said beside me.

I whirled around and faced the voice. Slim stood there,
arms folded, smiling contentedly.

"What in the hell are you doing vertical?" I demanded.

He goggled at me, startled. "*I* have to do push-ups, too?"

I made my eyes bulge and lunged for his throat. With
admirable speed he went horizontal, his arms pumping
before they hit the floor.

"I don't want to kill any of you," I said earnestly, walking among the prone ranks. "But I will if that is what it
takes to make the rest understand."

Five minutes trudged by, and sweat dripped off bodies groaning and shaking like old engines.

"Hurts, doesn't it?" I said. "What are you going to do when you've got a sucking chest wound and bullets are ringing your helmet like a bell?"

"I won't be doing goddamn push-ups!" someone said, and the martyrs proved they still had the strength to laugh.

"I thought you said these men were fit," I shouted at Slim. "Why, they're as weak as eighty-year-old junkies."

"C'mon, martyrs," Slim bleated. "Let's show the commander. Remember, One is watching!"

"One!" I shouted. "One is the last bastard you should be thinking about right now. It's the devil you need to worry about. And we all know who the devil is, don't we, martyrs?"

I was pleased to hear over half the martyrs had figured it out.

"That's right," I said. "It's *me*. Position of attention, move!"

They jumped to their feet, wobbling and swaying like rattled bowling pins.

"You men look tired," I said. "Would you like to go upstairs for a little rest? In fact, wouldn't you like to take the rest of the day off, just to relax, take it easy?"

They all wagged their heads, and a chorus of "Yes, sir" whined out of the ranks.

"Assistant," I said. "Take the men upstairs and let them do as they please. In fact, have the cafeteria send up some cake and ice cream on my authority."

Slim shot me a salute, and a smile jumped on his face. "Cake and ice cream, sir? Truly?"

"Sure," I said with a big smile, "They've had a hard time—they deserve it."

Slim saluted me again, grinning goofily. "Thanks for today's training, Commander. And I thought *I* was tough with them."

"No problem," I said, waving to the boys. "See you guys tomorrow. Is ten o'clock too early for you?"

"Oh, *no, sir,*" they stammered out happily.

"Good," I said. "See you then." I turned the formation over to Slim and began strolling away.

I was halfway to the elevator when I froze in my tracks, every muscle in my body tensing. I turned around slowly and faced the ranks where the laughter had died. "Who said that?" I hissed.

Slim looked confused. "Said what, Commander?"

I began walking back to the formation. "Someone said, 'Fuck you, Commander, you ignorant bastard,' clear as a bell." I could feel a vein rising on my forehead, throbbing a mean beat.

Slim looked back at the formation with horror. "I didn't hear anything, Commander. Did anyone hear any—"

"Shut the fuck up, you lying cur," I snarled. I paced before the ranks, staring into terrified faces. "Whoever said it better confess right now, or you're all going to pay a terrible, *terrible* price!"

The martyrs looked at each other, eager to turn out a sacrificial goat. Some of the larger martyrs went so far as to try and prod forward smaller martyrs, who fought back as if they were being pushed off a cliff into hell.

"Maybe you just thought you heard that," Slim said in a careful voice behind me. "Maybe he said, 'Good luck to you, illustrious Commander,' and it just sounded like, '*F*-word you, you ignorant *b*-word.' Gosh, I mishear things all the time. Why, just the other day Sailor said—"

I raised my hand, and he shut up. "Maybe you're right."

I sighed with a sheepish grin. "Maybe I am just hearing things. Sorry, guys. See you tomorrow."

I waved, and the tension melted out of their faces. I turned away, covering my mouth to cough, then swung back toward the formation, seething anger. "I suppose you'll tell me that was my imagination, too!"

The martyrs fell into chaos, making dire threats to the invisible perpetrator, screaming at each other to shut up.

"Oh, yeah," I sneered. "I suppose that was somebody wishing me a nice day instead of calling me a goddamn dirty shitbag! Is that it?" I covered my mouth to cough again, then I cried out savagely, "There it is again! Who said 'Up yours, you bastard'?" Real anarchy broke out in the ranks as martyrs began laying hands on each other.

"Knock it off!" I shouted.

They fell silent, snapping back to the position of attention. I began pacing in front of them. "So that's the way you want it, eh? I was hoping to become chums with all of you, make this course a pleasure for everyone, smiles and laughs the whole time. But no, I try to be a nice guy, I was going to give you *cake and ice cream,* for crissakes, and how do you show your gratitude? You call me a shitbag and a bastard!"

I wiped at big, angry crocodile tears, and my voice choked up. "Okay, fine, if that's the way you want it, then that's the way it's going to be. I guess I'm going to have to kill you, goddamn it, torture all of you to death. And I'm not your *chum* anymore, either." My voice cleared. "Guess who I am now?"

"The devil?" Nu ventured.

"Right! *Drop!*"

I spent the rest of the afternoon in a frothing rage, introducing the martyrs to various exercises and hardships.

I turned the urban mock-up at the rear of the gym into an obstacle course and made them jump, scurry and crawl like weasels. I howled while they climbed like deranged monkeys up and down the thick ropes hanging from the ceiling, I chased them around the indoor track like a tiger after a herd of panicked antelope. I ran them through drill after drill until I felt certain they loathed me with all their hearts. When 6:00 p.m. rolled around, I formed them back up.

"Are you motivated?" I asked.

"Yes, sir!"

"You see? I told you it would work. Next formation is at five tomorrow morning." I dismissed the formation, and they began shuffling toward the elevator.

"Freeze!" I shouted.

They froze in position, their eyes fearful and hunted.

"Let me clear up a few things right now," I shouted. "When moving from point A to point B, martyrs do not walk. Nor do they take elevators. They take stairs and move at a goddamn double-time! Am I clear?"

"Yes, sir!"

"Go!"

They swarmed up the stairwell with a thunder of steps.

All except a group of five martyrs who skulked in my direction, stopping a safe distance away. It was Slim and the ex-squad leaders.

"What do *you* want?" I snarled.

"Well, sir," Slim piped up, his body locked in the same cringe he had worn all day. "I don't think we got off on the right foot with you, and, uh, we were wondering, honored Commander, if you would care to join our special prayer group tonight. It's open to only a select few martyrs, and we'd like you to be one of them. It might even help you overcome your unfortunate proclivity toward swearing and blasphemy." He finished with a big, trembling smile that said he was bequeathing a great honor indeed.

I clenched my teeth and tensed my neck muscles until my face gorged with blood and their tentative smiles crumpled into expressions of abject horror. "I'm going to have to hurt you, aren't I?" I whispered, my voice trembling with rage. "Is that what it's going to take? A good beating?"

Slim choked on a mouthful of spit. "Well, uh, we were just wondering—"

"Drop!"

12

I stood in Sinn's office ten minutes later. A section of marble on the left wall had parted to reveal a bank of monitors, and together we watched what appeared to be a raving lunatic running amok before a crowd of men apparently paralyzed with fear. The madman seemed familiar.

"I've been watching your technique," he said, nodding toward the monitors. I looked closer and realized why the lunatic looked so familiar. "I can see you're going to give the martyrs the fire they need," Sinn said, grinning.

"I'll give them something, all right."

"Yes. They must think you're insane."

"That's what I want them to think. I want to be their deepest, darkest nightmare. I don't want to give them a chance to think about what they should really be afraid of."

"That being?"

"Taking the lives of their fellow men."

Sinn laughed. "There's no need to burden them with those crosses. Or have you forgotten you serve an unsentimental god now?"

I was silent.

"Well," Sinn said, "no use getting into metaphysics. What's your opinion of the martyrs as a fighting unit?"

"They're in better physical shape than I expected, but they lack unity and cohesion."

Sinn raised an eyebrow and glanced at the monitors. "Their ranks seemed quite straight to me."

"Unity is more than tight formations. When I accused them of calling me names they fell on each other like bleeding sharks. They were more concerned with saving their own asses than sticking together."

"I assume there are ways of correcting this flaw."

"There are. The first step is to give each martyr the opportunity to quit."

Sinn frowned. "How will that improve cohesiveness?"

"The cement of unity is morale. Nothing drags morale down more than knowing you have to be in that formation whether you like it or not."

"Well, you need not worry. Each martyr was selected for his excellent fanatic, fitness and discipline ratings, as determined by Set of One skill testing. And thanks to intensive indoctrination, each martyr has the perfect mind-set for the job."

"They have the mind-set of amoral killers."

"The same could be said of early Christian crusaders. I would think amoral killers make the best soldiers. Some of the most elite units in history could be described as such."

"Yes, but it took years of intensive combat to make them that way. They started with a foundation of humanity and emotion. I don't want killing machines. I want a cohesive unit that kills out of idealism, not bloodlust."

"Idealism." Sinn laughed. "Do you know how hard it is to find men who will kill and die for something as equivocal and insubstantial as a *cause?* I'd have to scour the entire City to come up with half the martyrs now in your ranks. Let's face it, the average man is a cowardly and self-interested creature. Set indoctrination, however, is capable of instilling that meek and average man with the desire to fight and kill and die for One, without being bothered with the whys and wherefores, all in a matter of days. Most military commanders would give their right arm for such men."

He was right. Most armies and death squads would be delighted to learn the set's methods. "All right," I said. "But once they're out of indoctrination, they're mine."

"Agreed. You have my permission to handle them as you see fit. When will they be ready for combat?"

I considered. "If they've been through as much military training as Slim says, three months."

"Three months." Sinn selected a white ostrich plume from a crystal decanter on the desk. "I was hoping for something shorter."

"How much shorter?"

"I was thinking three weeks," Sinn said, running a thumb up and down the spine of the feather. "Considering it takes us only a week to indoctrinate them, three weeks would seem generous."

"Making someone want to kill is easy," I countered. "Teaching them to do it well is something else."

"Are you saying three weeks isn't enough?"

"It could be done, but it would mean higher casualties during the first strikes."

"That's fine. Martyrs we have a lot of—it's time we're short on. So we'll shoot for three weeks, then."

I wanted to argue, but I felt I was just half out of the water and didn't feel like rocking the boat just yet. "All right. I'll intensify the course."

"See? That's what I like about you. A can-do attitude. I can see you are going to live up to all my expectations."

He put the feather back in the decanter. "Is there anything you want to discuss?"

"As a matter of fact, there is." I turned and wandered to a corner where a marble stand supported a delicate vase. I studied the vase for a moment, then gently picked it up, its skin as fragile as a promise. "What's the purpose of the Martyr Program?"

Sinn dispensed a quantity of his manufactured laugh. "I've already told you. It exists to stamp out evil, do away with the City's criminal class."

I rolled the vase in my hand, knowing I could crush it to shards with the slightest pressure. "I don't think that's it."

"And why not?"

"Because you strike me more as a ruthless corporate exec than a selfless holy avenger."

"More wolf than shepherd, eh?" he said, giggling. "Okay, Strait, I'm going to put all my cards on the table." He rose and moved to the elevator. "Shall we?"

I gently returned the vase to the stand. "Why not?"

We rode up to the God Hall and began our walk. Sinn clasped his hands behind his back and told me a story.

"Up to five years ago I lived the executive dream," he said. "I worked in the City Party's information bureau, I spent ten years telling the Party lie. I made good money, possessed all the material things I wanted, even wielded a certain amount of power—my creations held considerable sway over public thought. Do you know of Sal the Socialist Salamander?"

"The cartoon?"

"He was my creation. I also did the Bodies for Bucks spots for reclamation."

"The commercials that encouraged kids to look for dead bodies in transient areas?"

"That was mine. I was good, maybe the best in the City, and I had a good life. But you know, the whole time I felt as empty as a shell, haunted by the certainty I was missing out on something. Then one day I received a sign."

"A sign from One?" I said, sparing no sarcasm.

Sinn grinned. "You might say that. I was walking through the business district and I passed a crowd of execs gathered on a street corner. I was so bored I stopped to see what kind of contraband was being hawked. In the middle of the crowd was an old man." Sinn laughed. "Man, you should have seen this crazy cat. He was dressed in the robes of a Muslim holy man, yet he also wore a priest's collar, a Jewish skullcap, Buddhist beads, atheist tattoos, a Satanic pentagram and the symbols of a dozen other religions around his neck. He did this funny little jig and picked people out of the crowd with a crooked finger and the most crazy eyes in the world, saying, 'What's your faith, boy? Are you Catholic? These lips kissed the Pope's hand! Are you Muslim? These feet tread Mecca's dusty streets! Jewish? These eyes shed tears at the Wailing Wall!' He kept going on like that, and those people kept throwing creds at his feet. Then he looks right at me, points his finger and says, 'Are you an atheist, boy? I turned my back on all the gods!' And I'll be damned if I didn't find myself laying plastic on him!"

"So you were conned by a clever beggar. So what?"

"He didn't con anybody! We were buying faith, and he gave us all we could carry. He sold us a magnificent feeling of joy for less than the price of a couple of drinks in a high-up giddylounge. As I walked away, I thought to myself, man, if I could package and market what that geezer was handing out, I'd make millions, billions of credits. That's when it hit me."

"You decided to start peddling faith."

"Yes! It struck me that of all the products one could offer, faith had the best return. I mean, you're selling something you don't even have to manufacture, it's all in the promise. Do you realize how much the average man is willing to spend reserving a place in an afterlife?"

"A lot, I'm sure," I said. "But isn't the field a little crowded?"

"Oh, it's crowded, all right, but it's a slow race. The competition is down in the dirt, science has diminished mankind's capacity to believe in the old dogmas, their doctrines are too inflexible and outmoded to explain the complexities of a modern world, leaving a huge vacuum of faith."

"And you figured there might be a profit in filling that vacuum."

"Absolutely. But it couldn't be just *any* god. It had to be a fresh, properly planned god, unlike hodgepodge Jehovah or harsh Allah or the befuddled Buddha. It had to be a new *improved* god, a totally fresh mythos that appealed to everyone. That's what that crazy old man understood, the most basic axiom of marketing—make your product appealing to the greatest number of people. Do that and you corner the market."

"So you ran out and created a new god from scratch."

"Precisely. I quit my job, hustled together a board of investors and set up a research company. We invested millions of credits in thousands of hours of computer studies, opinion polls and market surveys. We found out exactly what kind of god the world wanted and we set about creating a god everyone would love."

"How could you hope to appeal to everyone?"

"It seems impossible, doesn't it?" Sinn said excitedly. "But listen, have you read *The Word of One*?"

"Yes."

"What do you think?"

"It was at once the most readable and ambiguous book I ever read."

"Exactly! That's it! That's the secret of mass appeal—ambiguity! Do you know who wrote that book? A computer! Every syllable, every turn of phrase is designed to flow phonetically, to capture the mind of the reader without actually saying anything. It rages equivocally, storms vague gates, expounds bold and important themes without taking any sort of stand, the very essence of every great philosophy. I could take any verse and read a dozen different meanings in it. That's why the Bible was so successful—it contradicted itself so often it was able to appeal to vastly divergent crowds. One section tells us not to kill, and another praises the massacre of rival tribes. We wanted a book that will be accessible ten thousand years from now, vague and flexible enough to change with the times. And to help the less-spirited reader along, we treated the pages with a suggestive drug, absorbed through the fingers by a process of osmosis."

"No wonder I couldn't put it down," I said. "Not particularly burdened with scruples, are you?"

"Oh, hell, no. Listen, the set's purpose is a good one, the best one going, as far as I'm concerned. Whatever means accomplish that purpose are justified, whether that means suggestive drugs, subliminal messages through the media or intensive programming. Hell, we have to use those methods just to be competitive. Other religions and the Party have used them for years, we just took them one step further."

"With no qualms at all."

"None," he said, wiping the glow from his forehead.

"Finding a name for my new god, now that was a problem! Couldn't be something like John or Harry, for crissakes. What name? What name? History runs in favor of a single syllable—God, Ra, Zeus, Thor. Or two—Allah, Buddha, Brahma. We did exhaustive phonetic research and massive marketing tests to come up with the best possible name for our new god."

"And One won."

"Yes! Simple, direct and powerful, don't you think?"

"What was the second choice?"

He looked down and smiled. "Bob."

I laughed cruelly. "You were one name away from calling your god Bob?"

He sold me a laugh. "Kind of funny, isn't it? Well, it was a big favorite, according to the surveys."

I lit a vitacig. "You make the whole thing sound as if you're marketing a new brand of laundry soap."

"The same principles apply! That's all religion has ever been, a huge scam, an appeal to everything foolish and gullible in mankind. The set is designed to exploit that weakness, make full use of that huge silly *faith* clause, that inborn idiot switch inherent in most of humanity. Generally logical and sensible people will shed all sense and logic and approach religion with a foolishness they would never tolerate in business or personal relationships. Oh, the money to be made, the immense power to be had. There is no more-powerful mantle than a religious one, a throne backed by a living and mighty god. It's fantastic!"

We stopped above a vast auditorium, by far the largest of the rooms beneath us. An orator directly below our feet gave a mute sermon to a huge crowd of worshipers, whipping them into greater and greater heights of orgasmic frenzy.

"I see you still rely on some of the old methods," I said.

"Vastly improved," Sinn said eagerly. "Just look at them. Have you ever witnessed such an ecstatic congregation?"

They danced and threw their arms in the air like dervishes, their faces rabid with glee. I looked to the speaker, expecting to find him rolling out a miracle a minute. He merely stood behind the podium and spoke somberly into the microphone. Four techs in lab coats and gas masks sat at a wide control panel behind him, busy with keyboards and monitors.

"What's the crowd so excited about?" I asked.

"Nothing! Well, nothing they can understand. They act that way because they're being subjected to monstrous amounts of stimuli. Our labs have worked out the sounds, scents and imagery that directly address the subconscious. Subsonic waves are stabbing subliminal ideas and key words into their subconscious, emotion-inducing light waves are bombarding their optic centers, the air they breathe is charged with psychoactive pheromones—we have it orchestrated to near perfection. There are mood detectors in every seat, monitoring brain activity, heartbeat, muscle stress and breathing rates, data which is refined and used to adjust the stimuli delivery. We have those poor suckers so tightly wound in an empathy loop they might as well be puppets on strings."

Sinn paused to laugh giddily. "I can turn a normal crowd into a band of loving pilgrims willing to embrace their most-hated enemies, or a bloodthirsty mob ready to rip their own mothers to pieces, all in the space of fifteen minutes!"

I looked down into the face of the mob. "Yeah, but you can't keep them in that cage forever. Sooner or later the drugs wear off and the strings are cut."

"Not entirely. A lot of the process involves compressed conditioning that remains in their subconscious minds long after a subject leaves the programming center. When subjected to a certain stimuli, a particular phrase or sound, the installed programming activates and the subject reacts immediately, just like that drooling cur of Pavlov's."

He stared down at the obscenely happy crowd with an air of propriety. "This mass-persuasion center is used only for indoctrination and experimental purposes right now, but with the information we've gained, we're constructing new worship-and-conversion centers all over the world. Believe me when I say Set of One is a great religion. We've already jumped into the top five on this continent. We're number three in Europe! We bumped off Buddha, and now we're knocking on Muhammad's door."

"Europe? I thought they were all atheists over there."

"Atheists are our biggest convert pool! They want to go to heaven just like everyone else—they just find the concept hard to swallow. The set wins them over in droves because we provide a sensible and scientific god, not just made-up stories and ballyhoo designed for uneducated peasants."

I looked down at the enthralled masses. Within the space of fifteen seconds I watched their looks of jubilation melt into masks of hate and anger. Fights broke out as the faithful hurled themselves upon one another. I watched for a moment, horrified. The congregation no longer seemed human, but mindless robots reacting to the whims of some greater, unseen machine. "Is this the same process you use at the mission?"

Sinn laughed. "What you were exposed to was a very crude version, comparable to what you see below only as a wooden club is to a cruise missile. But then winos don't need much to manipulate them." We started walking again, and Sinn slid me a sidelong leer. "I hope what I've told you hasn't soured your view of the set."

"You still haven't answered my question."

Sinn laughed. "Right to the bone, eh, Commander? All right, I'll tell you." He took a deep breath. "The Martyr Program was created by our PR department, as a means of establishing One's name. It's sad to say, but studies show organized violence is the surest way to get free press and build name recognition. Does that bother you, Commander?"

We started walking again, moving slowly over the beehive of cubicles crowded with medtechs and high-tech glass coffins. More of the coffins were occupied by bodies this time.

"To be honest, Sinn," I said, "I don't give a damn about why you want to kill criminals. Just as long as you do."

"Then why did you ask?"

"I wanted to know how far you were willing to take it." We stopped in front of the elevator, and I looked him straight in the eye. "Things are going to get very bloody."

Sinn smiled like a hungry ghoul. "The camera loves gore, Mr. Strait. The bloodier the better."

I nodded. "We'll see."

13

I paced at the front of the formation at seven the next morning, my face bathed in sweat after leading the martyrs through two hours of intense physical training. With each step their faces became more tense, as if they were trapped in an out-of-control vehicle hurtling toward a concrete wall and bracing for the moment of impact.

"So who wants to quit?" I asked.

Eyes flashed around, wary of a trick.

"If you raise your hand right now, I'll allow you to walk away from this," I said, "away from all the shit before it gets really bad. And believe me, it's going to get much, *much* worse. I'll arrange you a nice, soft job, passing out flyers in the burbs, or answering phones down in telemarketing—it'll be cake and ice cream from here on out." I stopped pacing. "So who wants to quit?"

The ranks remained silent.

"Listen to me closely, gentlemen. In less than a month, people you've never met before will be trying to kill you. Take a look around. Go ahead. Take a good look. Three weeks from now the man standing next to you might be dead. He might die right in front of you, his brains splattered all over your face. Or maybe it'll be *your* brains on his face. So who wants to quit?"

A lot of faces paled, but no hands went up.

"Just like lemmings stampeding over a cliff," I said, "too dumb to turn back and save your own lives. All right, if you want it, you got it."

I pushed them sixteen hours a day, seven days a week. I used every mean trick I knew to grind them down to the point where a man chooses between retaining his veneer of humanity and releasing the beast within. Between physical trials I taught them the finer points of how to kill their fellow man and do it well, whether with bare hands, garrote, knife, firearm, explosive or portable rocket. The martyrs proved to possess monstrous appetites for abuse and deadly knowledge. By the end of the first week I'd managed only to trim the initial roster of a hundred and eight to a mean eighty-seven. By the end of the second week the martyrs were stripped to a hard inner core of seventy-nine.

In only one area did the martyrs fail to excel. Though set indoctrination had rendered them utterly obedient, it had also imparted unto them the kind of meek unity found in a herd of sheep. They lacked that certain aggressive cohesion common to the wolf pack, the hallmark of every great fighting unit. I had hoped they would unite into a single front in the face of the hardships to which I exposed them, but instead they formed self-interested cliques.

Slim seemed to control a group consisting of most of the older and homosexual martyrs, and each ethnic group seemed to be more comfortable among its own in the cafeteria and barracks. It was the same schisms that predicated the breakup of units in the heat of battle, and I knew that if the martyrs were to survive, they would have to learn the kind of brotherhood that couldn't be taught in the classroom or gym. So I took the men dancing.

After a relatively light day of training, I loaded up the

entire company into set vans and drove them to a stadium-size revrock concert. I cut them loose in the slam-dance pit as individuals and let the organized elements of the pit take them apart. After an hour of being beaten and trampled, I formed them back up, gave them a lecture about unity, then dispatched them as a cohesive fighting force with a battle plan. One by one, the martyrs toppled the established pit gangs; the skinheads, the beatboys, the doomrockers and the greboes all fell to the martyrs. Before the gig was over, we conquered the protective ring of groupies and captured the stage, intimidating the band into improvising songs that proclaimed our valor and might. When the gig was over, the martyrs marched through the crowd in a solid phalanx with me at their head, feeling all the world like Caesar before his legions.

WE WEREN'T BACK ten minutes before I found myself standing in front of Sinn's desk, feeling all the world like Caesar before the tribunal.

"There's been some complaints about your training methods," Sinn said.

"Yeah?" I said. "Who's the fink?"

"No need to reveal names. Let's just say it was brought to my attention by someone who has the set's interests genuinely at heart."

I looked back at Slim standing by the door, his face bruised from slam-dancing. He looked away. "All right," I said. "What did this fink say?"

"Well," Sinn said gravely, "this concerned source feels some of your teachings contradict standards and canons of set indoctrination. For example, teaching leadership skills to the lower ranks might not be such a good idea. Sometimes too much initiative and freethinking can sway the pilgrim from his higher loyalties, and too much knowledge may only serve to confuse the simple soldier."

"That's a lot of crap," I retorted. "We're not organizing peasants here. We're about to embark on a very complex battle plan. Not every action we take will require a platoon, squad or even team-size effort. Some will require just two or three men, sometimes just one. Neither I nor the squad leaders will always be there to lead those strikes, since we'll be too busy with the larger missions. Therefore, each and every man will have to be able to make his own decisions. When I break a squad into six assassination teams, each team will have to be capable of directing itself independently."

Sinn's eyes flicked to Slim, then back to me. "Well defended, Commander." He turned a gray ostrich feather over in his hands. "There were also charges that you're downgrading the martyrs' faith, to the effect of glorifying yourself rather than One."

"Charges? Am I on trial here?"

"No, Commander, not at all. We are merely clearing up a few matters. My source merely feels you are perhaps unintentionally eroding the perfect obedience and faith installed by set indoctrination."

"Oh, they're obedient, all right. They'd jump off a cliff if I told them to, but who wants dumb bastards like that? Dead men don't serve any cause. I want soldiers who respect their lives enough to tell me to screw off and climb down the cliff." When Sinn continued to frown, I decided to make a stand. "Listen, Sinn, when I took on this job, you told me I could train the martyrs as I saw fit."

"Yes, but within certain guidelines, of course."

"I didn't hear mention of any guidelines. You wanted an elite unit to combat the criminal underground. That's what you're getting. Not bloodthirsty robots, not programmed mass murderers. Just well-trained soldiers. Once we get rolling, I think the martyrs' performance will speak for itself."

"Yes," he said, drawing out the word. "And how soon will that be, Commander?"

I tried to read Sinn's murky expression and came up empty. "You gave me three weeks," I said. "According to my mathematics I have one week left."

Sinn watched as his fingers bent the feather at its middle. "What if I told you I wanted them to strike tomorrow?"

I stood in silence, sensing walls closing in around me. "I'd tell you to go fly a kite. They're not ready."

Sinn studied me closely with hard blue eyes. After a moment his cold look warped into a smile. "You have one more week, then. By the end of that period I expect body counts."

"You'll get all you can stomach."

"I trust I will."

I saluted and went to the door. Out of the corner of my eye, I could see Slim shooting Sinn a begging look.

"One more thing, Commander," Sinn said.

I turned around. "Yeah?"

"You do believe in One, don't you?"

I looked into dead eyes and again failed to determine just how much leeway I had, how much honesty I could get away with, how much a con man had come to believe his own lies. "Is this a joke?"

"A joke? Why, I would think essential every key member of the set have complete faith in One."

There was no give in his expression, and I felt my back flat against some unseen, unbudging wall.

"Well, praise the almighty goddamn One, then," I said flatly.

"Praise him," Slim whispered beside me.

I glanced at him, sensing a challenge. "Great is his mantle, proud is his name," I snarled.

"Say it, brother!" Slim cried gleefully.

I rounded on him. "I say I am walking and talking at One's side," I shouted, trying not sound too ludicrous, "and I'll throttle any bastard who says otherwise."

Slim's beady eyes brightened, and his face lit up with rapturous joy. "Don't stop now, brother! Testify!"

"I say I am possessed by the spirit of One and cannot keep my peace!"

"I *hear* you, brother!" Slim whooped, and threw his hands in the air. "Take him back, One!" he slobbered happily. "Take this wayward brother back into the righteous fold of the holy set!"

I whooped it up and threw my arm comradely around Slim's shoulders. We left the office laughing like drunk brothers, and I waved happily at a beaming Sinn before closing the door. The door clicked shut, and I tightened my comradely arm until it became an uncomradely headlock.

"You're hurting me, brother," Slim croaked, and I linked hands and squeezed his head tighter to my side, my forearm closing on his windpipe. He began to struggle as I intensified the pressure. He reached up to claw at my eyes, but I turned my face away and wrenched at his neck. When I'd squeezed the fight and breath out of him, I let him go.

He rebounded off the unmanned receptionist's desk and collapsed to the carpet, wheezing and holding his throat. He curled into a fetal position, his tiny eyes shining up at me like a trapped and rabid animal.

I leaned down and put a finger in his face. "I'm *watching* you. *Brother.*"

I went back to my quarters, changed into shorts and

worked out furiously with Melvin. Two hours and a long shower later, my calm returned. I went out on the narrow balcony and leaned on the rail, drinking a vitabeer. A cold wind carried up the sounds and reek of the monstrous City below, spread before me as far as the eye could see, twinkling with a million lights, mocking the stars above. I stood on the edge of a long fall, contemplated how good my footing was and tried to understand just how much influence Slim had with Sinn and from where it sprang. I thought there was someone who could tell me. I finished my beer, put on a black flannel bathrobe and slippers and went for a walk.

I found Jackie's office unlocked and empty. I went behind the desk and examined the wall on both sides of the set symbol. I found a card slot behind a surprised-looking tribal mask.

On a whim I slipped my keycard into the slot. There was a click, and the plaque slid into the wall, revealing an elevator. Inside, I had a choice of three buttons, the same as Sinn's. I pushed the middle one and the car hummed up and opened on the God Hall. I stayed inside and pushed the top button.

The car went up one floor, the door slid open and there stood Jackie.

"So this is where you've been hiding," I said, admiring her apartment. I was pleased to find the walls were done up with shifting videoscapes instead of archaic weaponry. The sights, scents and sounds of a steaming jungle crowded the room. Bird calls and the patter of raindrops mingled with the rich, earthy scent of decaying vegetation, and a subtle humidity hung among the bloated, black-rubber furniture.

"What are you doing here?" Jackie asked.

"The card fit."

She gave my bathrobe and slippers the once-over, frowning.

"Self-confidence," I explained.

She nodded once and retreated to a black marble auto-bar squatting at the base of a mossy video tree. "Can I get you a drink? Double screwdriver?"

"You got my number."

"Where'd the bruises come from?" she asked as the bar mixed the drinks.

"Took the boys dancing," I said, sinking into a monstrous recliner in the middle of the sunken living room.

"Dancing? I thought you were trying to turn them into killers."

"Even killers should know how to dance."

She smiled. "I stopped by the training area yesterday to see how things were going."

"I don't remember seeing you."

"That's because you were too busy torturing those poor boys. Why are you so cold and cruel with them?"

"I have to be. I can't afford to like them."

"Why not?"

"Because when they start dying all around me, I don't want any cheap emotions clouding my judgment. If there was ever a time to be cold and cruel, it's now."

"But you're turning them into monsters."

"No, set indoctrination did that. Whenever I get the urge to lay a moral-justification speech on them, I clam up because they don't need any reason to kill. Your indoctrination techniques will revolutionize the murder industry." I closed my eyes and breathed in the humid jungle air. "I used to think I was ruthless. This new generation of killers makes me look like a kid shooting at sparrows with a BB gun."

"And you like that, don't you?" Jackie said from close behind me. "The comfort of knowing you're not the worst."

A cool glass slipped into my hand, and I took a long drink. "Nobody wants to be on the bottom of the list."

"Especially if God grades on a curve, eh, Jake?"

"You mean One, don't you?"

"We know what I mean. The question is, what do *you* mean?"

"I don't know what I believe, what's real and what isn't. Which means I know as much as anyone else in the world."

"Stay with the set, and maybe someday you will know."

"What's with you and Sinn?" I sneered. "You create a god out of computer studies and market surveys, then go around acting like you meet him for drinks every night."

Her hands settled on my shoulders. "Maybe we know something you don't."

"Maybe I don't want to know."

"Look how tense you are," Jackie said, rolling and squeezing the muscles of my shoulders and neck. "Why are you so stressed?"

"I'm having a little trouble with the chain of command. Slim's been finking on me, whispering secrets in Sinn's ear." I let my head loll forward, and she went to work on my upper neck. "Slim seems to have an inordinate amount of pull with Sinn. There's something special between those two."

She laughed. "Yes, I would think so. They're lovers."

"What?"

"You didn't know? That's how Slim got the head-martyr job before you came along. That's why he still controls security."

"Oh, Jesus. That explains a lot. It also complicates mat-

ters." I laughed. "If Sinn was sleeping with anybody, I figured it was you."

"I don't sleep with my superiors."

"How about your underlings?"

She laughed in a manner that lended neither hope nor
despair. Her fingers moved to my biceps, and she began
to sing softly, the same song she'd sung at the mission.

"What language is that?" I asked.

"It's the language of nothingness, of lies," she whispered. "Just phonetic sounds I memorized, created by a
computer. It's designed to lull the human mind into a state
of suggestibility."

"It seems too beautiful to be fake."

She giggled. "Too beautiful to be real, you mean."

"Ah, yes." My head drooped lower, and I slipped deeper
into a state of total relaxation. "Sing for me."

She laughed. "Even though you know it isn't real?"

"All the better," I said. "There's always more truth in
the lie."

As she began singing, I let the soft, soothing words
carry me away like the waves of a warm and gentle sea.
Somewhere above me a soft voice told me stories and
things to believe in as I slipped deeper and deeper into
bliss. *If this is what heaven is,* I thought dreamily, *book me
on the next boat out.*

"Hey, you," a voice said. "Wake up."

I swam upward and broke surface, feeling as if I were
returning from a long journey I could not remember.

"I know my voice isn't exactly exciting," Jackie said,
standing in front of me, "but I didn't think it would put you
to sleep."

I straightened up in the chair and shook out the cob-
webs. "How long was I out?"

"About an hour, I'm afraid."

"Why didn't you wake me?"

She shrugged. "You looked as if you needed the rest. How do you feel?"

"Super," I said, standing up. I stretched my arms to the ceiling. "I feel recharged, powerful." I regarded her closely. "Did you put a spell on me?"

She dropped hands to perfect hips. "Are you calling me a witch?"

"Are you?"

"I think you're confusing me with my sister." She walked to the bar and ordered a glass of red wine. "When was the last time you saw Heidi anyway?"

"The night I accepted Sinn's offer."

"You told her you were joining the set?"

"Yes." I lit a vitacig and watched a video panther lying atop a thick video branch above the bar, licking a paw. "You were right."

Jackie sat down in a rubber love seat across from me. "She tried to kill you?"

"No, but she behaved very strangely."

"You're lucky she didn't cut your throat."

I watched the smoke curling from the tip of the vitacig in my hand. "Jackie, did your father molest Heidi?"

Her body tensed, and she stabbed me with eyes as cold as winter lakes. "What makes you say that?"

"She started calling me Daddy at one point."

She frowned. "At what point?"

"Do you really want to know?"

"No, don't tell me anything about it." She looked away sharply, her cigarette smoke curling up to the ceiling. "Heidi seduced my father," she finally said.

"Seduced him? How does a daughter seduce her father?"

"You didn't know my father. He was a very weak man. She did it to get back at me. When father finally accepted my choice of faiths and we began to heal our wounds, she seduced him to keep him for herself, to blackmail him into turning on me. That's how sick she is. That's why I left."

"She tells a different story."

"I'll bet she does."

"She said she didn't leave the convent until your parents' funeral."

"That's not true," Jackie said in an angry tone. "She came home two weeks before my parents died." She glared at the coffee table between us. "Or they'd still be alive."

"Why do you say that?"

"Because she murdered them."

I regarded cool black eyes and a calm face. Over her shoulder, high on the wall, the panther stopped licking his paw and froze, scenting something.

"You gonna tell me about it?" I said.

"Why don't you ask Heidi?" she challenged. "She'll tell you."

I recalled my last words with Heidi. "Maybe it'd be better if you told me. If Heidi killed your parents, why isn't she in jail or dodging a death warrant?"

"There was never conclusive proof."

"But enough for you."

She nodded. "My parents died in a house locked up tighter than a meat bank. Yet there were no signs of forced entry, no triggered alarms. Just two bodies in a blood-soaked bed and Heidi in the room next door. They were butchered like cattle, and pure, sweet Heidi slept right through it."

"It's possible." I went to the autobar and demanded a screwdriver. A framed picture sat on the bar's black mirror surface. A brightly smiling Heidi stood before a backdrop of rose bushes, the sun illuminating her hair. Over her shoulder and in her shadow lurked a downcast and dour Jackie, looking as if she didn't belong there. I stared at the picture, and for a brief instant I pitied Jackie. "No security is perfect," I said, leaning back against the bar, looking at the back of Jackie's head. "Someone could have known how to get in without tripping any alarms."

Jackie lit a cigarette and inhaled deeply. She held the smoke for a moment, then blew a stream of haze toward the ceiling. "Someone like me, for example."

"For example," I said, then whispered over my shoulder, "Make that a double." I turned back to Jackie. "Tell me, exactly how did your parents die?"

"They were hacked to death."

A jolt went through my gut. "Triple," I whispered, and vodka jetted into orange juice. "With a butcher knife?"

"I don't know. The murder weapon never turned up. That's probably the only thing that kept her from being arrested for murder."

"What motive would your sister have for murdering your parents?"

"Because despite all her twisted manipulations and sick seductions, they had finally accepted my new life with the set."

I picked up my drink and swallowed half of it. Above me, on the branch, the panther was perfectly still, alert. I followed his lethal stare along the wall to an unsuspecting warthog nosing through the undergrowth, wandering straight into the ambush. "Heidi didn't like that, huh?"

"Oh, hell, no." Jackie joined me at the bar, ordering another glass of wine. "She won't tolerate that kind of weakness or betrayal. She'd rather kill something than lose it. She's so selfish and evil."

"If you hate her so much, why do you keep her picture around?"

She stared down at the portrait. "To remind me—" her eyes came up, as black and lethal as the panther's "—of what I might become."

I finished my drink and looked at my chrono. "I've got to be going."

A hand took my arm. "You can stay if you want," Jackie said, no ambiguity in her voice, and over her shoulder the panther pounced onto the back of the squealing warthog, ripping out its jugular with its razor-sharp claws. I looked into Jackie's eyes, and the hackles on the back of my neck stood up. She was giving me the same sleepy-eyed, hungry-shark look Heidi had laid on me just before she wigged and told me I'd be getting mine.

"Not this warthog," I said, muscling my way out of the powerful field she emanated. I backed out toward the elevator and leapt inside.

14

The final week of training flew by. I tried to cram every fundamental of murder and survival into their heads, but each day seemed twelve hours too short. I couldn't shake the feeling that we'd been thrown from an airplane and I was desperately trying to teach them how to operate their incredibly complex parachutes as we tumbled to earth.

On the morning of the final day of training, I mustered the company in the gym after PT and breakfast. They looked confident and hungry: they'd taken the worst I could give them and figured they were ready for anything. I could feel their excitement coming off them in waves, like a fever.

"Gather around," I said, and they formed a semicircle around me and the one-by-two meter videoboard I'd set up. "It all begins tomorrow," I said, looking from face to face. "Death, murder, mutilation, ultimate sacrifice. You'll wade and wallow in death and gore until it becomes the only thing you understand. And if that appeals to you, then you're a truly sick bunch."

They giggled like schoolboys, and I knew I was wasting my time. *They want to die,* I thought.

"We're ready to liberate the tragically heathen souls of

One's enemies," Slim piped up happily, "and, if need be, surrender our own souls for the almighty One." He looked around. "Aren't we, martyrs?"

They howled agreement, laughing and slapping each other on the back. I held up my hand until they shut up.

"I'm overjoyed you've sold your souls so cheaply," I said. "But I don't want you doing this for One."

Slim sneered. "Just who are we supposed to do it for, then?"

"For no one. I want you to do it because you're too stupid to live. Because you didn't know any better and someone tricked you into becoming killers. You can blame me. But don't you ever think you're doing it to please some bloodthirsty god or because you think you *like* to kill people. Remember your name, gentlemen. You're not heroes, you're *martyrs*. Martyrs are made to die, to die violently."

"What are you getting at?" Sailor asked.

"I'm saying this is your last chance to quit. Your last chance to walk away from shit too horrible to imagine. So, who's smart enough to save his own life?"

I waited, hoping just one hand would go up, that one body's worth of weight would be lifted from my conscience. Nobody so much as twitched.

"You poor, dumb creatures," I said, shaking my head. "Just look at you. Grinning like virgins going to the big dance with a pocketful of condoms."

They exchanged glances and snickers, and I gave up. *I cannot feel guilty because I tried my best to save them,* I told myself.

"All right, then," I said, turning on the videoboard. I slipped a disk into its controller and said, "Diagram one." A map of an urban park, ten kilometers distant from the tower, flashed onto the screen. "Martyrs, at 2100 hours tomorrow we will conduct an armed strike against the She Wolves of People's Park."

Looks of confusion went around the group.

"They're just a bunch of crazy castraters," Slim complained. "Why are we going after them?"

"Three reasons," I said. "First they're an easy target. That's how much faith I have in you. Second they're an independent operation, with no syndicate or major gang connections. If they disappear, no one will notice. And finally they deserve it. Over a period of four years they've carried out hundreds of attacks with impunity. They've left dozens of victims dead or wishing they were dead."

"But they're *girls*," Slim whined.

"Shut up, you sexist pig," I snapped. "Every criminal, regardless of race, sex, creed, religion, class, ethnic group or sexual orientation gets an equal opportunity to be liquidated by the martyrs. Our strategic planning will in no way resemble the bigoted crusades of suburban vigilantes.

"Now, here's how we're going to do it." I laid out the plan on the videoboard, then moved the company to the urban mock-up where we rehearsed the martyrs' coming-out ball.

Sinn called me up to his office late in the afternoon, after I'd released the martyrs to double-check their weapons and equipment.

"Well, this is it," Sinn said from behind his desk. "Are they ready?"

"For the She Wolves they are."

He nodded. "Public relations wants to know how many camera crews they can send along."

"I'd like to hold off on that for a while," I said. "I'd like to keep the Martyr Program covert for now. If we start beating a drum early on, the gangs and syndicates will unite and jump us before we can get our act together."

I expected an argument, but Sinn merely nodded. "I understand. Well," he said, sighing. "I must say I feel like a father sending my children off to war. Don't you?"

"I find it hard to think of them as children. They're more like rabid young wolverines."

"Yes, but I still worry. No matter, if things get bad, One will save them."

I smiled coldly. "Tell One to look out for the She Wolves," I said. "The martyrs will take care of themselves. I'll report tomorrow." I saluted and left.

THE KNOCK AT MY DOOR came around midnight, hours after I'd put the martyrs to bed. I got up from the command console I'd spent the past four hours hunched over, replaying the next day's operation through the computer's battle simulator, searching for flaws.

"Open door," I said. The door hissed open, and Nu stood in front of me. "Yes?"

He fidgeted nervously, glancing over his shoulder at his sleeping comrades. There was a striking restiveness in his face. "I'd like to speak with you, Commander. Privately."

"All right," I said, stepping aside. "Come in."

He walked hesitantly into the room, gawking at the accommodations. "Wow."

"The privileges of rank," I explained, sitting on the edge of the console. "What'd you want to talk about?"

His olive eyes flickered between me and the floor, and his restless hands began wrestling each other. "I wanted to talk about what you said this morning. About us being too stupid to live and not killing because we wanted to...." He halted, embarrassment choking him.

"Don't be so ashamed," I said. "Everyone's afraid of dying."

"I'm not afraid of dying," he said quickly. "It's just that I don't know if I can kill anyone else. Especially in the name of some god I don't think I believe in."

"Fall asleep during indoctrination?"

"No," he said. "I think I paid *too* much attention."

I nodded. "Well, don't worry about it. I don't believe in One, either."

He looked up at me. "You don't?"

"Hell, no, I'm just using the set like they're using me. Now, listen closely. Are you listening?"

"Yes, sir."

"Good. Because I'm going to give you some super advice. Get out of the martyrs. Pack up your shit right now and march your ass and soul right back to the burbs while they're both still intact. I won't think any less of you. If anything, I'd think you grew some brains during the past three weeks."

He looked back at the wall beyond which his comrades slept. "I feel bad about leaving the rest of them to go on without me."

"Screw them!" I said. "They're all wrongheaded and evil—why the hell else would they be here? Killing and dying is the only thing they'll ever be good for."

"If they're so evil, why are you teaching and leading them?"

"Because that's just the way the world is," I said, heating up. "Because I'm just like them. I tried being good and moral. It doesn't work—you slay the dragon, and the damsel in distress will slit your throat. Things have gotten so bad the only thing that will beat evil is a more ruthless evil. I wish it weren't that way, but it is."

"You're evil?"

"Yes, but only because I have to be." I slid off the desk

and put a hand on his shoulder. "But you're not evil. You're different from the rest of us—you can be something good."

"What about my responsibilities—"

"Your only responsibility in this big ugly world is to take care of your own skin and that's it. Anything anyone else feeds you is pure, unadulterated bullshit." I grabbed him by the shoulder and guided him to the door. "Open door," I commanded, and the door slid open. We stood in the doorway, and I pointed into the dark bay. "Look out there," I whispered, "and tell me what you see."

He squinted nervously at row after row of sleeping martyrs. "I, uh, see a lot of martyrs."

"No, you don't," I said. "Look harder, look *real* close."

Nu looked harder then shook his head. "I see sleeping martyrs. What do you see?"

"A bloody morgue! I see a morgue full of corpses that don't know they're dead yet because they're so stupid. Those men aren't sleeping, they're practicing death."

Nu goggled at his comrades with new eyes and said nothing.

"Listen," I whispered. "Do you want to lay down with them and wait for death to tap your shoulder or do you want to live?"

"Live, I guess," he stuttered.

"Then pack your shit up and get the hell out of here." I gave him a push, and he staggered into the bay. He looked back, unsure.

"Go on," I urged. "Don't be a fool." I backed inside and closed the door.

I went to the autobar and ordered a double vodka. *Not real supportive,* I thought, pouring the raw alcohol down my throat. *I am, however, saving his goddamn life.*

Fifteen minutes and three drinks later I crept into the

bay to check his bunk. His sleeping form lay as still as a corpse, covered by a blanket as black as a death shroud. "You dumb bastard," I whispered. I crept back to my room, had another drink, then crawled under my own shroud.

15

We traveled to the objective in a convoy of eight vans. I rode in the lead vehicle with half of First Squad. Slim sat across from me, hunched over *The Word of One* in the dim light, searching for inspiration in the manufactured lies. Nu sat next to me, closemouthed. The rest of the van was crowded with grim-faced martyrs, bulky with spider-silk body armor and battle gear, their knuckles white around their weapons.

"Anyone scared?" I asked.

Teeth showed between grimaces disguised to appear as jaunty smiles, and sweat-beaded faces shook no.

"Trust in One, and there is no reason to be afraid," Slim expounded, snapping his book shut. "'A hard rain is going to fall, brothers,'" he quoted from the gospel, looking at the faces around him. "'And it's not going to let up until the ground is very wet.' Wet with enemy blood is what One means by that." He looked at me with fevered eyes. "Right, Commander?"

"Who knows what that cagey bastard means?" I said. "I figured he was just talking about the rain making the ground wet."

Slim scowled and resumed reading.

"*I'm* scared," Nu whispered beside me.

Slim glared at him. "You yellow-belly pansy," he snarled. "I knew you'd—"

I cut Slim's tirade off with a chop of my hand. "What makes you think you're scared?" I asked Nu.

"I don't know. I feel jumpy and nauseous, like I might puke my guts out."

"That's good," I said. "Fear is your best friend. Fear is what's going to keep you alive. Don't worry about screwing up. Once the action starts, your training will take over and it'll all be an adrenaline blur, nothing to think or worry about. Just as long as you stayed scared."

"I'm not scared at all," Slim assured.

"That's because you're too stupid," I explained.

"Are you scared?" Nu asked me.

"Hell, yes, I'm scared."

"You don't look scared."

"Well, sometimes I forget." I looked out the porthole, then tapped the driver on the back. He pulled over to the curb, and I got out.

"See you boys later," I said, and slammed the door. I stood on the sidewalk and watched the vans depart. When they were out of sight, I took a seat on a scarred bench scrawled with graffiti and watched the sunset.

Am I scared? I asked myself. *I don't feel scared. In fact, I don't feel anything at all.* I wrestled with the idea until the sun had completed its daily fall from grace. I stood up, stretched and jogged into People's Park.

Moving at a comfortable pace along the broken asphalt path that wound through and around the park, I passed hunched groups of armed workers who gave me alarmed looks as they hustled home. They knew sane men didn't go jogging alone and unarmed through People's Park at night. When the sun went down, the wolves came out.

Twilight faded, and a full moon began crawling its way up the night sky, vainglorious as a sidewalk pimp. I jogged between overgrown hedges and moonlit fields of grass long gone to seed, glancing behind me every ten steps. The park had the pleasant odor of a midwestern plains video-scape I sometimes watched, and I imagined I could detect the rustle of small animals in the grass.

I heard them before I saw them. Like the pitter-patter of rain on tropical leaves, they skipped up behind me, closing the distance. I glanced over my shoulder and saw their sweating faces glowing in the moonlight, moving in a loose pack of about twenty. I judged the distance to a low rise to the left of the path ahead of me and picked up the pace a little, pretending not to hear the feet dropping behind me.

When they got within twenty meters, I turned around and jogged backward. They came up fast, running with long lopes, their breath a wild chorus. The ground began to rise on the left, and thirty meters ahead the path met a thick patch of shrubs and doglegged sharply to the right. I slowed to a walk and backed into the killzone.

They stopped running and crept up slowly, sniffing me out, eyes searching my tight running suit for the bulge of weapons or perhaps a trophy. They crept closer, shoulders hunched and breathing fast, eyes burning with bloodlust, their faces as cold and cruel as the surgical-steel claws they wore.

"Wrong place, wrong time, swinger," the apparent leader snarled, the long talons on her right hand flashing in the moonlight.

"Gulp," I said, backing away, drawing them in.

"Oh," she moaned, rattling her claws, "slice you and dice you, oh, how I need you to *bleed*." Howls went up from the surging pack, and she held them back with out-stretched arms. "No! This one's mine, *I* get first blood."

"You always get first blood," a malcontent complained.

"That's 'cause I'm chief," she said, creeping toward me. She threw back her head, whipping her long, tightly woven braids over her shoulders, exposing a necklace strung with what looked like withered roots. "Oh, you missed the boat this time, dickie," she said, rolling the words out one by one. "Oh, my, yes, you truly missed the boat. But before I slice open your belly and make you eat your guts, I'm gonna have a little fun with your swingy-dingy."

"Oh, c'mon now," I said. "What could be more fun than me eating my own guts?"

"Oh, you'll see." She reached up with her left hand and pulled down her sweat-soaked tube top, spilling out aroused breasts. "Now get it up so I can cut it off."

"Let's make him swallow his balls!" no friend of mine cried out.

"You ladies better back off," I warned in a high nasal tone. I held up a red plastic tube dangling from my neck. "Or I'll blow my official SPF crime-alert whistle."

"Woo!" the chief castrater howled, eyes flashing white under the silver moon, moving closer, close enough for me to realize the withered roots hanging from her neck were not the kind that grew in the ground. "Oh, you're a *mad* one, aren't you? A real *swinger*." She sprang forward, swiping at my stomach with razor-sharp steel.

I flinched back, and the flashing claws shredded the front of my jogging suit. My back hit the hedges, and they closed in around me, knowing I had nowhere to run.

"I warned you," I said, menacing them with my whis-tle. "In the name of human decency, good manners and dickless men throughout the City, I condemn you to death!" I dived to my right, flopped on my belly and blew the whistle.

Automatic fire erupted from the low rise and dense shrubs, the crisscrossing tracers grinding up the pack in a vicious cross fire. Expressions of bloodlust turned to terror and pain in the sporadic light of muzzle-flashes as bullets smacked into soft flesh with dull, wet thuds, twisting and jerking bodies in a mad and violent dance. After five seconds the din withered to a brief silence punctuated by the screams and moans of wounded and writhing She Wolves. I could hear fingers fumbling with magazines and I counted to four before short bursts began raking the wounded.

The shooting peaked and faded again. Then I shouted, "Cease fire!" I got off my belly, and martyrs began tumbling out from behind the rise and shrubs.

"Did we get them all?" Slim asked, gaping at the bodies.

"Many times over," I said, walking among the dead. Each She Wolf was hit at least a dozen times.

I faced the huddled group of martyrs. "Here's your on-site critique," I said. "You experienced what's known as premature ejaculation, meaning you peaked too soon. Instead of using controlled bursts as I taught you, most of you just held down the trigger until you ran out of ammo. During that brief period when your weapons were out of ammunition and you were fumbling with magazines, any survivors could have counterattacked or escaped. In the future, every other man will fire on semiautomatic until you learn fire control. Understand?"

"Yes, sir," they mumbled.

"Otherwise," I said, "you weren't bad."

Foolish grins grew on their faces, and they passed around secret smiles, silently congratulating each other.

"Get up into patrol formation," I said, "and move back to the vans. Keep alert, there may be other kinds of wolves out there." As they began forming up into wedges, I noticed a martyr doubled over and vomiting near the hedges.

When Nu finished emptying the contents of his stomach in the bushes, I walked over and crouched beside him.

"How do you feel?" I asked.

He shook his head slowly, wiping at the threads of saliva stretching from his lips to the puddle of vomit on the ground. "I didn't know they screamed like that. Like wounded animals."

"It takes some getting used to."

He shook his head. "I'll never get used to it."

"Yes, you will. I wish I could say mankind's nature was such he would never get used to something so horrible. But you do. You get used to everything. After a while even the tides of hell become common."

Excited talk broke out near the bodies, and I stood up to find Slim and his cronies scuttling among the dead. "I killed two of them!" Sailor cried out, bending down to hack an ear off a She Wolf. "Two!"

"I got at least *five* of these Jezebel *b*-words," Slim said, dancing a little jig in the moonlight, bloody bayonet in one hand and a handful of ears in the other. "Count 'em, five! Enough to make a necklace!"

"What do you think you're doing?" I shouted, and they froze like startled vultures.

"Just taking some trophies," Slim explained.

"Did I tell you to take trophies, Slim?"

"But they took ding-a-lings," Slim pouted, kicking at the bloody earth. "We should be able to take ears."

"There's something you need to understand," I said, enunciating my words carefully so there could be no confusion. "We are not like them. They're criminals. That's why we killed them."

"It's not fair," Slim sobbed, throwing his ears to the ground and stalking after the departing martyrs. "I'm telling Sinn," he wailed back at me.

Nu straightened up and watched the rest of the ghouls jog up to console Slim. "It comes so easy to them," Nu said. "I guess those who think they kill for a god make the best killers."

"No," I said as we began moving down the path. "They make the cruelest killers. The sensitive ones make the best killers."

16

The demolitions team pressed lumps of fusion clay against the hinges and lock of the heavy back door. I peered around the midnight alley, making sure the rest of the squad was pressed against the wall. I could barely make out the faces of the huddled martyrs, but what I could see I didn't like. On every face, in every smile, was the unmistakable arrogance of men who thought themselves immortal.

The three strikes since the She Wolves had gone off without a martyr casualty or major screwup, and like a deadly nightshade, an aura of invincibility began to flower in the martyrs, fertilized by Slim's bullshit about our good fortune being directly attributable to divine protection by One. I'd seen the same thing happen in combat units during the wars, young boys who got the idea they could not be killed no matter what risks were taken, that some big mover was backing them up, pulling all the right strings, surrounding them with the armor of immortality. Sooner or later the cruel wheel of Fortuna rolled over them, and once the bubble burst, the band of immortals would self-destruct, usually right on the battlefield.

I had worked against that day, experiencing perverse

trepidation over each mission that went off without spilling martyr blood, knowing the longer the piper of false immortality played, the larger his bill of death would be when he came to collect.

The demo team retreated from the back door of the Love Shack and looked to me. The night's operation was a simple squad-size action against a syndicate-affiliated gang called the Sex Killers. They ran their stim, cred-kill and guided rape-tour rackets out of the back offices of the Love Shack, a former corporate-era bank long ago converted to a giddylounge. I breathed deep and nodded.

With a bright flash and a dull boom, the door blew off its hinges. Martyrs on each side tossed in whisper grenades, which went off with dull pops seconds later, spraying the room with shrapnel.

I turned the corner and led a stream of martyrs into the room, moving left, spraying in a wide arc, my suppressed machine pistol fluttering like a sparrow's wings, double-tapping the sprawled bodies lit only by muzzle-flash.

Slim and his team fanned right, moving quickly toward a half-open door at the front of the room. The rest of the squad followed me down a hall.

At the end of the hall was a two-meter-high steel door with a spin wheel in the center. I stopped by the door and martyrs came up on both sides.

I put a finger to my lips. "The bank's old vault," I whispered.

The demo team looked at me dubiously, and I shook my head. I knocked on the door with the barrel of my machine pistol.

"Who's there?" a suspicious voice asked.

"Syndicate inspector," I said. "I've come to check your books."

A muffled discussion passed through the heavy door. "We ain't due for no inspection," said the voice.

"That's because it's a surprise inspection, you assholes. Now open this door before we yank your goddamn charter."

"How do we know you ain't someone else?"

"Who'd be stupid enough to razz a syndie joint? Open up, and I'll show you my syndie ID."

Another heated discussion took place. I grabbed a martyr's shoulder and whispered, "Tell Slim to wait in the alley with the vans." He took off as the spin wheel on the door began to turn counterclockwise.

"All right," a voice said, "but we're keeping the chain on until we see your ID and papers."

"Fine," I said. The wheel stopped turning, and I unclipped a fusion grenade from my belt. I flipped its cover and thumbed the activation button.

The door opened a crack. "Okay, slide it through," a voice said.

"Here it comes," I said, pulling on the wheel until the door snapped against the chain, giving me just enough room to push in the grenade.

I let go of the wheel and started counting.

"One." The door slammed shut, and the wheel spun clockwise.

"Two." Someone noticed the grenade, and the screaming started. I could hear hands fumbling and the wheel began to spin counterclockwise. I ordered the martyrs to move down the hall.

"Three." The door began to open, but something stopped me from leaning on it. *I'll bet they forgot to take off the chain,* an inner voice whispered.

"Four." The door snapped against the chain as wails of

horror echoed down the hall. *I'll also wager no one inside is collected enough to pick up the grenade and push it out.*

"Five." The door slammed shut, and above the doomed howling I could hear mad hands fumbling with the chain.

"Six." A dull boom shook the building, then silence.

Martyrs crept up behind me. "You gonna look inside?" Nu asked, staring at the door.

"Not me," I said. "I know what a fusion grenade does to people in a sealed room."

"What does it do?" Nu whispered.

"Let me put it this way. If you'd brought some peanut butter and bread, we could make sandwiches."

The blood left his face as he looked at me. "Oh, man, you're grossing me out."

The martyr I'd sent to find Slim came running down the hall. "Slim's not with the vans," he reported breathlessly. "He's not in the rear offices, either."

I thought quickly. If he wasn't with the vans and wasn't in any of the rear offices, then...

"C'mon," I snapped, moving quickly down the hall. I led the team back through the room we'd come in and into the front office that had swallowed Slim and his team.

The room was dim, and Sex Killers littered the floor. An opposite door was open, exposing a long, dark hall. I signaled the others to follow and rushed down the hall, my gut twisting with apprehension, my head amok with visions of dead martyrs.

Light seeped from a cracked door at the end of the hall, where I could hear an angry rumble of voices. I booted open the door and stepped into the light.

We spilled into the eye of a tight semicircle of martyrs squared off with a buzzing hive of humanity. It appeared we'd hit the Love Shack during happy hour. The music had died, and the mob was slowly getting its collective courage up, yelling insults and waving bottles.

"All right," I whispered to the martyrs, their bodies trembling with fear and kill energy. "Nice and easy, we're going to back right out of here."

"But some got away," Slim protested breathlessly, his wild eyes flicking back at me. "They're hiding them."

"That's okay," I said. "We're going to let these go."

"I'll handle it," Slim said, then addressed the crowd. "It's all right, folks," he shouted. "We just killed the criminals in the back and we'd appreciate it if you would turn out those who got away."

"You hear that?" the deejay roared over the PA. I could see him crouched in his elevated booth, his narrow, bird-like head peeking over the edge of his beat machine. "They've zippered Spazmo and the gang! Rush the mondo bastards! Rip their heads off! Suck out their brains! Gnaw on their skulls! Get out on the floor and dance to the new mondo death beat!"

He stabbed at his machine, and an aggressive death-rock beat began pounding from the speakers. Those of the mob not directly facing the row of machine pistols took to heart the deejay's pleas, shoving forward those in front of them.

The deejay continued his rant over the music, and I touched the elbow of a martyr cradling a grenade launcher. "The booth," I told him.

His weapon coughed, and deejay and beat machine exploded. The crowd convulsed like a monstrous amoeba away from the booth and toward the martyr line. "Fall back!" I shouted, grabbing paralyzed martyrs and shoving them down the hall.

"I'm gonna open fire!" Slim shouted above the din of the shouting crowd.

"No!" I shouted. "Just keep moving!"

A shot glass thrown from the rear of the mob arced gracefully through the air and, as if drawn by a magnet, bounced off Slim's forehead, drawing blood.

The room went suddenly still. Everyone watched the trickle of blood roll past Slim's right eye, causing it to twitch, then continue down to the corner of his mouth. Slim's tongue darted out to taste the blood, and his eyes rolled back like a shark's.

"You infidel *f*-words!" Slim shouted, and his machine pistol fluttered, slashing into the front ranks of the mob like an invisible chain saw.

I jumped forward and slapped the barrel upward, and wild bullets exploded a disco ball dangling from the ceiling. The magazine emptied, the screaming stopped, and a howling silence gripped the room. On the floor lay two dozen patrons of the Love Shack, dead or dying.

All at once the air filled with bottles, glasses, chairs and ashtrays, then shots rang out from the crowd.

A gyrajet punched at my ribs, exploding against the spider-silk vest, filling my nostrils with a sharp, acrid odor. The martyr next to me stumbled backward, his face a bloody mess, and another fell on top of him.

"Open fire!" I roared.

Machine pistols chattered beneath the horrified screams of the mob, mowing down the front ranks like wheat before a scythe, searching out the gunmen. Bodies crumpled and exploded as if caught in a monstrous invisible meat grinder, and the rest of the mob fell back before the onslaught, stampeding toward the front.

I shouted orders, and the now-receptive martyrs grabbed their fallen and retreated down the blood-slick hall. I followed in their wake, dropping booby grenades, catching up with them in the alley. Rocks and bottles beat the van sides like bass drums as we swung around the front of the Love Shack and roared away.

Inside the van, pandemonium reigned. Four martyrs lay dead on the floor, and the faces of many of the rest ran with blood from the shower of projectiles.

"Let's get the rest of the company and go back there and liberate all their dirty souls!" Slim raved, trying to stand in the rocking van, his eyes insane with bloodlust.

"Sit down!" I shouted. "There won't be any more massacres today."

Slim pointed at the four dead martyrs. "They killed four of our own!"

"If you hadn't opened up on them, it wouldn't have happened," I accused. "We're lucky we got off as lightly as we did."

"They hit me in the head with a glass!" he said, pointing at the wound on his temple. After a moment of showing the wound around, Slim sat down and shook his head violently. "I can't believe you're going to let those *b*-words get away with it."

"Those bastards are the very same people we're supposed to be protecting," I said. "That was the public."

"*F*-word the public!" Slim screamed. "I don't give a doo-doo about the public!"

"That's what I don't get," Nu said numbly. "We're supposed to be protecting them, but they wanted to rip us apart with their bare hands. Did you see how angry they were? Did you hear what they called us? We purged the criminals right in their midst, and they wanted to kill us for it. Don't they realize we're saving them?"

I shook my head. "The sheep have lived with the wolves so long they've gotten friendly with them—they've become willing victims. Don't expect any standing ovations. No one likes to be saved from themselves."

"Well, fuck them," Nu said. "At least we're heroes back in the burbs."

"And on the Hill," another added.

"I doubt it," I said. "It's their playhouses we're tearing down."

Nu's face screwed up. "Wait a goddamn minute. If we're not doing it for them, if there aren't any good people left, just who in the fuck *are* we fighting for?"

"For One, that's who," Slim interjected. "That's all the reason you need."

"I'm not so sure about that," Nu muttered.

Slim's face went livid. "You better gosh darn be sure! I think you need to go back to indoctrination."

"The hell I will!"

"Insubordination!" Slim cried, nearly frothing at the mouth. "You heard him, Commander. He's defying my authority and One's authority, too. I demand he be punished!"

"He's already been punished," I said.

"What? How?"

I looked outside the porthole at the dark City rushing by. "The truth. The truth has punished him."

WHEN WE REACHED the tower, I ordered Slim to run the squad through the set infirmary, then form up the entire company in the gym. When they'd piled out of the van, I stripped the four dead martyrs of their equipment, ripped the insignia and patches off their uniforms and drove the van to the local reclamation depot six blocks away. I wheeled around the back of the windowless and gleaming powder blue structure, no larger than a one-story cottage, to a conveyer belt manned by a bored-looking old man with a data board. I backed the van to the belt and got out.

"Slow night?" I asked.

"Dead slow," he said without irony. "What have you got?"

"Four reclaimables." I opened the rear cargo doors as the old man set the belt into motion. One by one we dragged the bodies onto the belt, and they disappeared into the humming machine. By the time the meat wagon arrived in the morning, the bodies would be scanned, cleaned, processed and ready for the protein vats.

"Looks like they all went out the same way," the old man said conversationally. "Gunshot wounds to the head."

"Yes," I said. We pulled the last martyr onto the belt, and the old man picked up his data board.

"Send the reward to the Homeless War Orphans Hooked on Whack Relief Fund," I said.

"Okay," the old man said, moving a light-pen across the board. "Do you want to give the circumstances of their deaths? It's optional."

"Suicide," I said.

He eyed me. "Yeah? All four? Did you see it?"

"See it?" I said, getting into the van. "I showed them how to do it."

THE COMPANY WAS FORMED up in the gym when I got back, the first rank decorated with fresh bandages. I sensed the news of the deaths had already spread through the three squads who hadn't participated in the raid, and in their frightened faces I witnessed the death of immortality. A dangerous silence hung over the formation, and I knew it was the moment of truth. I would soon know if the martyrs would survive as an effective fighting force or perish beneath a wave of fear.

I stood perfectly still before their ranks for long moments, letting the silence draw out the realization of what had happened. By degrees bewilderment and fear faded into despair, then trepidation. I could see in their eyes they expected me to conduct some solemn ceremony, say a few doleful words on behalf of the dearly departed, a speech that would explain away all the fear and horror.

"Roll call!" I shouted, my voice echoing through the big room. "Squad leaders, report!"

One by one the squad leaders saluted and gave me a tally of their squad's numbers.

"First Squad leader," I said. "You're four martyrs short. Where are they?"

Nu gave me a dumbfounded look. "You know," he said. "They were just kill—"

"You say they were last seen drunk and in the company of reputed whores?" I cut in. "Is that what you're saying? That one was heard to say, 'Commander Strait can kiss my ass, because I ain't coming back.' Is that it?"

Nu gawked at me for a moment, then nodded. "I guess so."

"Then say it."

Nu reported again. "Martyrs Shaw, Rashid, Blackmon and Ginsberg are AWOL, Commander. Last seen in the company of known prostitutes. Said for you to go screw yourself. It's unlikely they'll be returning."

"Well, looks likes those boys wised up," I said, and the martyrs learned what I had learned in the Rangers. Martyrs, like Rangers, did not die and they were not mourned. They merely passed from view.

17

I reported to Sinn the next morning after PT. After listening to my report, he sat while I stood in silence for a moment.

"We lost some good men," Sinn said.

"Yes. That's something we need to talk about. Replacements."

"Replacements," he said solemnly. He looked down at the bloodred ostrich feather in his hands. "Listen, Jacob. There was a board meeting yesterday. All the investors came down, and we had a long talk about the set and where it is going."

I studied his face closely. There was something about his expression that told me I wasn't going to like what I was about to hear.

Sinn suddenly snapped the spine of the feather between his fingers and began shaking his head with frustration. "I really went to bat for you and the Martyr Program. I really did, Jacob, you have to believe that."

He paused for a moment, and I stared out the broken feather on his desk. I knew something bad was coming, an ending, or perhaps worse, a compromise. Anger rose in my throat; we had come so far, risked so much, only to be undercut by fat rich men who didn't even understand death.

"All right," I said bitterly. "Let's have it."

"You wouldn't believe those bastards," he continued, mimicking my anger. "They don't even *understand* what we're trying to accomplish here, the *good* work we're doing." He shook his head, angrily this time. "They called for the termination of the Martyr Program. I'm afraid they don't think it's a viable project."

"Not viable? We're cleaning up the goddamn City."

"I know, Jacob. But you know how investors are. All they see is the bottom line."

"Bottom line? I wasn't even aware there was a bottom line. I thought we were operating on some kind of publicity angle."

"It hasn't worked out that way, has it? We have to keep the whole project secret so the criminal underworld won't rise up and stamp us out like upstart cockroaches. The martyrs sneak around like hunted assassins, defeating its very purpose. Now me, I am willing to keep the program going purely for altruistic reasons. But," he said, sighing, "my voice is a solitary one."

I turned and walked to the marble wall, trembling with mean energy. *No way out this time,* I thought, *I'm backed against the edge of the abyss.* I folded my arms, my right hand touching the solid bulk of the gyrapistol inside my jacket.

Suddenly it became clear to me, as clear as a shotgun blast on a still winter morning. I pictured the event, a black-and-white overhead shot in slow motion: I turn around slowly, pistol coming out of my jacket. Sinn's eyes register surprise and his mouth opens for a scream just as a gyrajet whooshes into the hole, blowing the roof of his mouth out the back of his skull. I move quickly around the desk and pitch his twitching body out the window. An anonymous call to reclamation and the War Orphans on Whack get another desperately needed donation. I purge Slim and the other wolves from the fold, seize control of the martyrs, and everything is as fine and sweet as summer sunset—the dream stays alive.

Do it, a ruthless voice whispered. Do it for the martyrs, do it for yourself, do it for the goddamn orphans, *right now.* My right palm slid inside my jacket and closed on the smooth, familiar butt of the gyra. Yes, it was the only way.

"There might be another way," Sinn said.

"What?" I said, off balance.

"There might be a way to save the martyrs."

I dropped my arms and turned around. "How?"

He picked another ostrich feather from the decanter, a green one. "I squeezed a one-week interim out of them."

"A week. And what's supposed to happen in a week?"

He stroked his cheek with the feather. "The martyrs will have to start turning a profit. It's as simple as that."

We locked eyes for a long moment.

"Is it possible, Commander?"

I teetered on the edge until hope crept up behind me and gave me a shove. Cheap, ugly hope, the eternal pimp. "It's possible."

"Excellent!" Sinn beamed. "I knew you'd take up the challenge." He spoke into the intercom on the desk, and an instant later the hulking receptionist carried in a gold tray with two crystal glasses of bourbon. "Well," Sinn said, rising and taking a glass. "Let's have a toast, then. To the new martyrs. Profit makers!"

We clinked glasses, and I shot the bourbon down my throat just to wash the bile down.

"Ah," Sinn said, "that's good stuff." He dismissed the receptionist with our empty glasses and sat back down.

"What about the replacements," I said, trying to salvage something, anything.

"Oh, we'll do much better than that." Sinn laughed. "Within a week a new class of three hundred specially selected converts will complete indoctrination, ready to be transformed into hard-driving martyrs. What do you think about that?"

I thought about it. With three hundred more martyrs, I could turn the battle for the streets into an all-out war. "I like it."

"Oh, it doesn't stop there. We've intensified and expanded our recruitment and indoctrination programs, and from here on out I can guarantee you five hundred martyrs a month."

"That might be too much," I said, "even for a City this size."

"Not to worry. As soon as they get some experience, I plan to ship the veterans to set centers in every corner of the globe to plant the seeds of new martyr armies, pass their holy knowledge on to new young minds. And all that knowledge will have sprung from you, Commander, the original seed." He leaned back in his chair and stared at something far, far away. "Soon I'll have an entire *army* of champions."

"Building an empire, Sinn?"

"I believe in expansion. Think of it, though, martyrs in every city, turning back the tide of evil."

"And earning fat profits."

"That, too."

"Funny, a minute ago you were ready to drop the entire program, but now it's going worldwide."

"That's how I operate. When I decide to do something, I go all the way."

I rubbed my jaw. "It's going be difficult for me to train the new class and carry on the campaign at the same time."

"I anticipated that," Sinn said. "I've decided that Slim and a select few other martyrs will form a cadre to carry out the training of the new recruits so you can devote yourself fully to the ongoing campaign. What do you think?"

"I don't like that idea."

"Why not? You just said you couldn't do both." He waved the feather at me rather effetely. "You're not jealous of Slim, are you?"

"No, I just don't like him."

"I'm surprised. He has a great deal of respect for you, Commander." He returned the feather to the decanter and picked up a remote. The marble wall to the left parted, revealing the bank of monitors. Men in glass coffins popped onto the screens. "You're dismissed," he said without looking at me.

As I walked down the long hall, I couldn't help feeling like a man sinking slowly into a pit of quicksand, trying desperately to hang on to a slippery vine. In such a situation, the mind of the average man would probably be clouded with many options. For a man such as myself, the choice was perfectly clear.

It was time to get ruthless.

I GAVE THE MARTYRS the rest of the day off to recover. I spent the afternoon above the City in my skimmer and the night at my command console, planning the next operation and rearranging the martyr roster. I abandoned the strategy of diluting Slim's power by keeping his followers spread over all four squads. I transferred his entire clique to Fourth Squad, appointing Sailor as squad leader. I rebuilt First Squad with the martyrs who seemed most loyal to my command. Second and Third squads were a homogenous mix of loyalties.

I announced the new roster in the barracks before the following morning's PT, using First Squad's losses as the reason. Sailor, Brown and the rest of Slim's consolidated gang seemed delighted at their unification, giggling and goosing each other. Slim appeared troubled by the new order but kept his mouth shut.

After PT I formed up the martyrs in the gym before a videoboard displaying a complex floor plan and three different photo images of the same sprawling one-story building.

I pointed at the images. "This is the Rainbow Building located at 2243 Enterprise Road in the City's industrial center, home of Rainbow Laboratories. Owned by the Pleasure Syndicate, it has the distinction of being the largest squeeze production facility in the region. Roughly a third of the squeeze distributed in the City and outlying areas comes from this building. The production line operates around the clock to meet demand. We strike the plant at midnight tomorrow."

The martyrs shifted a little, suddenly uneasy.

"Sequence A," I told the videoboard, and the floor plan suddenly animated with a descending computer-generated rotor. "The company will divide into three teams. Third Squad will arrive on the roof by rotor. Using suppressed machine pistols, they'll eliminate all enemy personnel and disable the microwave communication tower."

Tiny graphic martyrs shot tiny graphic guards, then threw whisper grenades into a microwave dish. Some of the younger martyrs stared at the board with childish fascination, more excited by the graphics than my plan.

"Third Squad will then break into four sniper teams and

one surface-to-air rocket crew. The sniper teams will position themselves on each corner of the building to pin down any reactionary ground forces. The rocket crew will shoot down approaching enemy aircraft. Once the rooftop is secure, Slim and Fourth Squad will arrive by rotor. They will quickly disembark and secure the stairwell in the southeast corner of the roof and wait for the radio command to descend."

"Wait a minute," Slim said, raising his hand. "You just said the rocket crew would shoot down any approaching aircraft. What makes you think they won't shoot down me and Fourth Squad?"

"I said approaching *enemy* aircraft. Your rotor will be equipped with an ID beacon. The foe-challenger beam of the rocket launcher will identify you as friendly and allow you to land safely. You will also be in constant radio contact, so nothing can go wrong."

Slim lowered his hand, not appearing entirely satisfied.

"Now," I continued, "while all this is happening, First and Second squads will arrive by van. One four-man heavy speedgun crew will take up position at the rear of the building and shoot anyone who comes out the back door. Anyone. The rest of First and Second squads will enter the building through the front door after neutralizing the door guards. They will fan out through the facility, eliminating all personnel encountered. Fourth Squad will descend the stairs ten seconds after the front door is breached, attacking the rear of any elements pinned down by the frontal assault. Once all enemy personnel in the plant proper are liquidated, we'll focus on the control office, a bullet-proof cubicle in the southeast corner of the building, near the stairwell." I pointed at a thick-walled blue cubicle on the plant's floor plan.

"Bulletproof?" Brown said. "What if they lock themselves inside?"

"Two two-man demo units drawn from Second Squad will follow in the wake of the attack. If the execs seal themselves inside the cube, the first demo unit will blow the door. After the cube is cleared, the same demo unit will locate and blow the safe, bagging whatever cash is on hand. While all this is happening, the second demo unit will arm a fusion bomb in the center of the building. Once both teams have finished their tasks, we reverse our movements and blow the building by remote once we're clear. We'll spend the rest of today and tomorrow rehearsing in the urban mock-up. Any questions?"

Sailor raised his hand. "How did you find this place?"

"It's common knowledge. I had the blueprints modemed over from City planning. The overflight vids I took myself."

Slim raised his hand. "Just how much security can we expect?"

"Very little," I said. "Perhaps two guards on the roof, two at the door and half a dozen inside. Plus whatever bodyguards the management team might have."

"What about the workers?" Nu asked.

"There won't be that many. The operation is mostly automated."

"No," he said. "I mean what do we do with them?"

I stared at him. "You kill them. This isn't a sensitive TV drama, and we don't have time to screw around with prisoners. If they don't mind producing a deadly drug, you shouldn't mind killing them."

Slim stared at the building layout. "It seems too easy. You'd think such an important syndicate facility would be more secretive and have a larger garrison."

"Their physical security has become a vestigial organ," I explained. "They think they have nothing to fear. On paper they're so safe they can hardly breathe. The Pleasure Syndicate is one of the more powerful criminal organizations in the City. The plant is located on safe turf, and they have ironclad protection contracts with the local gangs and militia. The SPF isn't a threat as long as the Pleasure Syndicate remains apolitical, and no one in the criminal subculture will approach the place because of a deeply rooted fear of the syndicate's symbolic power. The same way some people fear the devil."

Nu raised a hand. "Why aren't we afraid?"

"Because," I said, "we *are* the devil."

I DROVE THE VAN through the unmanned gate and stopped in front of the Rainbow Building. I jumped out, resplendent in a snappy red-and-turquoise uniform that matched the tacky decals on the van. I grabbed my boxes and pranced to the two guards loafing near the door. One was tall and thin, the other grossly fat: the Laurel and Hardy of the criminal underworld.

"Pizza dude!" I said brightly, stopping smartly in front of them.

The dark-suited heavies looked at each other. "We didn't order no pizza," Laurel said. "Did we?"

"No," Hardy said firmly. "We didn't order no pizzas."

I frowned slightly. "This *is* 2243 Enterprise Road, isn't it?"

"Yeah," Laurel admitted grudgingly.

"Then where's my goddamn money?" I demanded.

"We didn't order no pizza." Hardy scowled. "So scram, pizza boy."

I pouted, then firmed up my jaw. "I'm afraid I can't

leave until somebody coughs up the plastic for the pizzas. That's strict company policy."

They looked at each other incredulously. "Get the hell out of here," Laurel snarled.

"But you don't even know what the toppings are," I whined. "You're certain to like *these* pizzas."

The muscles in Laurel's neck became taut as steel cables, and his hands turned to claws. "I don't like no pizzas," he gasped. "I'm gonna tell you to get away just one more time, shit-for-brains."

"Hold on," Hardy said, sniffing the air. "What's on them pizzas?"

"I thought you'd never ask," I said, flipping up the lid of the top box. "Looks like we got soy ham, mushroom-flavored algae, kelp and a suppressed machine pistol."

"A what?" Hardy asked.

"Suppressed machine pistol," I said, blowing off the top of his head. Laurel gawked at me, and I tipped him over with a pair of silent bullets through the heart.

I dropped the boxes and signaled. The side door of the van popped open, and the speedgun crew hauled their weapon out, followed by martyrs with submachine guns. Two more vans powered up from the gate and disgorged more martyrs. When they'd formed up near the door, I gave the signal and we burst in, firing at anything that breathed.

It was over in seconds. Startled techs and guards, cut down by onrushing martyrs, fell among the humming production machines. We swept forward until we reached the bulletproof cubicle. Shocked, strangely detached faces stared out from behind the thick Plexiglas at the massacre happening outside, as if watching it on TV. Nu was a step from the heavy door before one of the execs tried to close and lock it. The exec leapt to the door with frantic energy and had it half-shut when Nu and two other martyrs drove shoulders into it, knocking the exec to the floor. The trio of martyrs stepped inside and opened up with their sub-guns, hosing down the four execs inside.

The three martyrs stepped outside and the first demo team rushed in. They scuttled about with a ferrous-anomaly detector until they located the safe behind a portrait of some smiling crook. They dropped their backpacks and dug out fusion clay, primers and a remote detonator.

Two teams of martyrs took up stations near the front and rear doors, and Nu moved the rest through the factory, double-tapping the bodies sprawled about the floor. The other demo team hunkered over a backpack-size fusion bomb in the center of the complex. The martyrs operated like a perfect machine, each component doing its job properly and efficiently without a word from me. None of the syndicate's guards or armed workers had even gotten a shot off—most died with startled expressions and holstered pistols. And not a single martyr had fallen.

The front door burst open as Slim and Fourth Squad hustled inside, shouting the running password, wild-eyed and out of breath. Slim jogged up to me and his men followed.

"You were supposed to come down the stairs," I said. "Remember?"

"The radio went out halfway here!" Slim frothed. "We were forty meters from the building, and the rocket crew on the roof fired at us! Missed us by a gosh-darn pubic hair!"

"They missed at that range?" I said incredulously. "Those boys need some retraining."

"We're lucky we weren't blown to bits!" Slim cried.

"What happened to the foolproof foe-challenger system on the launcher?"

"Must have malfunctioned," I speculated. "We'll have to go over that during the debriefing. Right now I want you to take Fourth Squad out the back door and set up a circular security perimeter around the building, got it?"

He scowled. "All right," he said, and motioned for Fourth Squad to follow him. About halfway to the back door he skidded to a halt and whirled around. "Wait a gosh-darn minute!" he howled. "Wait a gosh-darn almighty minute! Isn't there a speedgun team out there with orders to shoot *anyone* who sets foot out that door?"

I slapped my head. "Oh, Jesus, you're right. I forgot all about that. Maybe it'd be better if you went out the front."

"Yeah, maybe it would," Slim snarled, and he and Fourth Squad jogged away, throwing back glares.

"Fire in the hole!" the first demo team chorused, and the cubicle shook with a muffled explosion. I followed the team back inside once the smoke cleared. The wall safe hung open, and stacks of high-currency credit spilled out, only about half of it incinerated by the blast.

"Bag that up," I told the gaping demo team. "And take it easy on the fusion clay next time." They sprang into action, and I sought out the second demo team.

The ruddy-faced ogre of a martyr who'd packed in the heavy fusion bomb checked the casing for damage while a narrow Creole hunched over the blinking panel of fat bomb, punching in blast instructions.

I leaned over the Creole's shoulder. "What blast radius are you setting it for?"

"Ten thousand square meters, a shade less than the dimensions of the building, Commander. Just enough to implode it."

"Good," I said. I patted his shoulder, then keyed my throat mike. "Third Squad, how we looking up there?"

"Fine, sir," an uneasy voice replied, his voice reaching my eardrums by way of skeleton from the vibraphone strapped across my breastbone. "A rotor attempted to land but we chased it off with a missile. Fourth Squad, uh, never showed up," he said, making the connection right then.

"That's fine," I said. "We're about to scat. Once you hear the vans start up, pack up and rotor out. Give me an all-clear once you're a kilometer from the building."

"Yes, sir, but aren't we supposed to stay in position until the vans are clear?"

"There's been a change of plan. Fourth Squad will pull security until everyone is clear. You got that, Slim?"

"Check," Slim said. I waited for an argument, but much to my surprise it didn't come.

"Good," I said. "How far from the building are you?"

"We're right inside the chain-link fence."

"Super. The fusion bomb is set to implode and crater the building so you'll be safe."

"Sure," Slim said. No sarcasm, no emotion at all.

"I want you to stay in position until you see the building blow, then report back to me when it does."

"Right," Slim said.

I made a quick check of the situation. The fusion bomb was programmed, the credits bagged up, and it appeared as if our gig was done.

"Withdraw!" I shouted, and martyrs began streaming out the front door.

When the last martyr disappeared, I knelt over the fusion bomb, reprogrammed the blast radius and left.

We were four klicks from the complex when Third

Squad radioed they were clear. I slipped the sleek black detonator from my breast pocket, punched in the proper three-digit code and pushed the blinking red button.

I keyed my throat mike. "How's it look, Slim?" Silence and static answered me. I repeated the question, and a warm feeling began to glow in my heart.

"Looks great," Slim's voice crackled through my bones, and the warm feeling shriveled and died. "But it sure as heck didn't implode. That *f*-word went up like a volcano!"

"Did *anyone* get hurt?" I asked, trying to keep the hope out of my voice.

"No, we're all safe and sound and heading home. See you there."

18

After critiquing the men, I went upstairs to brief Sinn. I bumped into Slim as he exited Sinn's office.

He smiled at me. "That sure was a fine fireworks display you treated us to."

"Glad you liked it," I said.

"Yes. Of course, our view had a lot to do with it. I have the feeling if we had remained on the ground instead of going up in the rotor for a better look, we might not have been so appreciative." He smiled again and departed.

I spent half an hour briefing Sinn, leaving out the foul-ups. He wore an indifferent expression until a call from accounting announced we'd taken over 1.2 million credits from the safe. The rest of my report was met with enthusiastic nods and happy waves of a green ostrich feather. When I finished, he stood up and shook my hand.

"Success!" he cried. "Let those bastards on the board say the martyrs aren't pulling their weight now. And I won't even tell you how many friends you've made over in accounting. Why, a couple more hauls like this one, and I'll have the naysayers fighting to lick my boots!"

"Maybe it's best we laid off the big hits for a while," I said.

Sinn's head jerked up. "What? Why?"

"We've stirred up the hornet's nest, and they're going to want to go after someone," I explained. "Since we left no evidence or witnesses, they'll probably blame another syndicate or an ambitious militia. We should lay low and let them weaken themselves with infighting, attacking only the wolves that move in our direction."

I could almost hear the pop of Sinn's bubble. He settled down into his chair and sulked in silence for a moment, the green feather twitching in his fingers.

"You're right, of course," he said, sighing, working up a small smile. "We can't be too greedy, can we?" Suddenly his face brightened. "In fact, this is an excellent opportunity to take care of some trouble that has popped up." He reached into his desk and removed a disk. "A wolf has been baring his teeth at us. Have you heard of Faith No More?"

"They're that atheist group headed by the poet, Junes something."

"The loathsome Junes Dylan. One of our recent converts belonged to Faith No More. He has revealed that Junes and his organization have mobilized against us. He also revealed the location of their headquarters."

"Why is Faith No More moving against the Set of One?"

"Oh, you know how mean-spirited those atheists are. They'll attack any new religion that comes along. We have to strike them before they strike us."

"I thought Dylan and his group were pacifists."

"Our Intelligence tells us otherwise." He handed me the disk. "Everything is in there. I'd like it to be our next operation."

"I'll get on it as soon as I can."

"Excellent. There's something else I want to discuss with you."

"I'm listening."

He exchanged the green feather for a black one. He stroked the feather and grinned tightly. "Slim has fallen under the impression you are trying to get him killed."

I faked a laugh. "Most soldiers believe their leaders are trying to get them killed. That's just the nature of combat."

"Perhaps so, but Slim seems to think you are making a special effort to place him and Fourth Squad in harm's way."

"Now, why would I do that?"

"Slim believes you're trying to get rid of him and Fourth Squad as a means of taking full control of the martyrs. And history tells us that whoever controls the palace guard controls the palace. What have you to say about that?"

"I'd say Slim is dangerously paranoid."

Sinn smiled and tilted his head back. He closed his eyes and tickled his face with the feather. "Slim also believes that you have designs on my life," he said in a quiet voice, "that your intention is to stage a coup, installing yourself as set prophet."

I blinked at him and suddenly became conscious of the weight and availability of the pistol under my coat. "Oh, yeah? What do *you* believe, Sinn?"

His eyes opened to slits as he looked at me. "I believe you are guilty as hell."

"Then why haven't I been relieved of command?"

"Oh, there's no call for that." He leaned back in the chair, still stroking his cheek with the feather. "I understand your motivations, Jacob. You've been handed a good thing and you want to keep it—that's just human nature. What makes you different from the rest of us is that your peculiar disposition demands you go to rather ruthless extremes to hang on to that good thing. You play by, shall we say, a less restrictive set of rules than everyone else."

"Wasn't that why you hired me?"

"Indeed it was, and I knew precisely what I was getting. You've lived up to my expectations in every way. Please don't think I'm disappointed in you, because I'm not. I understand you, Jacob, and that's better than judging you."

I folded my arms. "Let me get this straight. You think I'm guilty as hell, but don't give a damn."

"Let me put it this way. I don't think you want my job. I don't think running a religion interests you. I think you just want to keep what you already have. If you did entertain any ominous thoughts about my safety, I think it was because you felt I was threatening your position. I want to make it clear right now that I am in no way a threat to you or the martyrs."

Sinn glanced at his watch, then touched a button on the desk's panel. A screen on the left wall lit up with the view of a bare-chested man being helped into one of the familiar glass chambers. "I have big plans for you, Commander. I just hope in the future you consider letting me in on your little intrigues."

I tried to make sense of the maze he was building around me. "What about Slim?" I asked.

Sinn smiled and shrugged. "It's a cruel, hard world, don't think I don't understand that." He reached into the desk, passed me a slip of paper, then turned back to the screen where white-suited techs frantically jumped around monitors and keyboards surrounding the man in the glass chamber who now appeared to be sleeping.

"What's this?" I asked.

"Your first pay slip. The amount at the bottom has been transferred to your scan account. Do you find it satisfactory?"

I looked at the number and divided it by the number of

lives I thought the martyrs had taken since I'd joined the set. It worked out to roughly three hundred creds per kill, which was about average for a death warrant. "It's about right," I said.

"Fine, fine," he said remotely. The still man in the glass chamber suddenly flailed to life, screaming. I was about to leave when Sinn pointed at the screen and said, "Why don't you stop by the Phoenix Program, Commander?"

I regarded the screen. "Why?"

"I think it'll clear some things up for you. Go to Bay Thirteen."

I nodded and left.

I walked down the hall lost in thought, trying to understand what kind of game Sinn was playing and what the new rules were, if there were any at all. A piece seemed to be missing; there was something I wasn't getting. I stopped in front of two swinging doors next to a plaque that read:

Phoenix Program
Resurrection Room 13
Authorized Personnel Only

I pushed open the door and went inside.

The air was sterile and faintly metallic smelling. A jumpy, chubby-faced lab technician met me at the door. "Oh, hello, Commander Strait. What a pleasure. How goes the battle?"

"Super. You boys are up kind of late, aren't you?"

He smiled. "The Phoenix Program operates twenty-four hours a day, seven days a week."

"That's super," I said, looking over his shoulder at techs bustling around behind him. "Tell me about your operation here."

"Certainly, Commander. My name is Herb, by the way. Not Herbert. Herb. I don't like being called Herbert."

"All right, Herb."

He adjusted his thick glasses and twisted on a smile. "Great. Now, what did you want to know?" I noticed he had planted himself between myself and the lab, like a protective mother.

"Everything," I said, brushing past him. Two other medtechs, a male and female with matching buzz cuts, appeared to be running tests on the equipment on and around the empty glass chamber in the middle of the room. Herb tagged behind me, quick as a sober host among drunks, afraid I was going to break something.

"What's that?" I demanded, pointing at the glass chamber.

"That's a resurrection booth. Actually, Commander, we're a little busy right now. Perhaps it would be better if you came back later."

I turned to give Herb a hard stare. "Are you questioning my credentials, Herbert? I'd hate to think there was a loyalty problem in this department."

His eyes flickered to the lightning bolts on my lapel, the red skull on my chest. "Please don't call me that. There's no reason to call me that."

"All right, Herb." I turned back to the chamber. "What happens in these glass coffins?"

"Resurrection chambers."

"Whatever."

"Well, we terminate then defibrillate the function—"

"In plain terms, Herb."

He pulled at his collar and cleared his throat. "We kill postlife pioneers, then bring them back to life after a certain period of time."

"For what purpose?"

"Why, to see what's out there, of course."

A sudden interest jabbed my belly. "Out where?"

Herb shrugged and went into his coy routine.

I folded my arms and yawned. "Well, it sounds dead boring compared to what we martyrs do."

Herb frowned deeply. "Why, it so happens, *Commander* Strait, that we of the Phoenix Program do some of the most important research—"

"Boring, boring, boring," I said, yawning again. "Jesus, would you look at me? I'm about to fall asleep here. Have you ever been in a firefight, Herb, baby?" I said arrogantly. "Have you ever even looked down the barrel of a rotor rifle in the hands of a squeeze-crazed psychopath? No, by the looks of you, I'd say you haven't."

Herb's face pinched up, and I could almost hear his departmental loyalties growl inside him. The two medtechs stopped checking the equipment to watch us, and Herb turned on them viciously. "Back to work!" he snarled, then rounded on me in a stern voice. "You martyrs may be out there confronting psychopathic criminals, mere *mortals,* but the bold pioneers of the Phoenix Program go out and confront *gods!*" He stretched his hands out wide. "Have *you* ever looked down the barrel of metaphysical *infinity,* huh, Commander? Have you?"

I pretended to doze for a moment, jerked my head back up, then blinked around. "Did you say something, pointy head?"

Herb shot up onto his toes, and his arms flapped around him. He wanted to hit me but he didn't know how. "I'm talking about exploring the *afterlife,* Mr. Strait. These brave and noble men and women venture boldly out beyond humankind's greatest barrier—death. That's right! Death! Have you ever *died, Commander* Strait?"

I smiled at his red, sweating face, inches from mine. "Sure," I said. "I've died of heartbreak at least a half-dozen times."

"Not the same!" he shrilled. "Not even close!" He wrapped his arms tightly around his chest and looked away angrily.

"What is it they see out there?" I asked.

Herb sulked and said nothing.

"I apologize for taking such a dim view of your obviously important work here," I said.

Herb nodded curtly but still wouldn't look at me. "Despite its magnitude," he said magnanimously, "your gargantuan ignorance is forgiven."

"Thank you. Where do you find your pioneers anyway? It must take a special breed to confront death."

He cleared his throat carefully. "Recruited out of our Resurrection Mission mostly. Volunteers all."

"What do you offer them?"

"Credit, a place to stay." He smiled wryly. "A chance to meet a god."

I nodded. "What was your line before you got into this racket?"

He shifted uncomfortably. "I worked at a hospital."

"Decided you liked killing people better then saving them?"

"I worked in a City casualty ward, Commander. Ever been inside one of those?"

"I've seen a few."

"Then you know the futility of it. You labor like a dog all day to save the lives of human animals, and for what?

Most of them aren't worth saving. I was attacked more times than I was thanked. After three hellish years, I transferred to medical research. It didn't take me long to realize the futility of *that*."

"Of what?"

"Of searching for ways to lengthen human life. Most people live too long as it is. The less time alive, the less trouble they can get into, the less they can screw up the world. Over the years I've learned human life isn't all that important, and anyone who tells you different is just concerned with his own precious butt. Beyond the egotistical point of view, human life has no redeeming value—it is a debt to the universe, a minus, a negative." Herb wiped a sheen of sweat from his face with a handkerchief. "Can't you see that?"

"There are times when I would agree. You sound like some atheists I know."

"I used to be one."

"But now you're a believer."

Herb smiled. "I challenge any atheist to work with the Phoenix Program and not become a staunch believer in One." There was a noise from the door, and Herb faced it. "Ah, the next pioneer."

Two burly orderlies wheeled in Leo, the wino I'd met in the mission. He wore only heavy trousers, and the sides of his head were freshly shaven. A tight smile creased his face.

"Hey, Sammy!" he said. "What're you doing here? Are you going for a ride, too?"

"Not today, Leo," I said.

The orderlies helped him into the chamber, then departed. The two techs took over, working harmoniously,

strapping down his limbs and rubbing a thin coat of petro-
leum jelly over his bare chest.

"They tell me it's as simple as giving blood and just as
safe," Leo told me as the techs taped two black disks trailing thick cables to his chest and sensors to his forehead.

"I bet it is," I said.

"Just like going to sleep and waking up, everyone
knows that." A smile hung on to his lips, but in his eyes I
could detect a lurking terror. "Well, here we go, boys, into
the wild blue yonder." He winked and gave me a thumbs-
up with his strapped hand.

The techs wrapped an injector pack trailing tubes of
fluid around Leo's neck, then secured an airtight clear
plastic oxygen mask over his nose and mouth. Herb
checked their work, then nodded. "Lower and seal."

The male tech moved to the control console at the head
of the chamber, and the female took her position by a bank
of monitors. The male tech clicked a button on the console, and the lid hummed shut. With a tiny rush of air, the
seals closed tight.

"Sealed," the male tech said.

"Introduce the catalyst," Herb instructed.

The male tech tapped a keyboard, and a nearly invisible
gas hissed into the mask. "Catalyst introduced," he reported.

I watched panic creep into Leo's eyes. His head began
to twitch, and his jaw began to chatter.

"How long, eh, Doc?" Leo asked, his voice muffled by
the mask and glass. "How long until…" He convulsed
once, and the dancing bead of light of his heart monitor
danced wildly. Leo clamped his mouth shut and held his
breath, jerking his head left and right, until terror made him
gasp for air. "Hold on now, Doc," he cried. "I'm not ready

yet, I've changed my mind." His hands and legs jerked savagely against the straps, the animal will to live overpowering all rationalization. "I don't want to die!" he sobbed. "I don't want to die!"

"You signed the contract, Mr. Beagley," Herb said. "It won't be long now."

Leo screamed and struggled more violently, sucking in more and more gas. He took one last convulsive breath, arced his spine and went limp.

"We have flatline," the female tech reported, studying the monitors closely.

"Good," Herb said. "Administer countercatalyst." The male tech touched the keyboard, and a low humming rose from the booth.

"Start countdown," Herb said, and a large digital readout on the wall above the monitors began counting backward from fifteen minutes.

"He's out there now," Herb told me. "Exploring the cosmos."

"Do they all go out like that?"

"Most. It's a good sign. It means they want to come back."

I stared at Leo. His chest was still; no breath entered his lungs. *He knows more now than all the living men in the world,* I thought. "What's happening to his body?"

"Well, he's dead. But then death is man's greatest exaggeration. We've administered a countercatalyst, a molecular-separation field that breaks down and neutralizes the gaseous compound that killed him. The chamber lowers the body temperature below freezing to prevent cell deterioration. All he needs now is the stimulus to return."

"Won't he suffer brain damage?"

Herb shrugged. "Most of them are already brain damaged by way of drink or drug. At least now they're doing it for a noble cause."

We stared at the digital timer for a while, like strangers waiting for an elevator.

"I wonder what he's seeing," I said.

Herb shrugged. "We'll know soon enough. Prior chemical and hypnotic conditioning has structured his subconscious to act as sort of a blank photographic plate, or a sponge if you will. When his extradimensional extension, what the layman terms the *soul,* returns, the subconscious mind will immediately absorb the details of the experience, or as much at it can take. It's almost as if he has a camera with him."

"Do they all come back?"

"Not all. One keeps some of them for its own purposes."

"Its? You're the first person I've heard address One as an object instead of a masculine entity."

He smiled thinly. "It's the scientist in me. Until One is revealed as having a specific gender, and I see no reason why it would, I'll address it as 'it.'" He slid me a look. "No disrespect to One, of course."

We spent the last five minutes watching the readout drop until it reached zero.

"Heat him up," Herb said, and the chamber began to hum.

"Temperature is go," the female tech said, staring at Herb expectantly, fingers poised over buttons. Herb stared at the flashing zero and moved his lips minutely, silently counting.

The techs exchanged a secret glance, then looked at Herb. "Shall we begin resurrection?" the female tech asked.

"No," Herb snapped. "Let's give him a bit longer. Make

sure he gets a good long look." He stared at the flashing zero while the techs fidgeted. Minutes passed.

"Okay," Herb said suddenly. "Begin resurrection. Let's bring this pioneer home." He held up a hand. "Ready, now!"

The male tech leaned on a big red button, and Leo's chest jumped under the black disks. Air hissed into Leo's mask, causing his chest to rise and fall.

"Nothing," the female tech said.

"Hit him again," Herb said.

The male tech pressed the button, and Leo's body convulsed again.

"Still flatline," the female tech reported.

"Up the joules to 360," Herb ordered.

Leo jumped. The female tech shook her head. "Still nothing."

"One hundred mils of Lidocaine," Herb snapped. The male tech pecked at a keyboard, and fluid rushed down a tube toward the injector pack on Leo's neck.

"Shock him," Herb said. Another current made Leo's body jump, but the heartbeat indicator continued its horizontal path.

"Nothing," the female tech said.

"Get out of my way," Herb demanded, shoving his way behind a keyboard. His fingers jabbed at the buttons, and more fluid pumped into Leo's system. He slapped the shock button.

Leo's body snapped like a whip under the bonds, his face animated with expression. The monitor beeped and the heart line danced up weakly. "We got him!" the female tech cried.

"Okay, now," Herb said, staring at the screen. "Now we just reel him in, slowly, slowly."

After a minute the heartbeat strengthened, then returned to normal. Leo's chest rose and fell rhythmically, and he appeared to be sleeping peacefully.

"He's back in the moorings now," Herb said, wiping sweat from his forehead with the drenched handkerchief. "Hopefully with stories to tell." He turned to the techs. "Take him to the Whisper Room."

The top of the chamber hummed open, and the techs unstrapped Leo's unconscious form. As he was being lifted from the chamber, Leo's eyes popped open and he began to scream. His arms flailed wildly, and he gasped like a drowning man breaking surface. "Let me go!" he wailed. "Tell him to let me go!"

"Restrain him," Herb commanded, and the techs muscled him onto the gurney and leaned on his shoulders. After a moment Leo stopped thrashing and seemed to relax.

"It's quite normal for them to behave in such an excited manner," Herb assured me.

"I'll bet," I said, stepping out of the way of the gurney. As it passed, Leo's hand shot out and grabbed my arm, his eyes alive with raging insanity.

"He tried to eat me," he whispered hoarsely, his mad eyes burning into mine. "He grabbed me by the soul and wouldn't let go. He tried to swallow me whole!"

"Take him away!" Herb ordered.

"Hold on," I said, leaning close to Leo's face. "Who was it you saw?"

His eyes goggled, staring right through me at a memory that twisted his face into a mask of terror. "*Huge.* Bigger than everything, and empty, a huge nothing, a big ugly idiot vacuum that goes on forever, an incomprehensible, drooling hunger with no end." His eyes refocused on mine, and the techs pried his fingers from my arm and struggled to push him away. "Don't send me back there, Doc!" Leo screamed. "I ain't going! He'll eat me next time, he'll eat us all!"

They hustled Leo out the door as Herb and I stared after him. "What do you suppose he meant by that?" I asked.

Herb shrugged. "Who knows? Postdeath trauma can really scramble the brain. It's up to the guys over in imprint extraction to sort it all out, cut away the trauma and get the picture. Sounds like he got a good look."

"Yeah, but a look at what?"

He shrugged again. "Everybody reacts to meeting the Reaper differently." He turned his smiling face to me, and his glasses went opaque under the fluorescents. "Death is what you make it."

"Yes," I agreed. "What happens to Leo now?"

"He visits the Whisper Room. That's what we call the imprint-extraction section. Memories are perishable, so it's essential we get the imprint as soon as possible."

"I want to see the Whisper Room."

He stared at me from behind his thick glasses. "All right, Mr. Strait." He led me down twenty meters of corridor and through two sets of swinging doors.

Most of the imprint-extraction section's two dozen couches were occupied by winos wearing bulbous black helmets with bulging eye covers and a snake's nest of cables, making them appear like strange insects. Their whispered words were picked up by microphones curled to their lips.

Two techs lifted Leo onto a vacant couch, strapped him down and fitted a helmet to his head. An injector pack was wrapped around his neck, and a clear fluid began trickling into his bloodstream.

"What's happening now?" I asked.

"A hypnotic drug is being fed into his system," Herb said. "The video goggles and earphones of the helmet produce visual and audio patterns that will slow down his brain waves and lower him into a deep hypnotic state."

Two orderlies appeared beside a pioneer and removed his helmet and injector pack. The dazed wino's haircut resembled Leo's mohawk.

"Why do you shave the sides of their heads?" I asked.

"Conductivity. You see, the pioneers verbal description of the postdeath experience is not enough to gain a perfect image. Asking a human mind to describe a memory is unreliable. Due to internal shaping, each subject describes the same object differently. To gain an objective image, we have to bypass the filters of the psyche and go straight to the memory centers. We draw out the raw data and let the computers refine it."

"You suck out their memories."

"No, we make imprints. Two rectangular plates inside the helmet are pressured against the sides of the skull. One plate sends powerful theta waves through the brain to the opposite plate, which acts as a receiver. Through hypnotism, we program the subject to focus on different specific aspects of the experience. The plates draw wave data from the brain using a sort of hammer-and-anvil technique. The most minute change in brain wave, electricity or blood flow makes up a complex cerebral language our computers understand."

"And from that data you're able to create an image?"

"Not exactly. Our data translators are not perfect—the messages tend to come out somewhat blurred, and sometimes the data is unique to other experiences. It's the computer's job to classify and compare each new string of data, match up similar pieces, then piece together those common bits into larger fragments."

"Fragments that will eventually form into an image."

"Not directly. Early on we determined that even at a vastly accelerated pace, it would take roughly eighty years and five million pioneers to get a complete and true image. You can imagine how distressed we were."

"That's a long time to wait for a picture to develop."

"Yes, it is. Fortunately we found a shortcut in fractology. Have you heard of it?"

"Sure. It's the computer process that creates elaborate graphic designs from a single repeating fractal equation. They make great calendar art."

"Aesthetics aside, you're basically correct. You see, everything in the universe follows a pattern right down to its atomic blueprint, based on a root equation. A certain equation, expanded outward, will equal, say, a chimpanzee, another equation will result in a teacup. There's even a specific equation for Jake Strait."

"So it's like being able to clone an entire creature from the genetic information stored in a single cell."

"That's a fair analogy. Because the molecular fabric of all matter follows a fairly uniform pattern, if you can obtain a big enough piece of an object, say the handle of the teacup, you can reverse the fragment back to the root equation. You then reverse the process again, and the equation will expand back out into the entire teacup. In concept, it's similar to the process paleontologists use to determine the size and shape of a dinosaur from a single bone."

"And that's why it's not going to take eighty years to achieve the whole image."

He smiled. "Precisely. Once we get a large enough piece, we can convert it to the whole image."

"And what exactly is it an image of?"

A voice behind me said, "The face of God."

We turned and Sinn dropped a hand on Herb's shoulder. "Showing our martyr the ropes, Herbert?"

"Yes, sir," Herb choked out, half bowing. "I knew it would be okay—"

"Of course it's okay," Sinn said with a big grin, clapping him harder on the shoulder. "Of course. Now, if you don't mind, I'll show Jacob what all this work is for."

Herb bowed away, stuttering goodbyes apologetically.

Sinn grinned. "I'm pleased to see you chose to explore the spiritual side of the set."

"I didn't think there was a spiritual side," I said.

"Oh, but there is. Come with me and I'll show you."

We started to leave, but I stopped, looking back at the Leo and the rest of the winos, their frail whispers just audible over the hum of machines. "What about them? What happens to them when you're through?"

"We let them go," Sinn said, giving me an amused look. "Did you think we killed them?"

"That would go along with the set's fine sense of ruthless efficiency."

"I agree, but we're dealing with an unknown commodity here. Killing them just might offend One. No, we just let them go. They're still functional. They may appear to act rather strange to the average man, but maybe they know something the average man doesn't." He left the room and I followed.

19

Sinn led me to the huge auditorium I'd witnessed from the God Hall. Dimly lit and empty, it reminded me of a large movie theater. We walked up the center aisle and stepped onto the platform in front of big red velvet curtains.

"What happened to the control panels?" I asked.

"Don't need them anymore," Sinn said. He moved to the podium and rolled back its steel top, exposing a keyboard and a row of tiny monitors. "It's all here now." He slipped his keycard into a slot and touched a button. The red velvet curtains began to part, exposing a twenty-by-forty-meter digital monitor.

"All the expense, all the effort," Sinn said quietly, pushing a button and facing the screen, "all for this."

The monstrous screen flashed to life, overwhelming me with a wave of color, shape and shadow swirling and flitting across a vast video landscape. Vague and ambiguous images came and went with turbulent swarms of color, and I had to move my head left and right to take it all in.

"When I first started out in the religion business, I played the game from a strictly corporate angle," Sinn said in a loud voice that boomed around the empty room. "And things went okay. We were turning a steady profit, but, you know, things weren't *skyrocketing*. We had a fine-tuned and efficient machine but we didn't have enough *soul*. So I turned loose my idea guys in marketing, and they came up with DER."

"DER?"

"Death exploration research, or the Phoenix Program. Oh, it was just a wild lark at first, a stab in the dark. Then they made an absolutely amazing discovery. Something that changed the entire direction and focus of the set. I had set out to create a money machine, then discovered something that goes beyond money and material wealth—that sort of power is always self-defeating and limited anyway. I learned materialism was not an end unto itself, it was merely a means to a higher end."

Sinn directed a hand at the shifting hues. "This is what it's all about," he said in a satisfied voice. "All the data, all the sacrifice, all the killing. This is why the martyrs must turn a profit—this is why the set must make money."

"What is it I'm seeing?"

He glanced back at me and smiled. "The landscape of the afterlife, Jacob. The forming soul of a god, the throbbing heart of eternity. This is the drawing board of the computers, computers so powerful it takes millions of dollars a day to maintain and feed them. This is the combined bits and pieces of what our pioneers bring back. Each passing moment adds a little more clarity, causes one more tiny piece to fall into place. Soon, my dear Jacob, we will know the face of One."

I looked at him. "How do you know it's going to be One's face?"

A big, wild grin grew on Sinn's face. "Because it's One our pioneers are seeing."

"How do you know that? Does he wear a name tag, for crissakes?"

He laughed. "Not exactly. We know by tests. Early on we discovered that no matter the faith of the pioneer sent out, they all basically experienced the same thing—a tunnel of darkness, deceased loved ones, a being of white light from which a feeling of complete peace and tranquility emanates. Yet a resurrected Muslim will say he met Allah, a Christian will say Jehovah or Christ, a Hindu will swear it was Brahma and so on.

"*Our* faithful, those who converted to the set, are certain they saw *One*. You see, Jacob, they use different names, affix to it different sets of moralities and personalities, but they all address the same pure, amoral force. A force that doesn't understand good or evil, a force of pure energy and power. It is the god of all religions and none of them. A power infinite and supreme, to be molded into any conceivable shape or form. Thus, One is real."

"Wait a minute," I said. "How can you say this supreme power is One when you earlier admitted you created One from surveys and polls?"

"That's just it! Worshipers create their gods, not vice versa. If enough people believe in a god, then that god *is* real, as real as love, hate or anything else built upon a foundation of faith. Gods are real because man believes in them. They don't exist until man makes them exist, and they die when they are reduced to myth.

"Listen to this—in the early days of the set, we hired special-effects techs to stage miracles for publicity purposes. Then we found out we didn't have to anymore. Once we converted a large-enough pool of believers, miracles started happening on their own. Two weeks ago, before a congregation of a thousand set faithful, a five-hundred-kilo bronze symbol of One levitated fifteen meters into the air at a set conversion center in Melbourne!

"In Naples a lightning bolt fell from a clear blue sky and exploded a car bomb hurtling toward a set administration center! The list goes on and on—it's as if we've tapped into some huge power source." Sinn walked to the screen, then turned around, throwing his hands in the air. "Do you understand the magnitude of this? I've not only created a new god, I've constructed a new heaven and hell! Through the creation of One, I've leased space beyond death! I'm selling immortality and paradise!"

"Who gave you the right?" I wanted to know.

"No one! I goddamn *took* it! I'm bringing back the afterlife concept, an idea the majority have abandoned. That's why this world has gone to shit. Everybody started thinking this existence was a dead-end road and started acting accordingly abominable. And why shouldn't they if the saint and sinner get the same reward in the end—nothingness? But I'm going to change that. The Martyr Program only attacks the symptoms, but my afterlife program is the cure!"

"Sure," I said. "You're going to solve all the world's problems selling tickets to paradise."

Sinn smiled. "Oh, don't be so cynical, Jacob. You're just like I am—we're both searching for the same thing, something more important than money and attacking the evil here on Earth."

"Free parking?"

"Eternal salvation!" he cried, throwing his hands into the air.

"Well, well," I sneered. "We've come full circle, haven't we? You started out wearing the robes of spiritual righteousness, then revealed yourself as a greedy businessman. And now you're the wild-eyed prophet again, babbling lies like all the crazies peddling paradise out on the street."

"But my offer is true," Sinn said softly, moving close, his eyes burning with the all-consuming, boiling insanity only prophets know. "Don't you see what I'm offering? Commit yourself fully to One, promise him all your heart and soul, and you won't have to roast in your Christian hell. I have the power to clean your slate and put you on the path to paradise. *One's* paradise."

I tried to laugh meanly at his tirade, but it came out dry and weak. "An objective man would say you're mad."

"Yes," he whispered huskily, his fevered eyes drilling holes into my doubts. "But you're not an objective man, are you, Jacob? I know what fears haunt you, I know what scares the bogeyman. I don't blame you for being doubtful. I was, too, at first, but the evidence is too overwhelming. One is real and he has an afterlife plan for you.

"Think about it, Jacob. No more fear of burning for eternity in lakes of fire, tortured at the hands of some senile, hypocritical god who would condemn you for trying to destroy the very evil he claims to oppose. How can you be loyal to a master who would damn you to eternal pain? How can you serve a god you don't want to believe in?"

His eyes lost some of their fervent intensity, and his voice softened. "I don't want to lose you, Jacob. You're perfect for the set because you're so devoutly ruthless. It takes devout and ruthless men to make a religion work."

I shifted my eyes from Sinn's hypnotic stare to the swirling hues of the screen. "One doesn't care if I'm a killer?"

"Hell, no! We have not affixed to One the burden of petty human moralities. One is not a judgmental or a moral god. He doesn't understand right or wrong—he merely rewards those who serve him and punishes those who do not."

"Did One tell you that or did you tell him?"

He laughed and his eyes dropped. "Indirectly I told him. I define the faith of my flock, and their faith defines the shape of their god." The fingers and thumbs of his hands formed an O. "A golden circle that leads right to paradise." He looked at me through the circle. "So what do you say, bogeyman?" he whispered. "Purpose and paradise or doom and damnation?"

Vertigo tipped me, and I could feel the very foundations of my worldview being shaken, reminiscent of the way I'd felt in a mission an eternity ago. "What would I have to give in return?" I asked.

"Devotion to One. Devotion unshackled by archaic moralities, by questions about what is right or wrong. Just pure, sweet devotion."

I felt adrift, lost in a swirling chaos of crumbling loyalties and cruel, hounding hope. When words finally crept out of my mouth, they sounded strained and faraway. "That's asking a lot."

"In exchange for *eternal paradise?*" He laughed, taking my shoulder. "I know how hard it is. I can recall my own hours of tortuous doubt. You've taken in a lot of information tonight, and you need time to sort it all out."

He turned to the screen and his voice became soft and distant. "Even now it's hard for me to understand," he resumed. "I still wonder what he will look like. I think about it all the time, trying to comprehend something that goes beyond all human experience, but there's no precedent to help me understand."

His voice choked up, and Sinn waved a hand at the shifting pigments, forming and dissolving, and in the flashing glare of his unfinished heaven I watched a tear roll down his cheek. "Just how can a *man* picture a *god?*"

"When will you know?" I asked after a moment.

"It's hard to tell," he said, his voice thick. "It could be a week or a month. We're expanding the Phoenix Program rapidly, working around the clock, sending out a hundred pioneers a day. Next week it'll be three hundred, in two weeks, a thousand. We've already embarked upon a massive advertising campaign to draw public attention to the set. Each week the campaign will intensify, like a growing wave. When that wave peaks, when the fickle, unblinking public eye focuses wholly on the set, it's essential that this screen reveals the face of One. Timing is so important, the difference between failure and...*everything*."

I laughed uneasily. "Today the City, tomorrow the world?"

He wiped away the tears and turned strange eyes to me. "Oh, more than that," he whispered, "much more. Don't underestimate One." He looked at the swirling screen. "There's no limit to what a god can do."

I stared at Sinn as he stared at the screen, consumed. "Well," I said, "I have to get ready for tomorrow."

Sinn didn't say anything, so I left him with his god.

I WALKED back to my quarters in a haze. I went straight to the bar and demanded a drink, not acknowledging the woman sitting cross-legged on my bed.

"Where have you been?" Jackie asked.

I swallowed the screwdriver and ordered another. "I just had a swell talk with Sinn about the Phoenix Program." I collected my second drink and faced her. "Why didn't you tell me One was real?"

"Haven't I always?"

"Yeah, but you never told me there was actual proof. Why didn't you tell me about the Phoenix Program?"

"Sinn didn't think you were ready." She laughed. "Look at you—you look positively haunted."

"Well, Christ," I said. "It's like scoffing at UFO reports all your life, then having a flying saucer crash-land in your living room. Why didn't Sinn think I was ready?"

She arched her brows. "Maybe he was afraid of what it would do to you. Maybe he wanted to see what kind of job you'd do without the promise of paradise."

"I guess he found out. He accused me of trying to stage a purge, then practically said it was okay. There's something I'm not getting, something I can't quite get a grip on."

Jackie laughed. "You sound like a paranoid captain who thinks he's losing command of his ship."

I studied her, unsure of her loyalties. "Is that what's happening?"

"You *are* paranoid," she said, slipping off the bed and moving toward me. "You'd do anything to hang on to the martyrs, wouldn't you?"

"Almost."

"Would you sacrifice heaven?"

I looked at her, then laughed. "I know what you're getting at. I sacrificed my shot at Christian heaven by following my warped sense of justice, so why wouldn't I do it again?"

"Would you?"

"I've made up my mind," I said softly, putting my hands on her shoulders and looking deeply into her eyes. "I'm going all the way this time. There'll be no looking back. I'm dropping every ounce of Christian morality and conscience and marching right into the gates of paradise waving a goddamn banner."

Her hands touched my ribs, then moved up, caressing my chest, my neck. Her eyelashes dipped, her head tilted, and suddenly I was kissing her warm lips, then squeezing her, pulling her closer, biting her neck.

"Oh, Jake," she whispered huskily into my ear, "I've waited so long for this moment, ever since I saw you at the mission. I had to come here tonight, I couldn't wait another moment. And now that you've accepted One, oh, can't you see, it's so perfect now."

"I do see," I murmured, and I did. I kissed the pulse of her throat and held her in my arms and I knew a powerful sense of satisfaction and completeness that had eluded me all my life. "I see everything now. I'm going to heaven with you."

We parted slightly, and her soft black eyes drooped with a genuine demureness that tugged at my heart. "What do you want, Jake?"

I lifted her chin until her eyes looked up into mine. "You, Jackie Pan," I whispered. "I want you. You're all I ever wanted. Just you."

"Tell me how much."

I leaned to her lips, and we kissed softly, gently, a kiss more phantom than real. "More than I know," I whispered, and meant it. "More than heaven itself."

I took her hand and led her to the bed. We stood at its foot, toe to toe, undressing ourselves, our eyes like matches, our sweat like kerosene, the flames rising, until, in flushed and burning nakedness, we lay down into the fire and released the volcanic passions trapped inside.

Making love to Jackie was like being chased by a tiger up a high mountain, clawing at handholds, afraid to look back, in constant danger of plunging to the jagged rocks of failed passion. Then at last, shuddering climax, reaching the pinnacle, that single crystalline moment when everything lay below in perfect clarity before tumbling over the other side, the moment I understood that I loved Jackie Pan completely.

An ashamed sadness passed through me then because I also understood that no future moment would match that instant of perfect realization and surrender, that unique lucid moment when I looked down at the rolling hills of heaven and saw the devil looking up at me.

I awoke to an empty bed and the melancholic self-contempt of a man who, having had paradise placed in his hands, was too weak to hold on to it. I knew then I would spend the rest of my life trying to regain that lost pinnacle of love.

20

We moved down the hall, quickly, quietly. Three doors confronted us, one left, one right, one at the end of the hall. I pointed at myself and the right door, and Slim nodded, continuing down the hall with Brown, Sailor and Nu.

I drove a heel into the door, surprising a man and woman leaning over a humming copy machine. Their eyes flashed to the two submachine guns leaning against a wall.

I shook my head. "Don't do it."

They dived toward the wall, and the speed rifle whirred in my hands. They jerked and groaned, dropping to the floor like punctured sacks of grain. I leaned back into the hall as Nu and Sailor stuck their heads from the other doors.

"Junes?" I asked.

"Nothing," Nu said. Sailor shook his head negative.

"Data and cash search," I said, and they disappeared.

I looked around the room. Computer equipment and printing machines were everywhere; it looked to be some kind of publishing center. I riffled through stacks of leaflets and posters. They were all searing indictments of the Set of One, designed to incite every possible audience. One flyer bewailed One as the Antichrist, another displayed a picture of Sinn with a drawn-on narrow mustache, claiming he was Hitler reincarnated with a meaner disposition. A pamphlet compared the rapid spread of the Set to the AIDS II epidemic of the early twenty-first century. I noticed none of the literature accused One of being a false god.

I collected all the data disks I could find and was about to exit when I heard a small sound. I turned to find the man on the floor watching me. His chest was a bloody mess, yet by some miracle he was still alive. As I walked over to the dying man, his eyes followed me across the room. I sat on my heels next to him, rifle across my knees.

"Sorry about shooting you," I said. "Nothing personal."

He made a shrugging movement with his shoulders and winced with pain. "No hard feelings," he said in a fragile whisper.

I gestured with the rifle. "Want me to put you out?"

"Naw, let me enjoy the sunset."

I nodded. "Still an atheist? Now that you're on death's doorstep?"

"Oh, yeah," he said. "One life's enough for me."

"Mind if I ask you a few questions?"

"I ain't going anywhere."

I leaned closer to him. "What made you decide to stop believing?"

He thought for a moment. "I guess I never met a god I liked."

"You never believed?"

He laughed, bubbling blood from his lips. "I've been a killer since I was twelve. How can a killer believe in God?"

He died before I could finish explaining it to him. I stood up when Nu poked his head in the door.

"We have a prisoner, Jake."

"Junes?"

"No, some kid. She was hiding behind some crates in the storage room. Slim's interrogating her."

"Where's Sailor and Brown?"

"With Slim."

"All right," I said, moving into the hall with him, speaking quietly. "I want you to go out the front door, go around the building and come in through the back door when the time is right. Understand?"

He squinted at me. "How will I know when?"

"You'll know. Do you know what to do?"

He nodded.

I put my hand on his shoulder and looked him in the eye. "I trust you, Nu. That's why I selected you for this mission. That's why there's only the five of us."

He nodded, diverting his eyes. He left me alone in the hall, and I wondered if Slim had got to him, if I'd misplaced my trust. I slipped a full magazine into the speed rifle and walked down the hall.

Brown and Sailor held the girl by her wrists, and Slim held her by her neck. I stood in the doorway and realized I wouldn't be able to shoot them without killing the girl. I began moving toward Slim's back.

"You're going to tell me where Junes is, you infidel little harlot," Slim told her gleefully, "or I'll twist your head from your scrawny little neck."

"Let her go," I said.

"Stay out of this, Strait," Slim said, tightening his grip on the girl's neck. "This is my business."

"She can't answer if she can't breathe," I snarled, stopping directly behind him.

His back twitched at my proximity, then he relaxed, his power assured. "That's *her* problem."

Her face was turning blue, and Slim's breath quickened with excitement as he screwed his hands tighter around her neck. I noticed his hips moved slowly forward and back as if it were a sexual act. Brown's and Sailor's eyes shot between me and the girl, between danger and pleasure.

Slinging the rifle, I grabbed Slim by the back of his neck, driving my thumbs into the nerves under his jaw. He howled with pain but wouldn't let go, so close to gratification. His crotch thrusts quickened, and I dug my thumbs deeper and deeper.

He shrieked with pain and released the girl. He spun around and faced me, holding the sides of his neck. His small black eyes glared at me from his red, sweating face, and he loosed a high-pitched animal scream.

I unslung the speed rifle the same instant Brown and Sailor brought up their rifles, but instead of explosions, a razor-thin hissing silence filled the room.

"Sinn told me you converted last night," Slim said in a low voice, "that you were one of us now. But I knew better— you can fool the old man but you can't fool me." Slim twisted his grimace into an evil smile. "Well, it looks like you're out-gunned, bogeyman." He drew his holstered machine pistol and pulled the girl in front of him. "Three to one. You lose."

A large, violent energy whipped around the cramped room, and I knew it was death looking for a dance partner. Just a trigger's pull from the incomprehensible void, I doubted my chances of getting all three. Their chances of getting me, however, were quite good, and Slim knew it.

"Show time!" Slim cried, crouching lower behind the girl. "It's time for you to exit the big picture, bogeyman. The martyrs will belong to me once again."

"I won't be going alone," I promised, the barrel of the speed rifle tracking his head as it bobbed behind the girl.

"I'm not afraid to die," Slim said, his voice cracking. He squinted at the barrel of the speed rifle, and sweat rolled down his strained face. "I know my place in paradise is secure!"

"Are you sure, Slim?" I stalled, wondering what was holding up Nu. "Are you one hundred percent certain? I think all that pious bullshit rap is a cover for your fear. I don't think you're ready to take that big leap of faith."

His head twisted and turned. "I'm not afraid of death! I'm not afraid of *you!* Shoot him, you *b*-words, *shoot him!*"

The back door crashed open, and Nu leapt into the room, shouting "Who wants to die?"

Sailor and Brown jumped, looking behind them.

"What are you doing, Nu?" Slim said in a slow sing-song voice without turning around.

"Following orders," Nu said. "Sorry, guys."

"Sorry won't feed the hogs," Slim said. After a moment he smiled and dropped his machine pistol into its holster, keeping the girl in front of him. "A misunderstanding is all this was."

"Let her go, then," I said.

Slim shrugged and shoved her to the ground. I started to pull the trigger, but Slim jerked a hand over his head. "Fusion grenade!" he hissed. "Shoot me and we all go up!"

The blinking red of the black sphere in his hand flashed urgently, set to explode on impact. The girl found her breath and feet and backed against the wall of crates. She probably wasn't in her teens yet.

"Get out of here," I told Slim.

"We can't let her go," Slim said, flashing his eyes at the girl. "She'll talk. She's an infidel terrorist."

"She's a child."

Slim screwed up his face at me. "How can you feel zero compassion for the adults and so much for their younger mirror? Do you think their *b*-word offspring will be any different? They'll grow into the same dirty monsters you so love to kill. They're all evil in the end, the black seed planted at birth."

"I don't give a damn about your philosophies," I said. I backed away from the door and gestured with the rifle. "Get out of here."

Scowling, Slim moved to the door, mumbling under his breath. Brown and Sailor followed him out.

"Watch them," I told Nu, and he followed them down the hall. I looked at the girl. She remained frozen against crates.

"Were those your parents up front?" I asked.

She nodded, tears blurring her wide eyes.

"You're an orphan, then. I don't know what to tell you." I started moving toward the door.

"He's right," she whispered. "I'll be just like them."

"Yes," I said. "I know."

I exited the building carefully, wary of an ambush. Nu sat behind the wheel of a gray sedan, the engine idling. Brown commanded the wheel of another sedan, and Sailor sat in the back, smoking a joint.

"Where's Slim?" I asked.

Brown smiled his slow, dead smile. "Don't know, man. Thought he was with you."

I looked at Nu, but he only shrugged and frowned. "He was just here," he said. I turned back to the warehouse just as Slim came out the door, smiling.

"What'd you do?" I said.

"Nothing, bogeyman," he said, leaping in the passenger seat beside Brown. "Nothing at all."

"If you touched her..." I said, moving toward the building.

"Too late," Slim said. "I flamed the place."

There was a huff and the windows of the warehouse blew out, showering me with glass. I stopped in front of the door, where black smoke poured out.

"She's okay," Slim said. "I saw her skipping out the back door, singing." Sailor and Brown laughed, and Slim motioned Brown to drive. "It's been great working for you, *Commander,*" he called out as they sped away. "Stop by the gym sometime, and I'll show you how martyrs are *supposed* to be trained." His laughter followed him out of the lot.

I climbed in next to Nu, and he pulled away in silence. We wound through the warehouse district and onto Hayward, heading uptown. I stared out the window, letting the numbness seep into me.

"We're not the good guys," Nu said suddenly, shaking his head. "And those weren't criminals back there. They were just activists."

"You don't know that."

"I can see, can't I? I know that goddamn little girl wasn't a criminal." As he turned away, I was surprised to see he was crying. "I know *that.*"

I sank down in the seat, weighted by cold, numbing resignation. "Maybe we never were the good guys," I mumbled. "Maybe it doesn't matter what happens down here on this shit planet. It's just what One wants."

He shot me a surprised look. "One? Since when do *you* believe in One?"

I shrugged. "Since I've learned a few things."

"But what about all the shit you say about him?"

"Just because I believe in One doesn't mean I like him."

I looked out the window. "I just want to make it through this shitstorm and go to his heaven, that's all."

Nu wiped angrily at his tears as we slipped into shadow of the set tower's underground garage. "Yeah, I guess that's what it comes down to, doesn't it? What price heaven? Just how much do we have to goddamn pay?"

I looked over at him. "It's never too late to quit, Nu."

He laughed like a madman. "Oh, that's good, Jake, that's rich. You throw me into the goddamn bottomless abyss then tell me it's not too late to crawl out." His laughter stopped abruptly. "Yeah, right."

Nu parked the van and we got out. We started for the elevator and I caught sight of my Oldsmobile lurking like an obsolete ghost among the sports cars and cruisers, squatting where I'd left it before I'd hocked my soul.

"What's wrong?" Nu asked, stopping beside me.

"Nothing," I said. "Go on, I'll be up later."

Nu gave me a strange look, then continued alone.

I walked toward the Olds; it drew me like a magnet. I stopped beside it and ran a hand over the dented hood, the peeling roof. When I reached into my pocket, the keys were there; I'd never lost the habit of carrying them. I opened the door, and nostalgia hit me like a pungent odor. I dropped in the driver's seat, and memories of a smaller, simpler life crowded in with me. Slamming the door, I started it up.

21

I parked in front of St. Christopher's Lounge and stood on the sidewalk, looking up at the windows of my office, smelling the perfume and dried sweat of passing whores, hearing the melodic lures of the porn callers. I stood there and reveled in the images and sounds that had once weaved the tapestry of my life. I put my hands in my pockets and crossed the street, swimming in a river of familiarity. Walking into the lobby was like a Christmas homecoming; each step up the stairs stripped away a layer of time passed by, and stepping into the office was like slipping into a dream.

I stood in the middle of the room for a spinning moment, soaking it all in. I sat in the swivel chair and laid my hands on the desk. I rocked in the chair and laughed; the squeaks were like the voice of a whiny old friend. I looked in the bottom drawer, and yes, there was a bottle of cheap gin next to *The Word of One*. I lifted out the bottle and shut the drawer, then poured a good slug into a dusty cup smelling of vomit. The cheap gin tasted as sweet as forbidden nectar.

I noticed the red eye of the answering machine was winking at me but I turned away. The little box was full of ghosts that I didn't want to acknowledge. I sat back in the chair with my drink and looked for the balance, the balance of good and evil, the final sum of the equation that made up Jake Strait. What did I hold in my hand, and what had I left behind?

All I ever wanted, I thought, *that's what I have.* A full pardon, a killer's redemption, a seat in a new heaven. I gazed around the ugly little room, my horrible little weasel den. I was a wolf hunter now, killing the *big* evil bastards. I was the big man at the controls, the overdog. *I was not only holding the line; I was winning the goddamn war.*

"I have to put all this behind me," I told the ugly little room. "This is a burning house full of garbage. There's nothing worth going back for, nothing I'd die over." I would shed the old reality like a snake shedding an old skin, because if I didn't, it would sure as hell sink its hooks into me and drag me back down. "And I don't want to go to hell," I told the silence. "That's the real bottom line."

I helped the bottle along, and the more I did, the more certain I was of my course.

A ringing woke me up. As the phone rang again, I stared at it. *That'd be the past calling,* I thought blurrily, *or maybe it's my conscience or maybe even hell. I'd be a stone-cold idiot to accept that call.*

"Hello," I said into the receiver.

"I thought we had a deal, bogeyman." His voice had lost all Ivy League pretension, but I recognized it anyway.

"Sorry, Marcus," I said. "There aren't any deals anymore. There aren't even any rules."

"You think you're killing for the good?" He tittered insanely, the laugh of a man on the gallows. "Do you *really* think you're cleaning up the City, bogeyman?"

"So what if I do?"

He laughed again. "You don't know, do you?"

"Know what?"

"We have to meet and talk."

"Talk to the set," I said. "I don't handle public relations."

"I've talked to them already. I told them our deal, and they just laughed. But I knew my man Jake wouldn't be pushing that line. I'm gonna tell you something that's gonna blow your mind. I'm gonna tear your rosy heaven down."

"Where you at?"

"The same place you saw me last. Come in the same way, too—I think someone's watching the front. They might even be listening to us right now."

"I'll be there in an hour."

I hung up the phone and stood, my head still hazy with gin. I knew it could very well be a syndicate trap. But there was something in Marcus's voice that told me he wasn't setting me up. He sounded like a man too close to death to lie.

I looked out the window at the animals in the street. I looked hard for some kind of dent, a tiny ripple of a turning tide. They seemed as arrogant and numerous as when I'd left, and I wondered how much more killing it would take to make them go away.

I WAS ABOUT to get into the Olds when two goons rudely lifted me from the sidewalk and tossed me into a narrow alley. Pinning me against the alley wall, they slapped the pistol out of my hand. A man in an overcoat strolled into the alley and stooped to pick up the gyrapistol in front of me. He balanced it in his hand, his eyes hidden by his immaculate gray fedora.

"Did you want to talk about something, Degas?" I asked.

"As a matter fact I do," Degas said, tilting back his hat

with the barrel of the gyra. "We checked out your missing-hand story."

"And?"

"We found out you were telling the truth. You wouldn't believe how shocked I was. The hand was tossed out with the Shamrock Café's garbage."

"Gee, that's too bad. Now, if you'll excuse me," I said, struggling against his gorillas, "I've things to do."

"They can wait. I want to talk with you about your new job."

I stopped struggling. "Don't lean on me, Degas. You don't know who you're fucking with."

"Oh, but I do. You're quite the big shot these days in the ghoul game. Why, I hear you got a whole brood of gunsels under you now, killing anyone who balks at your rules."

"Somebody has to do your job."

Degas laughed, then leaned into my face. "Listen to me, handchopper. You may think you're the general of a holy crusade, but to me you're still the same sack of shit that used to shoot pushers in the back just to meet your bar tab."

"That's a nifty line," I said. "I'd act more ashamed if I hadn't heard it few times before. Now tell your trained monkeys to let go of my lapels before I knock their heads together like coconuts and send them home bawling for mama."

The monkeys smacked me against the wall three times, then strained to lift me high to show me how well trained they were.

"See?" Degas said. "Now you've upset them. If I wasn't here to restrain them, they'd probably have ripped off your arms and shoved them up your ass by now."

I looked from one scowling goon to the other. "These

fags? If you weren't here, they'd probably be fighting over who would get to kiss me first."

For the next minute it seemed they were trying to rip my arms off. Degas finally calmed them down and put on his death-camp grin.

"You're working for some very ambitious cretins, Strait, too ambitious for their own good. I hate to say it, but I always thought you were smarter than that, in a weasely sort of way." His smile tightened. "Yes, they must have offered you something very special to be their house killer. The benefits must be sensational."

"Sure," I said. "It was the free uniforms that won me over."

"That's very funny. Unfortunately being funny won't save your ass now."

A meanness jumped into my head, and I suddenly tired of being pushed around by a big-mouthed spif and his cheap muscle. "Listen, Degas," I said. "If you're here to offer me occupational counseling, you can save your breath. I'm riding this train to the last stop."

Degas stepped closer until our noses bordered on intimacy. "You got me all wrong, bogeyman," he whispered. "I don't want you to quit. I want you to excel at your new job. I'm so damned interested in your career I want you to keep me posted on how well you and your new friends are coming along."

I laughed meanly. "Oh, it's a *stoolie* you want. Why don't you just send some of your own ferrets up through the ranks? I thought the SPF was good at that sort of thing."

"We've done that. None of them seem to get past their brainwashing program. Would you even believe they turned some of our own people? Sent them right back to spy on *us*. Is that nerve or what? That's why we have to come to shitbags like you."

"Yeah, and you figured you'd just lean on ol' scaredy-cat Jake and I'd start bawling and begging to be your weasel."

"Sure. I know you, Strait. If there was ever a man with a price, it's you, and I've been authorized to make a very high offer."

"Whatever it is, it's not enough."

"That's not the Jake Strait I know. You give us the inside angle on Sinn, and we'll set you up for life. You'll never have to worry about knocking off small-time hoods for booze money again. Maybe even enough to get you out of the City for good. How does that grab you?"

"A nice Party pension, huh? I suppose you'll even throw in a free one-way ticket to the protein vats once I stop being useful. Isn't that how it usually works?"

"Well," he said, "we could just kill you right now."

"But that wouldn't solve anything, would it?"

"It'd make *me* feel better."

"Go ahead, then," I sneered. "You got my gun. Who's stopping you?"

For a long moment he stared at me coolly, and I was beginning to think I'd blundered for the last time. Then anger shot into his eyes, and I knew I was probably going to live.

"You know what really bothers me?" he growled. "How all you creeps think you can invent gods to suit your own petty little concept of what's right or wrong. You're just a bunch of superstitious monkeys building idols with your own shit, terrified your slimy little egos won't have any place to go when you get your ass booted from this world."

"That may be so," I said, "but this monkey's going to heaven."

Degas glared, then turned away in disgust. "Get this piece of shit out of my face before I vomit."

The gorillas gave me a running start down the alley, and I ended up on my face. I got to my feet slowly, and my pistol rattled on the ground beside me. I picked it up and walked away, brushing the filth and grime off my clothes, not bothering to look back.

I couldn't walk right and I was having trouble breathing, and my legs were stiff and my chest tight. *What the shit does he know?* I thought. He was just a spiteful ghost from my past, a black world I no longer belonged to or believed in. I was on the high road now, above it all, walking away from the abyss.

I got into the Olds and powered into traffic. I drove down Hayward between the ranks of mean humanity, the hustlers and whores and thieves and killers of every shape, and for the first time in years I felt separate from them.

"And I ain't going back," I told them. "I ain't ever going to walk with shit-eaters again. I don't care what I have to do down here. None of this shit is real anyway—it's just a big, terrible nightmare. I just got to play One's game, and this monkey goes to heaven." My chest loosened up and I wheeled north. "I gotta remember that."

I parked up the street from the HPA building, then walked around the back. I slipped in from the balcony and moved quietly down the hallway, pistol in hand. The same light filtered from the bottom of the same door, illuminating the two dead men on the floor. Both were tall black men and both had been shot repeatedly in the head and chest.

I stepped over them and put my hand on the doorknob. I heard my heartbeat, then turned the knob slowly, until the latch gave with a tiny click. I pushed the door open with the barrel of the gyrapistol.

Marcus sat at his desk, or at least I thought it was Mar-

cus. A large-caliber bullet or a blunt instrument had caved
in his face, his eyes were gouged out and his ears were
missing. The loop of thin piano wire wound around his
throat and the high back of his chair had cut through his
windpipe to the spine, causing his head to droop forward.
His lips had been cut crudely away from his teeth, revealing the grinning skull inside. Clamped in the teeth was
what looked like a business card. I leaned across the blood-
splattered desk and took the card.

On one side of the card was scrawled: Hi Jake! Glad you
stopped by! Sorry I can't talk right now, but a cat got my
tongue!

I turned the card over. In black typeface it read: Find a
new path in life with the Set of One. Ring us up for a life
counseling today! Don't Delay!!

I stared at Marcus. His head was turned to the left a bit,
and his empty sockets seemed be staring at something behind his desk. I followed his dead stare and found Marcus
was not the only corpse in the room.

The body lay facedown behind the desk, the back of
his black uniform bloody with entry wounds. I came
around the desk and kneeled beside the martyr. I lifted
the head by the short black hair and looked at his face. It
was Nu.

All emotion flushed out of me then; every feeling in my
body rushed right out the bottom of my feet, leaving me
completely hollow inside. I leaned my back against the
wall and slid down to sit beside the body.

"Oh, shit," I whispered, shivering violently, drawing
my arms tight against the icy cold. "What the fuck are we
doing here?" I asked Nu hoarsely. I looked around a room
strange with shadows. "I don't think we belong here, Nu,
I don't think we ever did." A chill shook me to the mar-

row, and I drew my knees up to my chest. "Man, I don't know about you, but I'm getting cold, cold as the grave."

I suddenly scrambled to my feet, listening intently. Somewhere far, far away, I thought I heard the wail and cry of hounds. I jerked my head around but couldn't figure out from which direction they came.

"We gotta get out of here, Nu," I whispered frantically, "because we are sure as hell in the wrong place." I grabbed Nu by the back of his collar and tried to help him. "C'mon, get up," I said, grabbing him under his arms. "We'll go get a drink and figure this whole thing out. I'll bet you're ready to call it quits now, huh? C'mon, for crissakes."

I dragged Nu across the floor to the door, but he wouldn't get up. "Oh, shit," I whispered, letting him go, looking at the blood on my hands. "Oh, shit."

22

I drove to the set tower like a machine, trying not to think about anything. I knew something monstrous was closing the distance. Bare instinct carried me forward now; it would tell me where to go, what to do, who to blame, who to kill.

I parked the Olds in the same space I'd picked it up from, when I'd last seen Nu alive. I took the elevator to the barracks, thinking nothing, just listening to the buzzing in my head.

I found Slim in the barracks, sitting on his bunk, joking with Brown, Sailor and the rest of Fourth Squad. They turned when I entered.

"Well, well," Slim said, smiling as I walked toward him. "It's our errant commander. Where have you been? Out having a little drinky-poo?"

His lips spread for a giggle, and Slim laughing was the last thing I wanted to hear in the world. I hit him in the teeth with a hard right hook, knocking him off his bunk and onto the floor. Hands reached out to help him up, but he shook them off angrily.

"Get up," I told him.

He smiled slowly, touching the blood rising from his mashed lips. He looked at the blood on his fingers and laughed. "No, thank you, Commander. I like it just fine down here. What was that for, by the way?"

"That was for hitting the HPA without my approval." I took a step back and drew my gyrapistol. "And this is for killing Nu."

Fourth Squad jumped, hands reaching for weapons. Martyrs from the other squads reacted, teetering on the brink of mutiny.

"Hold on, now, Commander," Slim said quickly. "Let's not have a bloodbath over a misunderstanding. Your anger is entirely misplaced. Nu was killed by that pimp. He had a hideaway gat in his desk. Why do you think we did such a number on him?" He turned to his pals, who all nodded agreement. "Heck, I liked the kid, you know that. As for the hit on the HPA, you'll have to talk to Sinn about that. He gave the order."

"You're full of shit," I said, but I could feel the cold fury ebbing. I didn't have enough evidence to condemn and publicly execute him. I could also feel the eyes of martyrs upon me, watching their leader crack right in front of them.

"You're the one full of doo-doo," Slim said, knowing he was standing on firmer ground. "You weren't so squeamish about offing those pimps when they had a bounty on *your* head."

"What?"

"That's right. Your pimp pal Hayes had a lot to say before I painted the carpet with his brains. In fact, he asked me to relay a little message to you. He said to tell you that when you got to Hades there'd be something waiting for you. What do you think about that, bogeyman?"

Something clicked in my head. "Did he say Hades or hell?"

Slim frowned. "Hades. What's the difference?"

I looked at the faces around me. "Everything."

I PULLED OVER at the corner of Franklin and Hayward, in front of a long snake of flashing red neon. I got out and looked up at the sign. Hades's Playhouse, the buzzing neon said. More Sin And Pleasure Than You Can Shake Your Stick At!

Hades was one of many HPA franchises, a combination nightclub-bordello a small step above a mattress in a back alley. I entered the dim reception room, where a sloe-eyed mulatto woman looked up as I approached the counter. "You want some sin?" she asked.

"I'm here to pick up a package. From Mr. Hayes."

"Wha's yo name?"

"Jake Strait."

She reached under the counter and retrieved a postcard. "You the bogeyman?"

I looked her over. "You heard of me?"

"Yeah. You killed my brother six months ago."

"Small world," I said, taking the postcard.

"Not small enough," she said, her laugh slow and syrupy.

I turned my attention to the postcard. One side offered a picture of an overweight man suited up as the devil with his meaty arms around two bimbos in topless demon outfits. You'll Find More Than Fire And Brimstone At Hades, the logo promised. Come On Down And See Us Sometime Soon!

On the side you were supposed to scribble daring innuendos there was nothing but an address, a familiar one.

"Is this all?" I asked.

"What else did you expect, honky? A blowjob?"

"Is it so much to ask?"

"Gimme a hundred creds and it won't be."

"Even though I killed your brother?"

"I usually charge fifty."

"I see." I pocketed the postcard and left.

I drove quickly. I didn't know why a dead pimp wanted me to visit a blown-up building, but I was always willing to humor a corpse. When I pulled into the parking lot, the first thing I noticed was that the Rainbow Building looked pretty good for a building that had been recently blown up. In fact, it looked a whole lot like it looked prior to being blown up. After a while I even began to suspect it hadn't been blown up at all.

Two security men flanked the entrance, and I could see more men on the roof manning heavy weapons. Rotors and skimmers took off from the roof at regular intervals, and heavy trucks departed from the rear at a brisk pace. It seemed business as usual at the Rainbow Building.

I parked next to a sports car and approached the young black-uniformed martyrs guarding the entrance. They snapped to attention the moment they saw me coming.

"Good evening, Commander," the braver of the two said, his eyes flickering to my collar.

"Evening, boys," I said, not recognizing their faces. "You two fresh out of indoctrination?"

"Yes, sir," he said. "Graduated last week. Looking forward to martyr training."

"Good, good," I said, looking around. "Any trouble around here?"

"No sir, not really. Some of the Pleasure Syndicate's old customers are having difficulty adjusting, but I think they'll accept the status quo after a few more raids."

"Spoken like a true martyr," I said. "Mind if I come in?"

"Of course not, Commander." He stepped aside and I strolled in.

The automated production lines hummed busily along, and it looked as if most of the damage caused by the raid had been repaired. The place where the fusion bomb should have excavated a five-meter-deep crater was quite level and freshly mopped. At least now I knew why Slim was willing to hang around after the rest of the company left.

A monocled young man spotted me from the bullet-proof office and quickly made his way over. It was the same intense individual with whom I'd discussed the relative merits of poverty and condos.

"I didn't know we were due for an inspection, Commander," he said with an ingratiating smile.

"Just wanted to see how things are coming along."

"Well, we're running at about eighty percent efficiency right now," he reported in an officious voice. "But once the techs get the whole operation sussed out and implement a few modifications of my own device, we'll be producing more in a week than the syndicate did in a month. If you martyrs continue to deactualize the competition, we'll have the market cornered in no time at all."

"Exemplary," I congratulated, watching the squeeze roll down the line. "Deactualizing the competition is what we martyrs are all about. Well, thanks for the report. I'll be sure and put in a good word with Sinn for you."

"Thank you, Commander," he said in a groveling tone, bowing his head repeatedly.

"Not at all," I said, and went back to my car.

23

Sinn sat behind his desk, flanked by Sailor and Brown. A bearded man cringed in a chair in front of them, his face a patchwork of bruises and cuts.

"Commander!" Sinn beamed as I walked in. "Good of you to drop by."

"I need to talk to you," I said, glancing significantly at Sailor and Brown.

"We're all one big family," Sinn said. "Speak your mind."

"All right," I said. "Why wasn't I told about the hit on the HPA?"

"It was a simple operation," Sinn explained. "I was curious to see if the martyrs could operate without the guidance of their illustrious teacher and leader." He drew a black feather from the decanter and examined it closely. "I was also aware you had personal ties with the target group, perhaps had even reached a separate agreement with them. I didn't want to force you to compromise your sense of honor."

"I dropped my honor when I joined the set. I should have at least been told."

"I would have liked to, but you weren't available. You have to realize, Commander, the Martyr Program is ex-

panding so quickly it'll be impossible to keep you informed of everything. Quite frankly, there's going to be a
lot of things going on that you might not have full knowledge of."

"Yes, I know," I sneered. "The machines cranking out
squeeze in the Rainbow Building stand as a shining example."

Sinn's smile leveled out. "Ah, yes, the Rainbow Building. Well, Jacob, I was going to tell you about that, but I
was afraid you wouldn't understand, still burdened as you
are by your twisted sense of morality."

I laughed in his face, good and long. "*You*'re calling *me*
twisted? You? You're so twisted you probably need a cork-
screw to take a shit."

I laughed again, and for the first time I witnessed anger
rising in Sinn. His face flushed crimson, and ugly blue
veins bulged out of his head. His teeth ground, and he
squinted until his eye sockets became tight slits of hate.
The beast was amok in Sinn's heart, and it wasn't a pretty
sight. Just when I expected to see him start sprouting fangs
and fur, the emotion ebbed. Seconds later he was back to
his old self, patronizing smile and all.

"Yes, that's very good," he said, his voice just a little
off key. "But let me explain your misconceptions to you,
Commander. A man is a creature of vice—we have to accept that. If he wants to indulge his less-savory appetites,
he will. And as long as there's a profit to be made cater-
ing to those appetites, someone will be there to take the
risk. That's why every criminal we eliminate will be replaced by another and another. As long as the need is there,
a vacuum will exists."

"And you figured if someone had to fill that vacuum, it
might as well be you."

"Precisely. It's all very logical when you think about it. When we fill that vacuum with our own people, we stop the vicious cycle, thus taking power from the hands of the criminals."

"Yes, but I think you're missing the goddamn point," I said. "Our purpose was to eliminate the criminal underworld, not replace it."

"Oh, calm down. We're not putting on the goat's head, Jacob. We're just, shall we say, diversifying."

"A hostile takeover of the underworld."

"Exactly! It was bound to happen sooner or later. When you agreed to start robbing the criminals after you killed them, the martyrs became part of the underworld food chain, one of the animals. All I'm doing is eliminating the messy killing part and going straight to the well. The set can't afford to run your small-minded little crusade and let the big bucks slip away. Do you know how much capital they're taking in? It's amazing! The City's narcotic and prostitution trades alone gross over a billion a year—it's second only to religion in profit potential. Enough to fund the martyrs for years to come!"

"Until all the criminals belong to the set. What happens then? Just how far does it go, where does it end?"

"End? It's just the beginning! We're just warming up on the criminal world. Soon the martyrs will go after the real enemies of the set!"

"Who?"

"The gods!"

It came to me then, all the ugly lies and more-horrible truths came together, and the big sledgehammer of realization hit me right between the eyes.

"The Cassadys were working for you right up to the moment I shot them," I said, jabbing an accusing finger at him.

"They weren't renegades or blackmailers—they were bombing churches and killing clergymen on your orders. The old gods weren't dying fast enough, so you decided to give them a little push."

"Yes!" Sinn hissed. "That's right. Oh, it was just an experimental program, operated on a small scale, just to see if we could cause a ripple in our market surveys."

"And it did."

"More than we dreamed! We averaged a twelve percent jump in recruitment in each and every city they hit. The concept is so simple it's ingenious. You blow up a church or temple, kill the clergy, and wham! You've created a vacuum of faith. You flood the vacuum with advertising and recruiters, and the dispossessed come flooding into the conversion centers!"

"And now the martyrs will carry out the plan on a grand scale."

"Right! The old gods are down, and you better believe we're going to put the boot in. Josh and Marta were going to be the commanders, but tragically you shot them. It was while we were hunting you and the chip that I realized it was a blessing in disguise. You've given the martyrs something that the Cassadys didn't even understand. You taught them not only how to be superb soldiers, but you imparted just enough bastard conscience for them to attain the perfect killer's mind-set—you gave them the souls of *bogeymen.* You planted a seed that will spread across the entire world, strangling the old gods like deadly vine. Just think of it, Jacob, the entire planet under one god. No more religious wars, no more militias gunning down children in the streets because they call their god by a different name."

"With you on top, calling all the shots."

Sinn slapped the desk and jumped up. "That's *right!*"

he shouted. "Me! Who else has the power to get this world in order? Not the Party, not the SPF, not you cheap killers. It takes the power of a living *god* to get humanity in line, and that god is *me!*"

"You mean *One,* don't you?" I said.

He stared at me a moment, his mouth frozen open, his neck muscles strained, face gorged with blood. He dropped his eyes and sat down slowly. "Of course I meant One." He folded his hands on the desk. "But I can see you're still carrying those old crosses of morality," he said quietly. "You have yet to realize that crap won't buy you a ticket into One's heaven or save your soul from the hell you fear so much. There are no puzzling rules or mores or rituals. All you have to do is faithfully serve One. Period. As long as you do as I tell you, you *will* be saved."

He leaned back in the chair. "Is it really so hard to trade this miserable existence in for infinite paradise? I really don't think I'm asking that much of you." He squinted at me. "You don't *want* to go to hell, do you?"

I thought about it, about all the different kinds of hell, here on Earth and otherwise. "No," I said. "I'm pretty sure I don't want to go to hell."

"Super!" Sinn said sarcastically. "I'm glad you were able to figure that much out. Now, if you don't want to go to hell, if you don't want to burn for eternity, what must you do?"

"Stick with One."

"Hallelujah! You've made it! The great big leap of faith! Welcome aboard. Things are about to intensify in the martyr division, and we need all our soldiers, especially the leaders, *with* the program. Are you *with* the program, Jake?"

"Yes." I nodded slowly. "I guess I am."

"Excellent. I'd like you to do me a favor, then." He pointed the black feather at the bearded man. "I'd like you to kill Mr. Dylan for me."

I glanced at the battered poet. "Get Slim to do it."

"But I want *you* to. I trust you, Jake. There's a strange sense of loyalty in you that goes beyond serving the power that feeds you. You have that vicious brand of *faith* that has always fascinated me. Go with Sailor and Brown—I want you to remove this thorn in the side of One, this evil fool."

I regarded Junes Dylan. His eyes were nearly swollen shut, and his face was turned to the floor. By his expression I could see he had already accepted death. "I don't like shooting poets," I said.

Sinn released a long, disappointed sigh that petered out into a stiff silence. "Jacob, Jacob, Jacob. I thought you understood that you don't *need* any moral excuse to kill One's enemies. But I see the adjustment is going to take a little time. Very well. If you need a cheap moral rationalization, Junes here is also an arsonist and a murderer." He turned cold eyes to Junes. "Aren't you, poet?"

Junes dropped his chin to his chest. "One must do what has to be done."

Sinn laughed harshly. "Yes, doesn't One. Besides penning some very ugly anti-One literature, Mr. Dylan was also captured in the process of setting fire to one of our publishing centers. Three set faithful died in the fire." He looked to Junes. "Am I right, *poet?*"

"Sometimes," Junes said, "to save the angels, one must employ the methods of the devil."

Sinn's face suddenly flashed with hate. "That's a fine line coming out of your atheist mouth, poet. Get this godless charlatan out of here."

Sailor and Brown jerked Junes to his feet and dragged him away. I rose and went to the door.

"Great men can't think of the little things," Sinn said to my back. "They can't afford to. If you focus on the petty aspects of anything, you become nearsighted and lose your ability to see the big picture. Don't forget what you have gained, Jake, and what you have lost."

"A conscience for a soul, eh, Sinn?"

"Not a bad trade when you think about it. The two seldom go well together anyway."

I looked up at the black glass above Sinn's office. A twisted reflection leered back at me. "No, I guess they don't." I opened the door and went outside.

Sailor and Brown had Junes pinned against the wall of the reception room, and Slim was in his face. "You're lucky it's not me who's going to do you, you dirty blasphemer," Slim said. "I'd make it last, have you croaking poems of horror and death through a broken jaw and a mouth full of shattered teeth. I'd have you—"

"Shut up," I snapped. "And get the hell away from my prisoner."

Slim blinked, ground his jaw, then backed away from Junes. He bowed his head mockingly. "I defer to my intrepid teacher."

"I didn't teach you shit," I said. "Take him to the van." Sailor and Brown hustled Junes away while I squared off with Slim.

Slim said, "I hope you don't go soft and blow this one, bogeyman. Sinn might not tolerate another display of gutlessness."

"You're really hot after my job, aren't you, scumbag?"

He smiled. "I have only One's interests at heart. Wherever I serve my god best, there I will be."

"Sure you don't want to come along?"

He stared at me. "No, thanks, bogeyman. I think you have enough on your hands."

WE DROVE JUNES to a rail yard where the trains didn't run anymore. Sailor and Brown dragged him across the gravel lot to the tracks, and I followed, watching the puffs of dust my boots kicked up. Giggling like schoolgirls, Sailor and Brown forced Junes to his knees on the rotted ties between the rusted rails. I stopped in front of him, drawing my pistol. The poet closed his eyes to the light of the setting sun, and I pointed the barrel at his forehead.

I knew the execution was a test of faith, the last linger at the crossroads. It wasn't just Junes I would murder; it was what was left of my conscience, my past. Once I started down that darker road, there could be no looking back; my soul would belong to One and no other. And this monkey would go to heaven.

"Go ahead," Sailor said impatiently. "Blow his brains out."

"Yeah, man," Brown said. "Give the poet a bullet lobotomy."

As I stared at the patch of skull where the jet would enter, I visualized the simple pulling of the trigger, the explosion of gore spraying across the rotted ties.

"C'mon," Sailor snarled, glaring at me. "Shoot! Pull the damn trigger, *Commander!*"

"Slim said you'd pussy out," Brown said, "you pussy-ass pansy, limp-dick—"

"Shh!" I said, cocking my head. "Listen!"

Sailor and Brown looked around. "What?" Sailor said.

"Don't you hear it?" I whispered.

"Hear what?" Sailor asked.

"A train," I said. "A train's coming."

They looked up and down the tracks. Brown said, "I don't see no train."

"No, this way," I said, shooting Brown in the throat. Sailor backed away, clawing for his pistol. The gyra whooshed twice, and he pitched across the rails, his ruptured lungs and heart bare to the sunset.

After a moment Junes opened his eyes and blinked. "Is this the afterlife?" he croaked.

"The afterlife, yes," I said. I sat on a rail and ran a hand through my hair. I looked at the long shadows the dying sun cast across the rail yard and realized night was not far away. "I read a poem of yours once," I said. "A poem about heaven and hell."

Junes thought a moment, then said:

"Lie down not with lions tamed
Goodness and virtue is for the vain
In sin you'll find greater fame
For heaven lost is hell gained."

"Yes," I said. "Heaven lost." I looked at the horizon. The low clouds burned with a deep crimson, as if heaven itself were aflame. "Get out of here," I said.

His head jerked up. "What?"

"Get out of here."

Junes rose slowly, watching me. "Thanks," he mumbled, then shuffled away quickly, shoulders hunched, afraid to look back.

When he disappeared, I picked up a handful of gravel and let it sift between my fingers. "Well, bogeyman," I said. "What are you going to do now?"

I started walking down the railroad tracks, contemplating the failure of another dream. There didn't seem to be any crossroads in front of me, just a long series of bridges that crossed and recrossed the same stagnant river, each exploding into flame behind me until the river was black with ash and cinder. I walked between the rusted rails, stepping from tie to tie, bit by bit, stage by stage, working my way back to something. I didn't know what that something was; I only knew I had to find a circle that would hold me.

24

It was early in the morning, so it took a moment for Heidi to answer the door. When she did, I shoved my way in and threw the bolt behind me. I peered around a dim interior lit only by the gray, jumpy light of a small black-and-white TV.

"Has anyone come around?" I whispered.

"Who?"

"The goon squad. The goddamn wolf pack."

"No," she said nervously. "What's wrong with you?"

I went to the window, parted the venetians slightly and peered outside. All the killers on the street below looked local. "The set is after me."

"The set? What have you done?"

"Plenty," I said, closing the blinds tight and turning around. I spoke in a whisper and couldn't seem to stop. "I pawned my ticket to paradise to get my conscience out of hock. But I think it's busted, and I don't know how to fix it."

"Jake, what are you talking about?"

"I shot two martyrs and let loose One's archenemy yesterday. I spent the night under a railroad bridge." I lit a vitacig and moved into the kitchen. "Now I'm on the run and I need a drink."

"All I have is dinner wine."

"That'll do."

Heidi pulled an open bottle of white from an otherwise empty refrigerator. I took it from her before she could find a glass. I let a third of the bottle roll down my throat, then leaned back against the cupboards.

"Is getting drunk a good idea?" she asked.

"Sometimes you have to be drunk to be alert to certain things. Your flowers have died."

She turned to the withered tulips and petunias in the box near the window. "Yes. A blight killed them."

I looked at the soil. It looked as hard and dry as baked clay. I walked the bottle of wine to the armchair in front of the glowing TV. The brightness was turned too high, so it was like staring into the belly of a white-hot furnace.

Heidi came up behind me and put her arms around my neck. "I warned you this would happen if you joined her," she whispered in my ear.

"I blame that cruel pimp Fate. He tricked me."

"It's always someone."

"That's right. You know, I always suspected all the gods were against me. At least now I know for sure."

Her fingers kneaded at the tightness of my neck. "What are you going to do?"

"I don't know. There's not many places I can run. There are weasels in every bolt hole." A bleached-out rerun of an early Party sitcom jumped on to the screen with a roar of canned laughter. "Boy, I *really* screwed up this time. If I hadn't been so wrapped up in clawing and scratching to fix this miserable world, if I hadn't screwed up my chances at a good Christian afterlife, I would never have sold so much of my soul to One. Now so many gods hate me I'm not even sure whose hell I'm going to."

Heidi sighed. "Why must there be gods and devils and heavens and hells?"

"Because none of this horrible shit would make any sense if there wasn't. I mean, I couldn't have screwed up this much on my own."

"I think you're underestimating yourself. You know, if you'd accept we just blink out when we die, your life would be much simpler and happier."

"Just blink out, huh?" I said. "Like a lightbulb?"

"That's right."

"I'd rather burn in hell."

"That's your ego talking." Heidi's fingers squeezed the muscles of my neck, her hips warm against my back. "Look how tense you are," she soothed. "You need to relax."

Her fingers plied my bunched muscles, squeezing out the stress and tension like water from a sponge. "Relax," she whispered, and I began to drift. "Let all the fear and stress slip away. There's just you and me and we're safe here. Safe from everything."

Tension began to melt from my spine, and the angry buzzing in my head faded. On the TV a man wearing an outdated style of Party uniform whacked a fat corporationist with a rubber chicken, and I chuckled along with the laugh track.

"See," Heidi said. "Things aren't so bad." Her hair touched my shoulders as she lowered her head to whisper, "We could go to the bedroom."

"We could?" I murmured, tranquility and peace spreading through me like a drug.

"Sure," she cooed. "I can show you some new tricks."

"New tricks?" I said, pleased and completely relaxed. The sitcom melted into a commercial. An albino Sinn sat at his delicate desk, wearing a shimmering gold exec suit. "Hello, citizens!" he shouted.

I sat up quickly, startling Heidi. I shrugged her hands from my neck and leaned toward the set, turning the brightness down.

"Our competitors tell you to have faith," Sinn said. "They tell you to trust in things you cannot see, to believe in gods they cannot show, in promises that fade before the light of reason and truth." Sinn spread his hands and stretched his charming smile. "Yes, they treat you just like a bunch of blind, retarded, stupid *fools*."

He slapped the desk and stood up suddenly. "Well, you don't have to take it anymore! You can now put your faith in a new *improved* god!"

"Is that him?" Heidi whispered.

"Yes," I said.

"But," Sinn said, calming down, "why should you believe us at the Set of One? How am I any different from all the charlatans and con men who would lead you astray? Where is our *proof?* Well, I'll *show* you!"

He snapped his fingers and suddenly stood next to one of the resurrection chambers. "Do you know what happens in these chambers?" Sinn asked, touching it with a hand. "*People die!* Our postdeath pioneers have breached the greatest barrier known to man. That's right. Big scary ol' *death*. They venture into the vast reaches of the cosmos, range deep into the dark unknown—" his voice dropped to a low, reverent whisper, and the camera panned to a close-up of the attractive, well-groomed pioneer inside the resurrection chamber "—they explore the hereafter, then return to tell us what they saw. And what have these brave heroes to report? Well, let's ask our esteemed director of postdeath research, Herb. Herb?"

The camera panned, and Herb stepped into the picture, his face smooth with makeup. "After many thousands of documented accounts from our pioneers," Herb said in a deep, authoritative voice that sounded altered, "there can only be one conclusion—One exists! And what's more, One says there's lots of open space out there, plenty of room for *everyone,* sinner and saint alike!"

"Room for you!" Sinn exhorted, stabbing a finger at the camera. "Join the Set of One, and we will *unconditionally guarantee* you, yes, *you,* a place in paradise, regardless of all past sins. You heard me right! Unconditional guarantee! Complete forgiveness! Clean slate! Paradise! We'll put it in writing!"

An official-looking document in a gilded frame popped into Sinn's hand, and he pointed it at the camera. "Here it is, your ticket to paradise! How'd you like to have *this* hanging on your wall!" The excitement faded, supplanted by a quiet melancholy. Sinn linked his hands behind his back as he wandered away from the chamber, eyes on the floor.

"Ah, but I'll bet some of you, well, let's face it, a *lot* of you, remain skeptical. And I don't blame you, considering how long you've been swindled, duped and boondoggled by false prophets out for an easy buck. Well, I'm going to make you a promise, just between you and me. In the coming days I will present to you *definite* proof of One's existence, proof so irrefutable, proof so substantiated, you'll just *have* to believe." He dropped his melancholy like a used napkin and finished with a big winning smile and a wave. "See you then!" The screen faded back to the sitcom.

"Is this a City or World Party station?" I asked, rubbing my temples. My mind felt dull and itchy as if I'd just watched a Flash TV segment.

"City Party."

"Has it played on the World Party stations?"

"No, just locally."

"For how long?"

"Just since yesterday, I think."

I held my head in my hands and let the pieces jumble together. "Oh, Jesus, now I'm *really* screwed. The City Party and set are working together."

"Why would the Party take up with the set?"

"Maybe Sinn made the directors an offer no one else could. The fact that he's not broadcasting globally means the City is probably Sinn's test bed. If it works here, he'll sell the idea to other cities, maybe the whole World Party. He told me he was going to unite the world under one monotheistic banner, and now I know how."

Heidi giggled nervously. "The commercial isn't *that* good."

"It doesn't have to be—they're using subliminal bombardment."

"Who doesn't? They're just making the same claims as every other religion."

"Yeah, but they just might be able to back up their claims with heavy evidence."

Silence drifted for a moment. "What are you saying?"

"I'm saying One just might be real and Sinn just might be able to prove it. Judging by the commercial, I'd say he's getting ready to spring something on the public. And I think I know what."

Heidi moved around the front of the chair suddenly and took my hands, crouching in front of me. Her face creased with worry, her troubled eyes looked into mine. "Let's run away, Jake," she whispered. "Let's leave all of this behind. I have money, enough so we can run and run and never have to look back. We'll find paradise and stay there forever."

"Everybody wants to run away to paradise. That's what's wrong with this world. Nothing is ever put straight, and justice is backlogged right back to hell."

"I don't care about the rest of the world. I care about you, us. Why do you have to sacrifice yourself for a society that you hate and hates you?"

"Boy, you sure have changed," I said, standing up, suddenly restless. With the Party and set united, the hounds had doubled in number. I could almost hear them baying outside the door.

"You opened my eyes to the way the world is," she said.

"You shouldn't have listened to me. Cynics make the worst teachers." I began pacing the floor. "I stayed up all night thinking about this. It's up to me to stop them."

"Why you?"

"Because I built the goddamn bridge that helped them get this far. I was chasing some crazy dream about cleaning up the City through sheer firepower, and all the while they were setting me up to knock off Jehovah, Allah and the rest. I have to burn the bridge and wipe this goddamn blood off my hands, or the hounds will never leave me alone. I'll self-destruct."

The phone rang in the kitchen. I looked at Heidi. She looked confused. "No one calls here," she said.

I moved into the kitchen and picked up the phone. "Hello?"

"This the morgue?" a muffled voice asked.

"No," I replied.

"Sure about that?"

The line went dead.

"Who was it?" Heidi hissed.

"A warning," I said. I went to the window and peeked outside. "Oh, Christ."

"What's wrong?"

She came to the window, and I pointed at three gray vans parked in front of the Complan. "Martyrs. They've found me."

I rushed to the bedroom and looked out the rear window. A gray sedan idled in the alley, smoke curling from its exhaust. "Ah, yes, they've learned their lessons well."

"How did they know you were here?"

I moved back into the living room. "They probably figured this would be the first place I'd run." I looked at her. "Or maybe they're after you."

"Why me?"

"Jackie knows you sent me to rescue her."

Terror crossed her face. "How?"

"Some dirty bastard must've finked," I said, peeking back out the front window. It was impossible to tell if there were martyrs inside the vans or if they'd already entered the building. "She may just want you as a hostage. Bait to draw me in." I turned from the window, drew my pistol and checked the magazine. "If they follow my teachings, they'll send a team up the stairs and another up the elevator, leaving security in the lobby and in the back. There'll probably be another squad arriving by rotor on the roof."

"We're trapped, then."

"Not necessarily. They've already lost the element of surprise. We have a chance, but only if we act fast."

I went to the door and peered out the peephole. As much of the hallway as I could see was empty.

"What are you going to do?" Heidi asked.

"We'll take the stairs down a floor, then catch the elevator. We'll take whatever car isn't going up."

"What about the martyrs in the lobby?"

"I'll have to kill them." I opened the door, poked my head out and looked both ways. It was clear. "Let's go," I said, and slipped outside.

We hurried down the hall toward the stairwell. I put my ear to the fire door and listened. Silence. I opened the door a crack and peeked out. Nothing.

We descended the stairs swiftly, the gyra leading the way. We made the next floor, where I peeked into the hall. An old lady waited near the elevators. She didn't appear to be carrying a weapon. I opened the door, and we moved quickly to the elevator. One indicator said a car was descending from three floors up. The other said a car was ascending from the lobby.

"Jake," Heidi whispered. "Maybe it'd be best if we surrendered."

I gaped at her. "You're kidding."

"Well, think about it, Jake. If we surrender we might die, but there's only two of us. If we shoot our way out, many will die, perhaps even us."

"You haven't much of an ego, do you? Personally I'd rather have them die than me."

"That's very selfish."

"That's human nature." I noticed the old lady was staring at me. "What do you think?" I asked her.

She jerked her head forward and stared at the elevator doors. "I agree with the young lady," she said. "It's wrong to kill."

"It's more wrong to get killed," I said. The elevator chimed, and I leaned against the wall, pulling Heidi with me. The old lady scuttled to the other side of the door. The doors slid open and we all peered inside. It was vacant. The old lady looked at me and I nodded. "Looks okay to me," I said.

She glared as we all moved inside. The old lady pushed the button marked Lobby. As the doors began to close, Heidi jumped back into the hall. "Sorry, Jake. I can't be party to murder."

I made a grab for her arm, but smacked my knuckles on the closed doors. I wrestled with angst as we began to descend.

"What about you?" I asked the old lady as she backed into a corner. "Will you be party to murder?"

She shook her head vigorously. "Most certainly not."

"You better get off on the second floor, then."

"I am going to the lobby!" she said, her upper lip stiffening noticeably.

"Suit yourself," I said. I began checking the action of the gyra and loosening up my shoulder muscles. "Don't forget to duck."

She glared disapprovingly at the pistol and became more and more alarmed as we neared the lobby. Four floors from the lobby, I increased my breath rate and did some hops to jack up my heartbeat. The old lady shrank away, looking as if she expected me to make a lusty grab for her.

At the last possible moment, she jabbed at the button marked Two. The elevator doors opened, and she leapt into the hall. "Hooligan!" she muttered, and the doors closed.

She'd like me if she got to know me, I told myself. The elevator started moving again, and a restless, repressive silence crowded into the tiny room with me. There didn't seem enough air to go around. I imagined a lobby full of martyrs with me moving through them like a perfect knife, charging, ducking, shooting, an unstoppable killing machine. A low growl rose from my stomach as the first mean wave of adrenaline hit me like an amphetamine rush. My muscles tensed, my brain filled with a murderous red haze, I leaned toward the doors and, like the gates of hell, they opened.

I surged into the lobby, empty except for a clerk at the desk who didn't notice me or the gun in my hand. I stood on the carpet, breathing like a locomotive, blinking at invisible enemies. I exhaled a great breath, the kill energy seeped out of my muscles, and I jammed the pistol into my coat pocket.

I took five steps, and a dozen casually attired martyrs charged into the room, fanning out into a semicircular firing line, machine pistols pointed at my head and chest. Sinn stepped into the middle of the circle, resplendent in a shimmering blue robe, his head covered with a loose hood.

"Jake, we've found you!" Sinn shouted as if I were his long-lost amnesiac billionaire brother.

I paused before the phalanx of weapons, daunted by the sheer odds against dodging so many bullets. "Do I know you, mister?"

Sinn shook his head sadly, moving toward me. "Dear, dear Jacob." He stopped three steps away and spread his arms in a fatherly manner. "Don't you recognize your prophet? When we first met, you were a broken man without mantle or reason. But I looked inside and saw a wonderful psychopath held back by a lame conscience and a misplaced fear of hell. I freed you from those burdens, and look how far you'd come before being tragically undone by unsavory intrigues and moral traps. I know we have our differences, but it's nothing we can't work out. We need you back, Commander. It hasn't been the same without you. The martyrs miss you, I miss you."

"I miss you, too," a voice said, and I looked behind me to watch Jackie step off an elevator with another half-dozen martyrs. She brushed past me and took her place beside her prophet. She smiled seductively, and her abject beauty hit my willpower like a mean hammer. "Very much," she purred. "Come home, Jake. Come back to One."

Our eyes locked intimately, and I burned with conflicting fires. *I could go back,* I thought dizzily. *I could have it all—paradise, purpose, love, everything.*

"How do you know One would take me back?" I said. "I kind of screwed him over."

"How do I know?" Sinn said, and more than a little madness jumped into his eyes. "Why, my dear Jacob, he told me so!" He threw back his hood, revealing his freshly shaved mohawk. Above each ear was a red circular rash the size of a small saucer. "Do you see, Jake?" he whispered. "Right after you left yesterday, I went and had a little chat with One. I saw him, touched him, I know what he wants."

The light of madness grew in his eyes until it illuminated his entire face. "I want you to know him, too, Jake, I want all my top people to understand." He took a step toward me. "He wants to talk to you, Jake, he told me so. Go see him, and you'll never have to be afraid or confused about anything ever again."

I looked into the bonfire of his insanity and I hesitated at the crossroads once again: down one road lay salvation, meaning and the love of a beautiful woman; down the other lay doom, death, loneliness and the heavy cross of conscience. I was about to take the first step when an image came to me, the image of Leo's face when he'd come back. The unspeakable horror in his eyes, the terrible mien of a man who had looked over the brink into hell. *He tried to eat me!*

"I don't know," I said, moving slightly to put Jackie and Sinn between me and most of the guns. "I kinda like being confused and scared. It reminds me I'm alive."

Jackie shook her head with disgust. "You know, Jake, you had it all—wealth and power in this world, paradise and immortality in the next. You traded all that for pain and damnation. How can someone be so horribly stupid?"

"Stupidity is its own defense," I countered, and through the lobby windows, like an angel from heaven, a yellow taxi appeared over Jackie's shoulder, parking between two set vans across the street.

Sinn sighed and approached me with slow, careful steps. "Don't you want to go to heaven?" he asked, stopping a step away. "Don't you realize I have your ticket—" he reached out an empty hand "—right here in my hand?"

"That's a coincidence," I said, "because I have a ticket for you, too, right here in my hand." I pulled out the gyra-pistol.

"Mensch!" Jackie screamed, and the hand holding the gyra became extremely heavy, so heavy it fell to my side. I tried to move the connected arm, but it seemed to be made of lead. I frowned dumbly at the traitorous limb, then reached for the pistol with my left hand.

"Tensch!" Jackie barked, and the left arm fell heavy and limp. I looked at both arms, then at Jackie. "What are you doing to me?"

"You're a spiritual cripple," Jackie sneered. "It was only a matter of time before your infirmity manifested itself in physical form."

Sinn took the last step between us, arms wide to envelop me. "Come to One, Jake, he will heal you. Now and forever."

I lowered my head and charged him like a bull. He dodged to the right and I scurried past, arms flapping like wet towels at my
sides.

"Don't shoot him!" Sinn shouted, and the group of martyrs surged forward like a pack of stat-hungry linebackers. I hunched my shoulders and leaned into a break in the line, driving between two groping martyrs, sending them sprawling. Another martyr leapt on my back, but I twisted like an eel, shaking him off. I bounded out the door and stumbled down the steps, beelining for the cab. I could hear the boots of scrambling martyrs behind me and Jackie's voice.

"Lensch!" she screamed, and my right leg became a stiff lead pole. I caught myself with my good leg and hobbled toward the cab, dragging my right leg behind me.

"Open the damn door," I bellowed, dropping against the side of the cab. The startled cabbie reached across the seat and threw open the passenger door. I launched myself inside, and martyrs collided with the door, crushing my numb leg.

"Step on it!" I shouted, and the cab screeched away from the curve. A martyr held on to the door handle for half a block, then tumbled to the rushing asphalt. I crawled across the seat like a lame snake, and the door slammed behind me as we took a hard left turn.

"What the hell happened to you?" the sweating cabbie asked nervously, hunched against the wheel, peering fearfully into the rearview mirror.

"A god smote me," I said, trying to catch my breath. "Have we lost them?"

"I think so. Where we going?"

"Just drive," I said, "until I get my body back."

Feeling started to return less than an hour later. By the time I'd ran up two hundred creds on the meter and the driver had told me the unabridged version of what exactly the hell was wrong with the world, my body, if not my soul, was more or less my own.

25

The cabbie dropped me off behind the fortress that was SPF central. I lurked near the entrance of the underground garage until a car passed inside. I scuttled along its passenger side, crouching low so the guard working the barrier wouldn't see me.

I skulked down to the third level and hunkered down between the wall and the bumper of a rusting hulk. An honest cop's car, I thought, or one who tried hard to appear so. Less than an hour later my wait ended.

"Hello, Degas," I said, rising from my crouch.

Degas turned on me slowly, keys in the door, expression blank. His dead eyes went to the gun in my hand, then up to my face. "Beat the Reaper again, Strait?"

"By a rather bizarre stroke of luck. Thanks for the warning, by the way. It was a little late, but I figure it's the thought that counts."

"Why would I warn you? I don't even like you."

"I'm not concerned about the why. I just want to know when you started working for them."

"I don't have to tell you anything."

I leaned back on the hood. "Well, the tables are turned now, aren't they? What'd they promise *you*, Degas?

Money? Power? A postdeath pension? What does it take to turn a cheap flatfoot into One's lapdog?"

"Screw you," he said.

I pushed the gyra's snout at him. "I want some answers or I'll shoot you."

He sneered at the pistol. "A minute later and you'd be dead."

"Believe me, I've nothing to lose."

"Do it, then. Pull the trigger." He stared at me, as impassive as stone. I could hear the steady drip of a leaking pipe, a car starting above us and a distant exchange of voices. "You've really lost it, haven't you, bogeyman?" he taunted.

I lowered the pistol. "Ah, screw you. You didn't do such a good job shooting me when you had the gun." I started walking away.

"They wouldn't let me," Degas said.

I turned around. "Let you what?"

"Shoot you. The directive came down last week. Full cooperation with the set. Right from the top."

I rubbed my jaw. "You weren't trying to roust me, you were checking up on my loyalty."

"Yeah, and you passed with flying colors. Where's all that sneering devotion now? That's the difference between you and me. I do stupid and evil things because I'm told to. You do them because you're stupid and evil."

"It's that cruel pimp Fate, I tell you. What was on Cassady's chip?"

Degas stared at me, then something gave in his eyes— a bridge was crossed. "Contacts, safe houses, account numbers, munition caches. Everything you need to run a terrorist operation. The City was just a stopover. They were just beginning their world tour when you lucked on to them. There was enough evidence on that chip to put a death warrant on Sinn and turn his tower into a hole in the ground."

"Since when does the SPF need evidence?"

"The set has some highly placed members within the Party who might object. But as long as we had proof the set was making a power play, they'd have to keep their mouths shut."

"How did you find out about the chip?"

"Junes Dylan told us."

"So that's why Sinn was so hot about taking him out. How'd Junes know?"

"The Cassadys once belonged to Faith No More. After they converted to the set, Junes kept tabs on them. He was losing a lot of his members to Sinn and wanted to know why. Junes also claimed to have an agent high up in the set hierarchy."

"Who?"

"Junes wouldn't tell us."

"And when Junes came to you a couple of days ago, you set him up for the set to capture."

He nodded. "He wanted us to help him flame some set buildings. I guess his agent forgot to tell him about the new allegiances."

"That's because he's a double agent. Sinn turned him. What made the Party team up with the set, anyway?"

"The same reason the Party has ever done anything. To stay on top. They don't care which banner the masses rally around, just as long as they rally."

"So the Party gets another means of control, and the set gets use of the Party propaganda machine."

"Among other things."

I leaned against his wreck and took it all in. "Well, at least I know just how far up shit river I am."

"You gonna do something about it?"

"Maybe. Is your interest personal or professional?"

He didn't answer.

"Thanks for the data," I said, and started off.

"Good luck, bogeyman," he said, and I thought I actually heard embarrassed sincerity mixed in with all the sarcasm.

I CAUGHT A CAB to the corner of Hayward and Bukowski. The noon sky flashed and rumbled with SPF air strikes against the southern boroughs. People along Hayward stood on the hoods of parked cars, oohing and aahing at the more spectacular explosions. The Christian and Muslim militia lands in Barridales and Riverside were getting a good pounding, and I wondered just how far the Party was willing to go for the set.

When I called Heidi's apartment from a combooth, a male voice answered. I hung up and walked half a block to a Party Bank cred dispenser. I scanned into my account and skimmed off the maximum-allowed two thousand credits from the nest egg the set had deposited. I put the plastic and my hands into my pockets and brooded on the corner of Hayward and Bukowski.

Well, now, I thought, gazing around, *let's take a look at the situation. On the down side, all the gods are mad at me and I'm being hunted by a huge violent religion, its superbly trained militia, the criminal underworld and the SPF. On the up side, I have credit, a gun, and nowhere to run. Which means there's no place they can wait for me.* I looked around some more. *Yes, sir, definitely no paddle on this trip up shit river. No paddle, no plan, no ticket to paradise.* I sighed and started down Bukowski. It was high time to seek spiritual advice.

It was immediately evident the City's damned soul had taken a meaner turn. The neon temples and carny churches appeared to have had a change in management; the video preachers now extolled One as the oversoul, coin-fed confession booths now demanded change for One's forgiveness. The street corners were bare of ghetto prophets and whiskey evangelists, most of the missions were either boarded up or bearing One's sign, and the sidewalks were rife with winos with mohawks and red circular welts on the sides of their heads.

The closer I walked to the original Set of One Resurrection Mission the thicker they got, until I stood across the street from the mission itself. They swarmed around its front like bees around a hive, on the move, possessed with restless and directionless energy, moving yet always returning to the mission.

The neon Jesus hadn't fared too well in the new order. His steel torso was battered and dented, his right arm torn from its socket, his head hung sorrowfully on his left shoulder, dangling from a snake's nest of wires. Both neon eyes had been jabbed out, and his chrome teeth had been forcefully extracted.

Zach's kiosk next to the mutilated messiah had also been victimized, its plastic exterior battered and burned. Heretics Die and Charlatans Out! was crudely spray painted across the closed shutters, and I heard a rustling sound inside. I knocked on the shutter and the rustling sound stopped.

"Who is it?" a voice whispered.

"A customer," I said.

"Shop's closed."

"I need some help."

"Sorry, but I'm going out of business."

"I thought business was good."

"That was before a jealous god decided to lean on me," the voice said, and the shutters parted an inch, then slid open. The mystic hipster peered fearfully across the street, then resumed packing his inventory into plastic boxes. "Do me a favor and tell me if these punk zombies start acting funny."

"All right," I said, leaning back against the booth. The winos continued to mill. "What happened to Jesus?"

"The zombies stomped him," he said. "The same bastards that attacked my place. It happened all at once. Screaming Jesus was laying out his usual spiel when all of a sudden one of them whacks Jesus on the head and then they all just fell on him like a pack of robot sharks."

"Weird," I said.

"Oh, yeah. At first I wasn't too concerned, you know. I was a little tired of hearing that bastard's voice anyway, then all of a sudden they turned on *me*. I barely got the shutters closed in time. Funny thing is, I used to know some of those bastards, before they turned into zombies." He grabbed a stack of boxes and carried them out the back door to an alley. He loaded the boxes into a minivan and returned for more.

A bell clanged across the street, and many pioneers rushed into the set mission. Suddenly the streets were eerily empty except for a handful of bewildered passersby.

"Oh, shit," the hipster said, redoubling his packing efforts.

"What's happening?"

"Chow call. Three times a day a guy comes out and rings the bell and they herd in like sheep. I don't know what they feed them, but they emerge twenty minutes later like a pack of deranged wolves and attack one of the other

missions or sometimes just people on the street. I saw
them tear a whiskey evangelist limb from limb two days
ago. Half an hour later they were walking around docile
as lambs, his blood still on their hands. If you're smart, you
won't be around when they come out."

"I need to talk to you."

"About what?"

"I need spiritual advice."

He finished filling the last box. "Right place, wrong
time."

"Can we talk somewhere else?"

"Okay. You help me carry out these boxes and we'll—"

The mission door banged open, and I turned in time to
see Ted step outside.

"Him!" he screeched, pointing a damning finger at me.
"Kill him!" Wild-eyed pioneers poured out of the mission
like starving wolves, led by Leo, racing right for me with
bloodlust in their eyes.

I drew my pistol, and a long burst of gyrajets chewed up
Ted and the first rank of zombies. The pistol's magazine
emptied, and the zombies bore down, stumbling over their
dead brothers without removing their fevered eyes from me.

"Run!" the hipster shouted, bolting out the back door
with an armload of boxes.

I took off down the sidewalk at a dead sprint, pumping
my arms like pistons, my jacket flying out behind me
like a cape. I collided with a lone junkie, rolled off him
and got back up to speed. I heard a scream and glanced
over my shoulder to watch the zombies roll over the young
junkie, stomping him into the concrete without animosity
or mercy—he just happened to be in the way. They rushed
on, hot on my trail and very fast for programmed winos.

My mean pace soon had most of the mob strung out,

but an elite pack of eight stayed close enough to count. I swung left, colliding with a gaggle of whores in front of the Silver Spoon Café. They scratched and screamed, and I fought my way to my feet, then lurched away, my right knee sore from hitting the sidewalk. I glanced back to find the zombies had closed the distance to twenty meters.

I ran limpingly as the zombies closed, block by block. Stiff jolts of pain shot up my leg, and my knee stiffened with each step until I had to resort to a lurching hop. The chorus of labored breathing grew loud behind me as I lurched grimly forward, gritting my teeth against the pain. A hand hooked my shoulder, but I lashed back with my elbow, breaking free. I hobbled across a side street, lunging out of the way of an onrushing pimpmobile. Tires screeched and the long black cruiser struck two zombies, throwing them like papier-mâché dummies onto Hayward. The rest swarmed over and around the stalled machine, their voracious eyes never leaving my back. I reached the corner of Haiti and Hayward before my knee gave out. I struggled to my feet, wobbling on one good leg, and decided to make a stand. I drew the empty gyrapistol and held it by the barrel, raised high to crush skulls as the zombies swarmed in.

A red blur jumped the curb, crushing three zombies under its front bumper. The side cargo door slid open, and I dived into a mountain of boxes. The van screeched off the sidewalk, losing the zombies hanging on the rearview mirrors like an elephant shaking off monkeys. I shoved the door closed, then turned to watch the zombies stumbling after us as we roared down Hayward. Four blocks later they fell hopelessly behind, and the van settled into a more conservative speed. I climbed over the stacked boxes to the passenger seat.

"Thanks for the lift," I said, sitting down.

"The name is Zach," the hipster said. I introduced myself and we shook hands. "I figured I owed you a ride for diverting them from me," Zach said.

"It was me they were after."

He eyed me. "Why's the set after you?"

"That's what I wanted to talk to you about."

He shook his head. "I'm not messing with the set. Those cretins are ruthless."

"I know. I led their death squads."

"You killed for them?"

"Yes."

"Why?"

I looked out at Hayward. "You know when you're driving and you hit a patch of black ice on a corner, near a tall cliff, and you lose all traction and began to slide toward the edge? Steering wheel, brakes and accelerator mean nothing—you're totally at the mercy of elements beyond your control, sliding silently toward the cliff with that gut-wrenching, paralytic horror of helplessness. You know what I'm talking about?"

"I guess so."

"Well, every day of my life used to be like that, one long power slide toward a cliff. Then I ran into the set. They gave me the power to change the world, for the better, I thought. When that fell through, they promised me something more."

"Like what?"

"An afterlife. A pleasant one."

He nodded. "Oh, yeah, they all say they hold the keys to heaven. Shit, you should have come to me. I could have sold you a plastic god and saved you a whole lot of trouble."

"One isn't plastic. He's real."

"Yeah," Zach said, smirking. "They all are."

"No, he really is. I've seen proof. The set kills hypnotized winos and sends them out into the great unknown to rap with the bastard. That's where the zombies come from. They're the ones that come back."

"Whew," Zach said, shaking his head. "The whole thing seems like one bad trip. I'm sure glad I'm not involved."

"Oh, but you are."

"No, not me."

"Sure you are."

He eyed me nervously. "How do you figure?"

"Are you kidding? That cruel pimp Fate dropped it right into our laps."

He scowled. "That bastard Fate would do something like that, wouldn't he? Can't we call the SPF in on this?"

"No, they're working with the set. Even as we speak, their rotors are helping the martyrs crush the old religions."

"Whew. Who can you turn to?"

"No one. We're going to have to stop them ourselves."

"We?"

"Sure. Somebody has to do it."

"Yes, but why does it have to be *us*?"

"Oh, c'mon, you know how Fate is. He always screws over the least deserving. The set may also be holding my ex-client hostage. We have to rescue her."

"Client? What's your line when you're not battling gods?"

"I'm a private enforcer."

"Great karma!" He shifted uncomfortably. "Whew. I don't know, I'm more clairvoyant than commando."

"That's exactly why I came to you. You see, we're not just up against a physical enemy—we're also fighting a spiritual force. Are you qualified to advise me on that level?"

His face shifted gears and his spine straightened. "Advice I can give. I'm a fully qualified neo-New Age shaman, registered mystic, multidimensional channeler, hypnotist, clairvoyant, a recognized scholar of the entire metaphysical field, and informed sources will tell you I'm the best psyche surgeon east of the Topeka vortex. And my rates are extremely reasonable."

"What do you know about magic spells?"

"What kind?"

I related to him how Jackie had selectively paralyzed parts of my body.

"Hmm," he said thoughtfully. "Tell me, previous to this encounter, did she ever hypnotize you or put you into a trance?"

I shook my head. "No."

"I don't just mean with a swinging watch. She might have done it without you knowing, with speech patterns or a video, during which you blacked out or fell asleep."

I thought back. "I fell asleep while she was giving me a massage once. She was singing, too."

"Ah-ha," Zach said with a sly triumphant smile. "We know her game."

"We do?"

"You're damn right. But before you can even think about taking on the set, we're going to have to get their hooks out of you."

"What does that entail?"

"It entails going on a trip to the desert." He wheeled off Hayward and headed north on Hunter. "We'll stop by my house and pick up my skimmer. How much credit do you have on you?"

"A couple grand."

"Give it to me," he said, extending a hand.

"Why should I?"

"Hey, spiritual comfort doesn't come cheap these days."

I dug out the plastic and handed it to him. "Yeah, I'm catching on to that."

26

Red earth and red stone mesas passed beneath the shadow of Zach's rotor. I'd slept for the first six hours of the flight, fatigue finally wrestling down nervous fear.

"We don't have the power to meet their machine head-on," I explained from the contoured passenger seat. "It's too large and organized. But if we can get inside, we can screw up the controls, rescue Heidi and bring the whole bastard down. We'll have to infiltrate."

Zach eyed me uneasily. "I wish you'd stop this 'we' stuff. I'm just going to advise you, remember?"

I shook my head sadly. "I'm afraid your karmic responsibilities don't stop there."

"They don't?"

"Hell, no. The entire universe as we know it may well be at stake. We've been empowered with the task of setting things straight."

"Empowered by whom?"

I looked him dead in the eye and kept a straight face. "The cosmic."

"The cosmic?"

"Sure," I said. "Don't tell me someone as spiritually tuned as yourself hasn't picked up on that yet."

He watched me for a moment then nodded slowly, turning his attention back to the desert. "Yeah, I think I'm starting to pick up on those waves."

"Heavy waves," I said.

"Whew, are they." He seemed to shrug under the weight of the brutal cosmic bombardment. "Oh, yeah, I feel those bastards now, like lead hammers dropping right on the back of my neck."

"You can handle it," I said with absolute confidence. "Where exactly are we going, anyway?"

"Right down here," he said, and the nose of the rotor dipped toward the red sands. We spiraled down over what appeared to be a primitive village among huge red stone formations and set down on a large tarmac landing pad painted with exotic Native American symbols and crowded with late-model skimmers and rotors. We hopped out and stretched.

"Breathe in that pure air," Zach extolled. "Feel those positive vibes. We're right in the middle of a powerful network of psychic energy vortexes."

The warm breeze blew across the pad, smelling of sage and sand. I felt hardy and somehow heartened, just being out of the City was exhilarating. Zach led me off the pad with a righteous step, and we followed a trail to the village I'd seen from above. Chanting and drum beats floated among the squat adobe buildings, long-haired and silent tribespeople stared from the mouths of shadowy doorways, skinny sunbaked children ran and played in the dust.

"These are the new spiritual children," Zach said. "Except for weekly food and medical shipments, they live as the gentle Hopi did a thousand years before."

Wisps of a dream I'd once had floated back to me, a dream of fleeing all the ugliness in the world and escaping to the desert—before I'd realized there was no escaping what lay within, at least not for me.

A withered old man wandered into our path. He was dressed as a medicine man, his skin the shade and texture of old leather. He made a curious sign with his hands, and Zach returned the sign and bowed slightly.

"How grows the corn?" the old man asked.

"Tall and strong," Zach replied. "I take many pleasures in its cool shadow."

"Then bring me a husk to hang above my door so I, too, may know of these shady pleasures."

Zach bowed again, and the old man moved on.

"What did all that mean?" I asked.

"Who knows?" Zach replied. "Peyote and the sun cooked his brain a long time ago. It's best just to humor that type."

We passed through the center of the village and began moving into a more affluent neighborhood. The dusty path turned to cobblestone, and the adobe buildings began to resemble town houses. I followed Zach into one of the larger adobe structures.

Shock hit me along with the chill of the air-conditioning. Except for the adobe walls and the expensive Native American furnishings, the office belonged in an exec tower. The floor was a gleaming turquoise tile, the gleaming chrome desks were loaded with sleek computer equipment and monitors on every wall showcased various properties for sale. The voices of slick salesmen extolled the spiritual attunement and incredible investment opportunities to be had in Spirit City. Racks of colorful brochures were everywhere. I touched the adobe of the doorjamb. It appeared to be molded plastic.

"Dust screws with the computer equipment," said a watching salesman wearing a black exec suit and turquoise necklace.

"We need a meditation cave," Zach said, approaching the salesman's desk.

"What size?"

"Something small and isolated, with good ventilation. We're going to be doing some cooking."

"I have a suite for two hundred wampum per night, but the fire permit's going to cost you fifty wampum more."

"Fifty wam—" Zach rolled his eyes. "All right, what's the current exchange rate for wampum?"

"Two to one."

"Two wampum for one cred?"

"No, the other way around."

Zach grimaced. "Why didn't I know that?" He dug into a pouch on his hip and pulled out my wad of credits. "Give me two thousand creds worth."

The salesman took the plastic squares and handed back a number of intricately beaded circles of cloth. "That's eight hundred wampum."

Zach frowned at the handful of beads. "That's about two hundred wampum short."

"There's a twenty percent conversion charge," the clerk politely explained.

"Well, *of course!*" Zach cried. "Why did I think the money changers hadn't set up office in Spirit City, too?" He handed over some of the wampum, received a keycard, and we marched out into the sun.

"The new spiritual children are wise in the ways of finance," I noted.

"Stinking commercialism, that's what it is," Zach said. "Why, I remember when it was *four* wampum for *one* credit. Think of all the bad karma those bastards are building up here." He shivered. "Whew, I can feel it all around me!"

We stopped at a medicine stand, where Zach traded a sizable hunk of wampum for clay bottles of strange liquid and bags of various roots and powders.

Our cave was in the side of a sandstone formation two hundred meters outside Spirit City.

"Good, an isolated one," Zach said. "That damn chanting gets on my nerves after a while."

I followed him through the door-size entrance into a cool interior. Smooth sandstone arced to a high ceiling, and carved stone tables and chairs rose from the floor. It appeared to be of recent excavation. Zach slipped the keycard into a steel panel near the door, and overhead lights came on. He adjusted a dimmer switch until the lighting approximated that of a single candle.

Zach went to the cooking pit, selected a black iron pot and said, "I want you to tell me exactly what happened when this set priestess rendered you helpless."

As I told my story, he nodded a lot and poured most of the purchases from the medicine stand into the pot. When I'd finished, he said, "Yeah, we got her number, all right." He ignited the gas burner in the center of the fire pit and set the small pot to simmer. He stood up and dusted his hands with a satisfied air.

"Making some stew?"

He grinned. "You might say that."

I thought about what he had put in it. "What kind of stew?"

He looked at me and smiled wickedly. "Mind stew."

"Nothing dangerous, I hope."

"Only to our enemies," he said, sitting on the stone bench in front of me. "When she paralyzed a limb, how exactly did this limb feel?"

"Powerless. Drained. Frozen. You know, paralyzed."

"You say 'drained.' Was it as if someone pulled a plug inside you and all the energy rushed out of that particular body part?"

"Yeah, that's it."

He nodded vigorously. "And when this happened, did you get any image flashes, fleeting pictures or sensations?"

"No, not really. But I did have a feeling of déjà vu, like I'd heard the word before."

"Mensch?"

"Yes."

He nodded slowly. "I think I know what your problem is."

"What?"

"I can't be sure until you've been hypnotized." He rolled up his sleeves. "I'm going to have to go in and see what's what. Probably have to go all the way to the core."

I eyed him suspiciously. "The core of what?"

"Your psyche. It's possible this sèt priestess Jackie put you under hypnosis and installed posthypnotic command mechanisms in your subconscious. Now, do you have faith in me as a mystic?"

"I suppose so."

"Good. Then I want you to take a walk with me, a walk down some steps. Now close your eyes, clear your mind and imagine you're standing at the top of a long, winding stairwell."

"I think I'm too tense to be hypnotized."

A frazzled and sweating Zach stood up and stretched. "Don't worry, it's all over."

"What's all over?"

"Look at your watch."

I did. It told me it was eleven in the evening. About four hours later than it should have been. "I've been out for four hours?"

He nodded. "I didn't get far. We're not dealing with an amateur. That Jackie must be some sort of witch."

"I often suspected as much."

"She installed more blocks, double binds and booby traps than you'll find in hell's labyrinth. How long did you sleep after she sang to you?"

"An hour, tops."

"Whew, that's scary. She must have had a program laid out for insertion. Or she could have used some sort of machine."

The insectlike winos of the Whisper Room flashed in my mind's eye. "They have those. What exactly transpired over the past four hours?"

Zach rose and checked on the stew. He moved stiffly, as if he'd spent the afternoon sprinting up sand dunes. "It's called psyche surgery, the hypnotic version of exploratory surgery. I wasn't able to go very deep. I got past some of the blocks and binds by using the *mensch* code word to go through a subconscious back door, but I couldn't risk dismantling her command structure without triggering the booby traps she installed." He crouched to stir the stew. "Just probing was like walking in a minefield."

"Let me get this right," I said. "You're saying there's a bunch of bombs in my head?"

"Psyche bombs."

"How can she do that?"

Zach laughed morbidly. "Hypnotism has come a long way in the last twenty years. It's not just a party game or memory device anymore. New techniques have made it a lethal and powerful weapon."

"What happens if one of these bombs goes off?"

He shrugged. "Could be a lot of things. Something as

minor as memory loss or a sudden fear of weapons, or something as major as a powerful and urgent manifestation of a death wish."

"And she can trigger these words at will?"

"By uttering a single key word. Probably some nonsensical term or a foreign word like *mensch,* something that wouldn't be encountered in day-to-day conversation."

"If that's so, why don't I freeze up when you say *mensch?*"

"It has to be said in her voice. Or a similar one. Just as a properly trained attack dog will respond only to his master's voice."

"So I get to go through life waiting for some sensually voiced German girl to say the right word so I can throw myself out a window?"

"Not necessarily," he said, slowly stirring the stew. "I anticipated that I might not be able to breach her programming through hypnosis. So I prepared another option."

My eyes dropped to the bubbling pot hissing with foul-smelling steam. "You're talking about the horrible stew option."

He lifted the wood spoon from the pot and smelled the ooze dripping from it. He wrinkled his nose, then smiled. "It's about done."

I HELD THE CUP of stew at arm's length. "What's this going to do?"

Zach poured half a cup for himself and set the pot between us. We sat under a blanket of stars, side by side on a sandy hill overlooking the cave. "It'll wreak havoc with her programming, I can tell you that. Probably rip it out by the roots."

"What about the booby traps?"

"Oh, you'll be in no condition to obey any of those suggestions. The stew will grind them up into mush."

"Mush, huh? And just what is this stew going to do to *me?*"

"Nothing terribly extreme. It'll rearrange some synapses, maybe shift your worldview a little."

"I like my worldview as it is."

"Relax. See, I'm going to drink some, too."

"How come?"

"It'll refocus my psyche for what lies ahead. When the psychic wave hits, I'll lock into a meditative state and direct my mystic energies toward the set. By the time I come up, I'll be calibrated to do battle with the set like a programmed missile."

"What do I do when the wave hits *me?*"

He smiled. "Just ride it out." He lifted his earthen cup and clunked mine. "Bottoms up."

Drinking the stew was just a shade worse than having a shit-eating dog vomit in my mouth. My stomach immediately decided it wanted no part of it, and I fought the gag reflex for five horrific minutes, feeling as if I'd swallowed a live bullfrog coated with hot tar. Eventually the stew settled on the bottom of my stomach with a queasy weight.

"Not bad, eh?" Zach gasped.

"Not good," I croaked, and we settled down to watching each other to see who would start wigging first.

"Just what was in that horrible shit?" I asked.

Zach shrugged evasively. "Many fine herbs and medicines. It opens the mind for the entry of powerful spirits." Zach suddenly flinched. "Whew, did you feel that? A goddamn spirit just flashed by us. He laid a jolt right through me."

"A spirit?" I said, peering around. "Are you sure?"

"Of course I'm sure. What else could it have been?"

"All those fine medicines and herbs we just drank."

"Don't be silly. The stew is merely the key to locked portals. What lies beyond is something else entirely. We are about to embark on a wonderful mystic journey into the spirit world, a world of infinite wisdom, noble meaning and unmatched splendor."

"That's good," I said, settling deeper into the sand. "I was afraid we'd get high and start running around on all fours and barking like dogs."

He slid me a look. "Well, that might happen, but if it does, I'm certain it will have deep and significant spiritual meaning."

"I'll remember that when I start drooling."

We sat quietly for a minute, moving steadily toward the brink on the vast unknown, nervous with anticipation. "I don't know," I said. "I don't feel any differently."

"You weigh more than I do, so it'll take longer. But remember, you drank twice as much as I did, you poor bastard." He flinched again, as if cracked with a bullwhip. "A goddamn death spirit is trapped in my rib cage!" he howled, clawing at his chest. "Get the hell out of me, you evil bastard! Get out of my heart!"

"He's gone!" I shouted at him, fearful of his fit. "I saw him leap out and zoom off behind those rocks over there."

Zach stopped clawing. "Whew, thank the cosmic for that. Did you see what the mean bastard looked like?"

"Well, he was sort of a transparent orange hue, and he had these big, slanted black eyes with glowing red centers and a long forked tail."

"Great karma! That sounds just like a Sumerian air devil. What is he doing here? The vortexes are supposed to keep that kind of scum out. Where did you say he went?"

I pointed at a jumble of moonlit boulders atop a distant hill. "He shot over those—*Jesus,* there he is!"

"Where?"

"Right there!" I said, pointing at an orange, shifting shape with fiery black eyes lurking behind one of the boulders. "He's hunkered down behind that big rock on the left. Jesus, he's seething with hate. I think you really pissed him off, rejecting him like that."

Zach squinted along my finger. "I don't see any goddamn spirit." He frowned at me. "I think you're hallucinating."

I laughed maliciously. "You'll be seeing him soon enough. Once he comes over to stomp the shit out of your karma, you dumb brute."

"And you'll probably help him, *won't you?*" he snarled.

I shrugged. "I might be talked into it, depending on what he offers. There might be some prime power involved in this deal."

"You ungrateful cur!" Zach snapped, and staggered down the hill. He stopped at the bottom and shook a fist at me. "Tell your demon buddy to come and get me! I'll have a little surprise waiting for *both* of you!" He laughed wickedly and loped off toward the cave.

I laughed at him and rose, gazing in every direction. Canyons and rock spires confronted me on every horizon, and I realized I stood in a long-dead riverbed. Yet I could hear rushing water somewhere close. I closed my eyes, trying to place the source of water with my ears, then realized it was all around me.

I opened my eyes to find the hill on which I stood was actually a low island, surrounded by a swirling phantom river that washed through the dry canyons and had done so since the beginning of time, a wildly rushing torrent of psychic energy toiling madly toward some distant mystic sea. And the river was rising, fed by storms crackling in the distance. The flood currents swelled and rose until the rushing waters whipped at my feet, then my knees. Then I was floating, and the current carried me away.

I washed up on a bank where the river met a wide sea. A monstrous paddleboat lay moored in the delta, and a long line of people made their way up the gangway, handing their tickets to the great white-bearded captain at the bottom. *The High Road* was painted across the ship's magnificent bow.

I got in line because it seemed the thing to do. As we shuffled along, I noted the passengers represented every stratum of society, including more than a few seedy types. When my turn came to walk up the gangway, the captain blocked my way with a huge arm.

"Your ticket, sir?"

I checked all my pockets, then smiled at the bearded giant. "Don't seem to have one."

He grunted and lifted a huge book from under his arm. "Name?"

I eyed him speculatively. "John Smith."

He eyed me back. "Name?"

"Mike Jones."

He glared harder. "Name?"

"Jake Strait."

He leafed through the book, then followed his finger down a page. "No, no Jake Strait on the manifest." He snapped the book shut with finality. "Sorry, you can't come aboard."

"Oh, well," I said. "All the good berths are probably already taken." I stepped back, and the captain marched up the ramp. He turned around at the top and gave the order for the gangway to be retracted. The ship's rail was crowded with spectators, staring at the lone man on the bank.

"No hard feelings," the captain called from his place near the big wheel. "It's the rules."

"That's okay," I said. "I'll catch the next boat."

The captain gave me a strange look. "Yes, I guess you will."

The paddles of the boat churned to life, and the boat pushed off from the bank toward the wide sea. The passengers on the rail waved goodbye, and I waved back. The ship slowly melted into the horizon.

I put my hands in my pockets and waited. I figured the next boat would be along soon enough. I kept checking my pockets to see if a ticket would appear. They stayed empty.

The next boat arrived about fifteen minutes later. This one wasn't nearly as resplendent or large as the paddleboat. In fact, it bore more than a casual resemblance to a rowboat manned by an old wino.

"Oh, good," he muttered as he rowed to the bank. "We have one today." He gestured to the plank seat beside him.

I stayed where I was. "Sorry," I said, smiling apologetically, "but I don't have a ticket."

"Are you certain?" he asked. "Perhaps you overlooked it."

"No chance," I said. I patted my pockets to show my good faith and felt a flat bulge in my breast pocket. I slowly removed a cardboard stub. "Well, what do you know. But I'm certain it's for another boat."

"No," the old man said, reaching out a hand. "There aren't any more boats along today. Won't you come aboard?"

"I don't think I want to. Where's your manifest?"

He laughed. "Don't have one. I just pick up whoever is left behind. Besides, where else can you go?"

"I dunno," I said, looking across the river at the opposite bank. It was cloaked in fog. "I could swim back across."

"No, you can't. The other side is Limbo and you won't like that. It's horribly boring."

"How boring?"

"Ever been to a museum curator's cocktail party?"

I sighed and stepped aboard the boat, handing him my ticket. The old man scooted over on the bench, and I sat next to him. "I suppose you're Charon and this is the rowboat to hell," I said.

He nodded and took an oar. "Won't you help me row?"

"I didn't see any of the customers paddling on the paddleboat."

He smiled. "Getting to heaven is easy. You have to work at going to hell."

I took the other oar. "I got myself this far, so I suppose I can help with the rest."

We began rowing upstream, against a strong current.

"I always figured the current pulled toward hell," I said.

He smiled. "No, it takes a lot of effort to get there. Especially these days. So few get to make the trip anymore."

"Why's that?"

"Oh, it's that new forgiveness clause they have." He threw an irked glance over a bony shoulder. "They'll take anyone these days—atheists, murderers, deviants, sinners of every shape and form. Sometimes it's hard for me to get up the motivation to make the trip down—too often the bank is bare of souls." He slid me a sideways glance and smiled. "You must have done something particularly despicable."

"A long series of tragic misunderstandings," I explained. "It's funny, I always figured I was at least in the upper fifty percentile. That if I did go to hell, I'd have loads of company."

"Yes, well, there was a time when I piloted the big boat and Pete came down in his tiny craft. But that was before they lowered their standards. New administration, you understand."

"What?"

"Didn't you know? Jesus ousted his father. Thought him too conservative, too harsh, too much a boor. The first thing that snot-nose messiah did was declare a general amnesty, pardoning most of hell's wards." He pulled at the oar and shook his head. "Hell's quite lonely these days. Even some of the most vile demons have defected. Why, we even lost Aleister Crowley the other day."

I clucked sympathetically. "So what's eternal damnation really like? Is it as bad as its rap?"

"Well, it's not all fire and brimstone, if that's what you mean. We've kept up with the times." He shrugged. "You'll get used to it after the first five million years."

"Five million years? How can you say that? Mankind hasn't been around that long."

He smiled nefariously. "No, I guess he hasn't, has he?" He threw back his head and cackled.

We continued to row, making slow progress. I mopped my brow with a hand. "Getting hot."

"It'll get hotter."

"I bet." I leaned on the oar as if to catch my wind. "Boy, that's a strong current."

"You're more than strong enough," Charon pointed out.

"Yeah, but I don't think I'm motivated," I said, driving my elbow into his Adam's apple. He released the oar and clawed at his crushed larynx. Putting one hand behind his neck, I used the heel of my other hand to drive his forehead back down. Then, snapping his neck like a dry branch, I pitched him into the river.

I started paddling back toward the sea, trying to think of a good plan. I knew heaven didn't want me, but I didn't see why that meant I had to go to hell. After a while I stopped paddling and let the current carry me past mist-shrouded banks echoing with the sorrowful calls of lost souls. I wasn't sure where I was going, but I was very certain where I *wasn't* going.

27

The rude glare of the morning sun woke me. I lay halfway down the hill, half buried in the sand. I had an audience.

I struggled to my feet, spine and muscles stiff. "Beat it," I told a girl of about five and a boy perhaps three years older. They both wore Native American costumes and war paint.

"You're not going to do any more tricks?" the girl asked.

"No," I said, spitting grit out of my mouth. "Fresh out of tricks."

"No more Gila-monster impressions?" she asked.

"Nope."

"Are you going to eat any more sand?" the boy inquired.

"No, I think I've met my daily requirement of sand. Now run along back to your tepee."

They wandered away, obviously disappointed the show was over. I staggered back to the cave, where Zach was hunched over the cooking pit, stirring a big black pot. He glanced over his shoulder and smiled.

"How do you feel?" he asked.

"Like a grilled lizard."

He laughed. "Want some stew?"

"Screw you."

"But this is real stew. With vegetables and broth. From the village's greenhouse."

I sniffed at the pot suspiciously. "Any herbs or medicine in there?"

"Just the kind that are good for you."

"That's what you said last night."

He smiled. "Yes, well, this is different."

"Okay," I said. "But just a little. I already hit the sand-and-gravel buffet."

He ladled out two bowls and handed one to me. We sat at the rock table and ate our stew. "So, tell me what happened," Zach said.

"I died and went to hell."

He stared at me speculatively. "Are you speaking literally or figuratively?"

"Both."

"Hmm." He chewed his stew thoughtfully. "Tell me what happened exactly."

I shrugged. "St. Peter wouldn't let me on the big boat, so I caught a ride with Charon up the River Styx."

"And?"

"I killed him and threw him overboard. Rowed back out to sea."

He nodded. "Good, good. I think I can interpret that for you."

"I can't wait."

Zach ignored my petulance. "You died symbolically to cleanse your karma, to satisfy your kill guilt. But instead of accepting your fate in hell, you destroyed the means that would take you there. This proves your fear of hell is stronger than your sense of remorse. Dying removed the thin layer of guilt, and defeating Charon resolved your fear of hell. You are now spiritually pure."

"Just like that?"

"Sure. It used to take years and years of intense meditation and self-denial to address the inner psyche. But with the aid of advanced psychochemistry, we accomplished the same end in a single night. What it takes a Tibetan monk a lifetime to achieve, we attain in a matter of hours."

"You're starting to sound like Sinn."

"This had nothing to do with sin or any other Christian concept," he said, misunderstanding me.

"I don't feel particularly pure."

"How do you feel?"

"Poisoned."

"That'll pass. Now that your karma is balanced, you can absorb the mystic skills needed to overcome our powerful enemy. But first I'll hypnotize you to make sure you've been completely deprogrammed, then install suggestions that will accelerate the learning process."

We walked down the stairs again, and two hours later Zach informed me Jackie's programming was wiped clean. We spent the remainder of the day and most of the night sitting cross-legged in different caves. In exchange for various amounts of wampum, self-styled magi and shamans taught us how to form psychic-protection bubbles, invoke invisibility shields, employ psi power words that would smite helpless any fool who got in our way and other sundry mystic knowledge.

When the last shaman chased us out of his cave at three in the morning, we shuffled off to doze like torpid iguanas on the slimy rocks of a medicinal steam cave, letting the heat and vapors suck physical impurities right out of our skins.

In the morning we gathered our things and staggered to

the landing pad, so in tune and purified that we could barely walk.

"Whew, I feel great!" Zach croaked heartily as we stepped among the maze of machines parked on the pad.

"You don't look great," I said. "You look dehydrated and crazy."

"That's because I've been drawing energy from my physical shell to feed the furnaces of my supercharged spiritual machine. I'm positively giddy with karmic energy." He giggled to prove it.

At Zach's skimmer we were confronted by four teenage girls brandishing meter-long sabers.

"Castraters!" I announced, dropping into a fighting stance.

"It's all right," Zach soothed, "they're sword dancers. I've arranged a portent reading before we leave. Go ahead, girls."

The girls formed a foursquare on the tarmac, laying their swords at their feet. A tall plump girl barked "Play!" at a boom box a few meters away, and they began dancing to the chant of neo-Native synth beat.

"Warriors in druid Scotland had maidens dance over their swords before they went into battle to portend their fate," Zach explained. "If the maiden representing the warrior touched the sword with her feet, it was a sign the warrior would be wounded or killed."

I nodded and watched. They leapt and twirled above the blades with various degrees of grace.

"Two of the girls represent fate and chance. The other two represent us, each carrying an object imbued with our essence."

"I was wondering where my sock went."

"The redhead represents me," Zach said, gesturing to a

slender elfish lass who danced above her sword with the grace of a ballerina, her feet never coming near the blade.

"Look's like you're in fine shape," I congratulated. "Which one is mine?"

"The plump one."

I looked the group over. "You mean the one who's stomping on the sword like it was a snake?"

"That's the one."

"Super."

Zach frowned. "Well, it's just a hokey old tradition, doesn't mean that much." He clapped his hands once. "All right, that's enough, ladies."

The dance ground to a halt, and they picked up their swords. Zach tipped his dancer with the rest of the wampum. My dancer walked up to me, digging into a pouch on her belt. "Here's your sock," she said.

I took the sock and she lingered, smacking her gum loudly, holding out her open palm expectantly.

"She's waiting for a tip," Zach whispered in my ear.

"I know what she's waiting for," I said. "Did she earn a tip is the question. I mean, she pretty much danced me right into the frigging grave. The goddamn skimmer will probably explode the minute we lift off."

She wouldn't go away, so I dug into my pocket and came out with a five-cred note. "I want you to spend this money on dance lessons," I told her. "You need to work on your technique, baby."

"You need to work on your karma," she snarled, snatching the bill. "I just do what the spirits tell me."

"Yeah, well, next time get possessed by a spirit that knows how to dance."

She made a rude gesture and waddled away, dragging her sword.

"You have any more portents arranged?" I asked Zach.

"Nope."

"Praise the merciful Lord."

FIVE HOURS LATER we arrived in the City and exchanged the rotor for Zach's minivan. We checked into a downtown motel that Zach assured me was located on spiritually safe ground, where we had to spend at least twenty-four hours reacclimatizing to the harsh karmic vibes of the City. After moving boxes of Zach's gear from the van into the room, we settled down before the TV just in time for the afternoon news.

The lead story was about SPF rotors pounding various religious militias around the City for "committing atrocities too numerous and gruesome to mention."

"Whew," Zach said. "Looks like a bad day for old-time religion."

"Yes," I said. "It's all about creating a vacuum of faith."

Zach nodded, and a special news bulletin interrupted the weather report with a camera shot from a buzzing rotor high above the City, closing in on the top of a familiar barrel-shaped tower. A man dressed in a stunning gold lamé robe danced on the rooftop, his arms and face raised to the steadily descending rotor, until his joyous face filled the camera.

"The moment has arrived!" Sinn shouted excitedly into the camera, his robe whipping and flashing in rotor wash. "It's here! The moment you've been waiting for! I promised you something big was coming, remember? Didn't I promise you that? Well, *it has arrived!*"

Sinn vanished and reappeared in front of the huge, red velvet curtains of the set auditorium, wearing a sparkling crimson exec suit, his mohawk fluffed and spiked. "A *se-*

cret!" Sinn hissed, jerking a thumb back at the curtains. "But not for long! The hardworking Set of One computers have targeted the time, and guess what? It's *tonight!* That's right! Tonight at precisely 8:31 p.m., on this and every City Party station, these luxurious red velvet curtains will part and reveal in perfect digital detail," he paused, threw his hands in the air and screamed, "the *face of God!* The *One* god! Your god! Get ready! It's coming! Tonight! Eight thirty-one p.m.! Tune in for the greatest event of the millennium! The televised warm-up begins at 7:00 p.m.!" He gave us a broad salute. "See you then!"

The screen returned to the newsroom, where the anchors were in a stuttering frenzy. They babbled about Sinn's announcement with the unbridled enthusiasm of freshman philosophy students who'd just discovered LSD. They videolinked with a wild-eyed reporter on location outside the set tower who slobbered over a just-released list of the all the bigwigs who would be personally attending the exclusive unveiling ceremony.

"The guy in the commercial was Sinn," I said.

"The old punk rocker?" Zach exclaimed, startled. "Great karma, we're up against a real loon. Did you see the look in his eyes? Power has not only corrupted him, it drove him crazy."

"Power may have corrupted him," I agreed, "but it took talking to One to make him crazy."

Zach waved a skeptical hand. "Ah, they all claim to talk to their gods."

"Yeah, but he really did. He had himself killed, then brought back to life in one of his resurrection chambers."

"Resurrection chambers?"

"It's part of their Phoenix Program. They've developed a system of killing people, letting them hang out in the afterlife for a while, then bringing them back to talk about it. They're using that information and computers to form an image of One. That's what's behind the velvet curtains."

Zach stared at me. "You mean this face of God stuff is for real?"

"Maybe."

"Whew! We really *are* in deep spiritual shit." He sank deeper into the armchair. "They're exploring death, huh?" he said, envy in his voice. "Just think of all the knowledge they must be gathering. Wow, that's heavy."

"We're going to have to go in tonight," I said.

His head jerked up. "But we're not reacclimatized yet. Our karma is way off-line for this vibe."

"We have no choice. If Sinn pulls this off tonight, it'll be too late to do anything. We have to stop One now or never."

"What if we can't?"

"I don't know. If the show goes over in the City, it'll probably get worldwide Party coverage. One will win a lot of converts and many believers. Who knows what might happen then."

"All right," Zach said, leaping to his feet. "It's up to us to save the world, then." He rushed to one of his boxes and dug out red-tinted goggles, headphones and a vial of fat white tablets. "I'll immediately drop into a Ganzfeld cocoon and astrally project myself to the set tower for a crash reconnaissance mission." He opened the vial and began gobbling pills. "You're going to have to get me something."

"What?"

"Something that belongs to the client you want to rescue. Preferably something very dear to her heart."

"Why?"

"So we can find her once we get inside. I'll tune in to the possession's vibrations and follow her aural residue right to her cell. It's called psychometry."

"All right," I said doubtfully, putting on my coat. "I was going to scout her place anyway. I'll be back in a couple hours."

Zach put on the goggles and headphones and dropped into a lotus position in front of the TV. I slipped out the door as Zach was sliding into a trance.

THE CAB DRIVER PARKED across the street, and we watched the front of Complan B together. There were dangerous men lurking on every corner but none had that earnest psychokiller look common to martyrs. I paid the cabbie and slunk inside the deserted Complan lobby. I took the elevator to the twenty-seventh floor, walked down a flight, then crept to Heidi's door. I drew my pistol, put my back to the wall and knocked. Nothing stirred inside. When I tried the knob, the door opened.

I rushed in, half expecting a bloodbath, or at least lurking martyrs. Instead, I found an empty apartment. No tables were overturned, no lamps were smashed, no bullet holes riddled the walls.

I searched the apartment, looking for possessions. The cupboards and fridge were empty, the bed was made, the bottle of wine I'd drank was still on the bedroom dresser where I'd left it.

Near the bottle was a small, facedown picture. I picked it up and sat on the bed. It was an identical copy of the portrait that sat on Jackie's bar. Heidi beamed, Jackie scowled, and I wished I had a strong drink. I moved the picture close to my eyes, studying it closely, particularly the face of

Jackie. Her black mood captured by the photo seemed so consummate, an aura of darkness seemed to emanate from her.

"Oh, it's a treacherous world," I told the picture. "A mean, treacherous world." I got up and left the room, picture in hand. I was about to exit when a thought hit me. I went back to the bedroom, stopping in front of the bed. I put my fingers under the edge of the mattress and flipped it off the bed.

Like a black snake on a bed of snow, Heidi's heavy-bladed butcher knife lay on the box springs, near the edge for easy access. A new, sinister light fell on Heidi's offer to show me new tricks, and a chill squirmed up my spine. I put the picture back on the dresser and picked up the big knife. The wood handle was smooth with use, and the wide blade was extremely top-heavy, definitely designed for hacking meat. I slipped it carefully into the waistband of my trousers and covered the hilt with my jacket. I left the apartment.

28

Zach was more or less conscious when I returned. He sat on his bed, sifting through what looked to be the inventory of a Navajo souvenir stand. There was a similar pile on my bed.

"How'd it go?" he asked.

"Fine." I pointed at the gear on my bed. "What's this?"

"Our tools," he said with a smile. He squinted at the strange clothing, bead necklaces, amulets, rattles and other curiosities. "I think I've got every angle covered."

"Yeah? Think we'll need it?"

"Yes," he said, suddenly troubled. "According to my reconnaissance."

I sat on the edge of an armchair, facing him. "Tell me what happened."

"My father murdered me."

"Your father? How'd he do it?" I asked.

"Well, I was walking down this misty corridor, somewhere in the set tower, and I saw him up ahead. I was surprised because I haven't seen him for eight years, since he left me and Mom and went to live on skid row. So I went up to shake his hand and say 'Hi, Pop, how ya doing?' He put his hand out, except it wasn't a hand, it was like a god-damn *talon* or something, and instead of giving me his old limp-rag one-pump he reaches up under my rib cage and rips out my heart and *shows* the goddamn thing to me, still pumping out blood like it had a reason.

"So I say something like 'Gee, thanks a lot, Pop, that's just what I needed, I mean, who needs a goddamn pulse anyway?' Then he presses the slimy, beating thing into my hands and says with this big, demon grin, 'That's what nosy little backsliding heathens get, son, and you're lucky I'm leaving you with your *balls.*' Then he turns around and walks away, leaving me holding the bag, so to speak."

"Christ," I said, shaking my head. "That doesn't exactly smack of good tidings. What does it mean to us, portent wise?"

Zach smiled grimly. "Why, it means I get to keep my balls, that's what. Let's get to it."

It took us roughly an hour to get geared up. When we were more or less finished, we looked at ourselves in the full-length mirror.

"We've got to be kidding," I said.

"We most certainly are not," Zach assured. "These items will get us unnoticed into the heart of the viper nest, spiritually safe and sound."

"How could they not help but notice? We look like hard-core Navajo Elvis impersonators out for a wild weekend in Vegas. Do we really need all this crap?"

"Absolutely. I've arranged each talisman so its inherent power complements, parlays and interlocks with the other talismans so as to direct their energy toward a higher purpose."

"You mean besides making us look foolish?"

"Yes! Look," he said, pointing at a spherical stone dangling from my feathered headpiece, "this crystal will deflect psi mind whips. Our beaded vests will neutralize any passive detection fields, not to mention distorting any psi bubbles they might throw at us. These feather headdresses will signal their mantra probes that we are of the kishna class, which we are not, thus throwing them off the mark completely. These weasel-skin leggings were cured and flayed by Masgar juju men, spiritual masters of stealth and deception. These mondo turquoise belt buckles will allow us to penetrate psi power fields. These Huichol shaman dream disks, indexed to the aura of Heidi, will—"

"That's enough," I said. "It's probably best I don't know their full portent. I might get heady with power and storm the tower straightaway." I reached under my mystical trappings and came up with the gyrapistol. I inserted a full magazine, checked the safety, then jacked in a jet.

"What's that?" Zach asked with a frown.

"It's a mystical tool forged by the sacred fires of the holy Myers Firearms factory. It exudes a powerful blast of kinetic energy which can profoundly disrupt an enemy's life force."

He looked away and pouted. "It shows a lack of faith."

"I'm wearing your goddamn rattles and feathers, aren't I? Why can't my stuff be magical and exciting, too? You just handle the spiritual side, and I'll handle the rest." I looked at my chrono. It was 6:18. We had just about two hours until the curtains parted. "Let's hit the road. I want some time to think up a plan once we get inside."

We loaded into the van and powered toward the set tower. "Remember," Zach said from the passenger seat, "the instant we pass through the door, start looking inward and ohming. Center all your energy inside, your thoughts tightly collected, exude nothing but passive waves of invisibility. See no one, judge no one, relate to no one. If you do not recognize their existence, they will not recognize yours."

I looked at myself in the rearview mirror. My face was painted with cryptic designs and swirls, my eye sockets and lips blackened with holy soot. "That shouldn't be too hard," I said. "I don't even recognize myself."

"That's the attitude," Zach said, double-checking the many tiny leather bags of powder hanging from his belt. After making certain he hadn't forgotten anything vital, he reached into a black nylon bag and pulled out a huge vampire-killing crucifix. He kissed it, then dangled it around his neck.

"What's that for?" I asked. "I didn't think you went for the Christian angle."

"It's to ward off my father's Catholic spirit," he said quickly. "While it has no intrinsic power, it may serve as a totem to draw him away from their circle of power."

I looked at the huge cross. "If that fails, you can whack him over the head with it," I said.

"I'd start trying real hard to lose those hostile vibes if I were you, Jake. They'll only get in our way, karma wise. Did you remember to get something that belonged to Heidi?"

"Oh, yeah," I said, reaching for the knife.

"No, don't let me see it. Not until it's time to psychometrize."

"Fine. Well, look who's showed up for the dance," I said, and we pulled onto Korangar Boulevard. Chauffeurs and bodyguards leaned against expensive machines parked for blocks in every direction from the set tower.

"Whew!" Zach said. "It looks like they turned the place into a used-limo lot."

"All the bigwigs seem to have afterlife concerns, as well," I said. "If Sinn pulls this off, he'll be calling the shots

from here on in. Uh-oh, here comes trouble," I said, pointing down Korangar. Fifty meters from the tower stood an
SPF roadblock.

"What now?" Zach said. "There's no room to turn
around."

"We'll just flow through," I said. "Let me do the talking."

"Hold on," Zach said. "I have some cooperation-induc-
ing harmony dust somewhere on my belt, I'll…"

I dropped a hand on Zach's shoulder and gave him a
cold stare. "Let *me* do the talking," I repeated slowly for
emphasis. Zach nodded, and I halted the van in front of the
steel barricade. One of the half-dozen SPF troopers on
hand leaned in my window. He got a good look at our getups and drew back in alarm, clutching at his assault rifle.

"Who the hell are *you?*" he demanded.

"We're part of the gig," I said.

"The gig? Let's see your invitations."

I frowned. "Didn't you just goddamn hear me? We're
part of the goddamn show, we don't need no invites. You
think we dress like this because we like to? Now move this
shit out of my way before I call Prophet Sinn."

He gaped at me, then started to say something.

"All right," I snapped, cutting him off. "What's your
goddamn name?"

He frowned. "What difference does that make?"

"What difference does it make? *What difference?*" I
threw a incredulous look at Zach. "Did you hear this
swine? He asked me what goddamn difference it makes!"
I returned my glare to the guard. "You better answer my
question before you get in deep trouble!"

"Higgens," he stuttered. "Micky Higgens."

"Higgens, eh? What precinct are you from, Higgens?"

"Twenty-third."

"That's what I thought. You're a Presbyterian, aren't you, Higgens? A goddamn Christian, am I right?"

He shifted uncomfortably. "Lutheran, actually."

"Lutheran! Jesus, did you hear that? We got a goddamn *Lutheran* on our hands! That explains *everything.* You better mend your ways, Higgens of the Twenty-third Precinct, because times are a-changing. There's a new god in town, and he ain't taking any shit from any of you reactionary types. I'm gonna give you a break this time, but if you don't open that goddamn gate this minute, I'll turn you over to indoctrination before you can say hallelujah, you ungrateful heathen pig."

Higgens wavered, glancing nervously over his shoulder. "I better clear it with Sarge…"

"Sure," I said, "bring Sarge over. Bring them *all* over. I'll have them arrest you on the spot, you backsliding bastard. We'll have you trussed up and cattle-prodded into right thinking within the hour."

He looked fearfully over his shoulder at his new enemies and was about to hustle to the gate when Zach threw a handful of black powder in his face. "Cooperate!" Zach commanded.

"What's the idea?" Higgens screeched, backing away from the window, wiping at his eyes. A husky guard wearing chevrons closed on the van and peered inside, hefting his machine pistol.

"He's blessed you," I explained to Higgens, moving my hand inside my beaded vest. "At no charge!"

"Out! Out!" Higgens screamed, jabbing the barrel of his rifle at us, and the gate flew up.

I looked at the unblocked road, then at the sergeant with his hand on the hydraulic switch. "You're clear to go."

He smiled while Higgens gaped. I dropped the transmission into low, and we flowed through the gate.

"Pretty impressive, huh?" Zach said after we passed through. "Did you see that? I dusted him and the gate went up."

"It was weird, all right," I said. "So weird I don't want to think about it."

A phalanx of valets stood by the lobby doors, but there didn't appear to be any exterior security. I parked in front of the tower, and Zach and I regarded each other. The utter absurdity of our getups caused me to break up into hysterical laughter. Zach chuckled along, waiting until I finished.

"Feel better?" he asked.

I exhaled heavily, sighing. "Much."

"Time to go?" Zach asked.

"Yes," I said and the butterflies hit my stomach in a swarm. "Are we really ready for this?"

He giggled, a little manically. "Hell, yes, we are." He dug into a leather pouch on his belt and came up with a handful of mushrooms. He pushed all of them into his mouth. "Magic mushrooms," he explained, chewing rapidly. "To focus my powers of concentration."

"You're not going to start wigging, are you?"

"If the need arises. Do you want some?"

"I'll pass." I said. I drew several deep breaths, psyching myself up. "Well, shall we see if the god is in?"

"Why not?"

We stepped out of the van and gave each other a final check. I tossed the keys to one of the unnerved valets, and we strode purposefully into the high-security Set of One complex.

29

We moved through the lobby quickly, looking inward and ohming like bastards. I tried to keep my attention passive and pointed into a dark corner of my soul, but it kept whipping around, trying to get out. I shot a look at Zach. His eyes were rolled back in his head, and his lips mumbled frantically. Past him I got a good look at the alarmed faces of the beefed-up martyr contingent at the security station.

An empty elevator opened as if on command, and we moved aboard, not turning around until it closed. I punched button thirty-eight, and we surged upward.

"Man, did you see that?" Zach cried excitedly. "We went through there like invisible leopards. Their psyches didn't even recognize us."

"I think their conscious minds refused to accept we were real," I said, watching the numbers of the elevator's digital readout climb. "We'll get off three floors below the auditorium and work our way up the stairs."

"Then what?"

"After a quick recon, we kill the bad guys and rescue Heidi."

"Just like that?"

"Sure," I said. "We'll make it up as we go along. Right

now we need to worry about what happens when these doors open."

"Right," Zach said, scratching at a handful of gaily colored rattles. I drew my pistol, and we both stood poised by the doors. We reached the thirty-eighth floor, but the elevator continued upward.

I punched the emergency Stop button without effect. "Uh-oh," I said. "Looks like we've been hijacked."

"Stand back!" Zach cried, and hit the button panel with a large rattle. The rattle shattered and we continued upward.

I took a step back and drove a heel into the panel's chrome plate, crushing circuitry. The elevator shuddered, then jerked to a halt, throwing us to the floor.

The lights dimmed, and the panel began spitting sparks and smoke.

"Lucky for us you were wearing Masgar juju leggings," Zach pointed out.

"Yes, it certainly was," I said, getting up. The readout blinked three zeros. I pushed the Open Door button on the crushed panel, and after a grinding noise the door opened an inch.

"Hold this," I said, handing Zach the gyrapistol. I wedged my fingers in the gap, set my legs and strained to pull the doors apart. After several moments of monstrous exertion, I'd managed to increase the gap by half an inch. I stopped trying and caught my breath.

"You're not visualizing properly," Zach coached. "Imagine the doors are mere cloth curtains, picture them in your mind parting with a mere wave of your hands. Become the door, will it to open."

"I'll bet that's pretty effective for opening jelly jars," I said, "but this is a little different."

"Get rid of that negative energy! You're fighting against yourself, that's the problem. You have to ask yourself what part of you *doesn't* want that door open. Confront that counterself and sway him to your side. All of you has to want to open that door."

I looked at Zach. The mushrooms had dilated his eyes to the point they appeared completely black, like a shark's. "All right, goddamn it," I said and got another grip. "All of me wants to open this goddamn door."

I heaved, and the doors parted as if on well-oiled wheels. Zach shook his rattles fiercely and bounded into the martyrs' cavernous gym, looking around. I followed, the elevator doors screeched closed, and the car began to grind upward.

"How about those doors, eh?" Zach said.

"I think I loosened them on the first try."

"Ha! You know better than that. You overcame that inner deterrent, and they parted like the Red Sea." Zach looked around the room. "What now?"

"First off, give me back my pistol." I held out my hand as I looked around the room. A moment passed. I looked at Zach. "Gimme my pistol."

"I think I might have left it on the elevator."

"*What?*" I said with horror. "You did *what?*"

"It was seriously interfering with my mantric vibe anyway. We're much better off without it."

I shook my fist at the ceiling. "Fate, you mean pimp!"

"Relax," Zach said, adjusting his gear. "We have plenty to work with. What do we do next?"

"All right," I said, feeling naked and daunted. "Let's get off this floor before they trace the elevator."

"Right," Zach said. He dug at the gang of small bags of powder on his beaded belt. He opened several and began pouring blue-and-green powder into a circle around him, chanting ferociously.

"May I ask what you are doing?"

"I'm creating a multidimensional displacement portal so we can segue our physical selves into the auditorium."

"Have you done this before?"

"No, but I saw it in a movie once."

I put a hand on his shoulder. "Let's just take the stairs."

He stopped pouring powder and looked at me. "Why?"

"Because I'm crazy."

"All right," he said, frowning. "Whatever you like."

We moved up the stairs, creeping past the martyr barracks like mice in a ferret den. The stairway ended on the forty-third floor, and I peeked through the window of the door that opened onto the hall, ducking back quickly. Martyrs, set execs and late-arriving bigwigs hurried down the hall at odd intervals. I maintained surveillance, waiting for a gap in the traffic.

"Get ready to move fast," I whispered to Zach. "When a gap opens, we have to run like hounds." Zach got a firm grip on two rattles and nodded.

A squad of martyrs marched by, followed by two wary-eyed crime bosses in their best suits, then a gap appeared.

"Now!" I said, and we barreled into the hall, loping to the corner of the T section that led to the Phoenix chambers and Jackie's office. I peered around the corner, then jerked back. Four martyrs with machine pistols marched toward us.

"Quick!" I ordered, diving into the nearest door, pulling Zach with me.

The room was alive with flapping arms and animal howls. The hulking instructor, smartly attired in a black rubber jumper and gorilla mask, stopped screaming obscenities at the blindfolded initiates and turned on us.

"Did we miss anything good?" I asked.

He pointed his cattle prod at us. "Who are you?"

"We were told to report here for indoctrination." I gave him a sloppy salute.

He blinked. "Why are you dressed like that?"

"We heard it was a costume party. Did we screw up?"

"Oh, completely!" he snarled sadistically, prowling toward us.

"Sleep!" Zach cried, and smacked him on the chest with a rattle.

The instructor looked down at where the rattle had hit him, then at Zach. A tremor went through his thick body, and his voice lowered to a quivering, aroused hiss. "I'm going to hurt you now," he said, raising the cattle prod.

"Sleep!" I said, driving a fist into the side of his jaw. He staggered back, dropping the cattle prod and groping blindly, the eye holes of his mask askew from the blow. I picked up the prod, thumbed the Continual Pulse button and dropped it down the front of his tight rubber trousers. He howled with pain and spun into the inductees, clawing at the prod.

"Follow my voice!" I yelled at the class. The blindfolded mass rushed toward me, stampeding their instructor to the floor. I opened the door and steered them into the hall with shoves. "Run amok!" I commanded. "Scream hallelujah and don't stop until I say Rumpelstiltskin three times! This is your final test!"

The classroom emptied, and we followed the rampaging class into the hall, leaping over initiates grappling with wild-eyed martyrs and indignant execs. We turned left at the corner and rushed down the hall into Jackie's office. We reeled around wildly for a moment before realizing it was empty.

"Whew!" Zach cried. "Look at these Tonton Macoute voodoo masks! And the golden-dawn initiation dagger! A Mau Mau spear of spiritual vengeance! We're standing in a seething maelstrom of occult energy!"

I jammed my card into the slot next to the set plaque. I groveled to any god who cared to listen, and the door hissed open. "Never mind these pagan tools," I said. "Let's go!"

Zach backed into the elevator with me, shaking his rattles at Jackie's decor.

"She *knows*," Zach said as we rode up a floor. "She *understands*. We may be in deep, deep trouble."

"Gee, you really think so?" The doors parted to reveal the God Hall. I stepped out and Zach gasped.

"Jake, you're goddamn levitating! You're a juju man!"

I crouched down and rapped on the invisible floor. "Solid one-way glass."

Zach stepped out in low crouch. "They can't see us?"

"That's right," I said, looking down. "We'll recon and plan our next move from up here."

It was standing room only in the auditorium, and there wasn't much of that. Movers and shakers of every description packed the hall. City Party execs, militia leaders, captains of commerce and crime, anybody who had their hands on any lever of power. Mixed in like weasels among fat cats were a half-dozen camera crews, crowding the aisles and bobbing in the wave of humanity, directing their cameras and commentary at the stage and curtain. A monstrous digital clock hung above the curtain, counting backward, ticking off the seconds until One made his world debut. It passed the one-hour mark and marched on.

On the stage stood a single man, bathed in a barrage of spotlights, his arms raised above his head, his lips forming words we could not hear.

"Sinn knows how to work a crowd," Zach said. "They're practically groveling at his feet."

"He has a little help," I said. Sinn finished a salient point, jabbed a finger at the giant clock, and the crowd applauded wildly. Sinn smiled, then looked up, his eyes staring directly into mine. Terror shoved me against the wall and dropped me into low crouch.

"Get down!" I cried. "Hide! The bastard's spotted us!"

Zach flinched then hunkered down, looking back at me accusingly. "You swine! You said this was one-way glass!"

I blinked at him without comprehension for a moment, then got a grip on my nerves. "That's right," I said. I looked down at Sinn, and his eyes were back upon the crowd. "There's no way he can see us. I just imagined he did, that's all."

"Give me Heidi's possession," Zach said, holding out a hand, "and I'll try to locate her."

I drew the blade and handed it to him. He eyed it speculatively. "This item was dear to her heart?"

"Very," I assured.

Zach shrugged, petting the blade with one hand. He closed his eyes and began to moan. "I'm picking up something," he said. "I'm getting a clearer image, yes, yes, here it comes, powerful vibes here, it's a...it's a— Aaarrrggghhh!" He lurched back violently, dropping the knife as if it were white-hot, wiping his hands frantically on his beaded vest. "Get away from it!" he shouted desperately, backing away from the blade as if it were a hissing cobra. "Whatever you do, *don't touch it!*"

I skirted the knife and moved to Zach's side. "What the hell happened?"

"Murder!" he cried out. "Terrible murder. I saw a vision of that blade rising and falling, hacking, rending the flesh

of loved ones mercilessly, coldly, blood on the bed, everywhere, death, death, everywhere death. It's a spirit eater,
the souls of its victims imprisoned inside the vile steel,
screaming to be released." He looked up at me. "What kind
of girl did you say she was?"

I shrugged. "I didn't say she was *perfect.*"

He shook his head incredulously. "Man, you must be
really hard up for clients. You must have dredged the low-
est pits of hell to find this one." Suddenly he flinched. "Oh,
man, I just felt something."

"Oh, sweet Jesus, what now?"

"I'm starting to feel his presence," he whispered, rotat-
ing slowly.

"Who?"

"One! Oh, yes, this bastard is *powerful!* He's all around
us! We're surrounded!"

"Enough of that kind of talk," I warned, backing away
from him. "I have to think of a plan."

"It better be a very good one. Man, do you realize
what's going on? We're standing in a vortex of massive,
conflicting energies. I can feel them shifting around us like
lumbering leviathans, infinitely powerful entities grinding
against and confronting each other, old against the new.
And here we are, bringing all the focused powers of the
mystic circle into the fray like a torch among powder kegs.
The implications are staggering—this battle could spark
the Apocalypse! This could be the Ragnarok! The down-
fall of all the gods! We might doom the entire universe to
chaos and destruction!"

"Well, doesn't that goddamn figure," I said. "The
Apocalypse arrives, and I don't even have a goddamn
gun."

"Hello, Jake," a voice boomed at us.

We crouched and whirled, peering in every direction. "Telepathic message bombardment," Zach hissed.

"Hidden speakers," I corrected, straightening up. "Hello, Slim. How's the murder business?"

"Quite good, actually," Slim cooed, his voice carrying the calm and politeness of a sadist with his hands on all the controls. "In fact, it can be said you have arrived at our finest hour. I would have invited you personally, but we had trouble locating you."

I signaled Zach to follow and we began moving around the circuit. I said, "I hope you're not upset about me crashing the party."

"Not at all. I see you brought a friend."

"I hope you don't mind."

"Of course not. Speaking of friends, someone of your acquaintance is with me right now."

"Who might that be?"

"I'll let her introduce herself." After a moment of silence, a frightened voice called across the speakers.

"Hello?" Heidi said. "Is it you, Jake?"

"It's me," I said. "Are you okay?"

There was a muffled sound, and Slim came back on. "I'm sorry, but she can't speak right now. She's, shall we say, in a bit of a jam."

"Where are you, Slim?" I asked. "Maybe we can talk."

"I was hoping you'd say that. Why don't you take a look down."

I looked down. Herb and Slim stood in the center room of the Phoenix section. Slim watched a monitor with a view of Zach and I, and Herb stood over the control panel of the resurrection chamber. Inside the sealed chamber, like a surreal Snow White in her crystal coffin, lay Heidi, her eyes bright with fear.

"Why don't you come down to resurrection room thirteen," Slim said. "And we'll talk this over."

"Come and get us!" Zach shouted, and began laying down a circle of powder.

"Well," Slim drawled, "I could just send up a squad of martyrs, but I'd hate to disturb tonight's historic ceremonies with frivolous gunplay. Wouldn't it be better all around if you two came down here and we talked about it, *mano a mano?*" Slim moved next to Herb and raised a finger over the mortal black button on the control panel. "And as an added incentive, if you don't come down this minute, the pale princess here is going to take a little nap, and she won't be waking up."

"Hold on," I said. "I'll be right down. Make sure the hall is cleared of traffic." Slim gave me a smile and a big thumbs-up.

"We can't go down there," Zach whispered as we retraced our steps. "It's an obvious trap. And according to my psychometry reading, the damsel in distress isn't exactly a kind-eyed princess. She's a cold-blooded killer."

"Yeah, but who isn't these days? We have to do something. Maybe I can get really ruthless and turn the tables on them." I stopped to retrieve Heidi's knife and put it back in my waistband. "Besides, isn't it obvious the cosmic is directing us down there? Don't you feel the pull?"

Zach eyed me skeptically. "Okay, but I'm not taking any chances. As of this moment, I'm erecting a psi protection bubble because this is turning into an extremely twisted fairy tale." He launched into a chant.

We took the elevator down to Jackie's office, then crept nervously down empty halls, expecting martyrs to pop out of every doorway.

"What is that gesture symbolic of?" Zach asked from behind me.

I glanced back at him. "What gesture?"

"You keep pawing at your left side with your right hand every third step."

I looked down at my hand. I watched it closing on the air above my shoulder holster. "It's a type of animist Oriental hand dance," I said, "used by early samurai warriors to bring good fortune during an impending battle."

"I think I've heard of it," Zach whispered. "What is that style called? The scratching bear?"

"The declawed monkey."

We reached the door of resurrection room thirteen. I took Zach's arm and pulled him back to resurrection room twelve. I peeked inside. The room was empty.

"I want you to wait in here," I whispered.

"What? Why?"

"Like you said, it's obviously a trap. We need a trump card. I want you to wait in here for five minutes, in case they check outside, then come back out into the hall. Keep your ear to the door, and when you hear me say 'karmic,' I want you to leap into the room like a rain dancer from hell. When you distract them, I'll make my move."

"I'll do more than distract them," Zach assured. "I'll hit them with a psi whip that'll scar their Kirlian auras for eternity. In the meantime I'll slip into an invisibility field in case they come looking for me." He slipped into room twelve, his eyes rolled back, focusing his energy inward.

I confronted the door marked Resurrection Room 13 and took a deep breath. After making a couple more symbolic swipes at my shoulder holster for good luck, I went inside.

"Good of you to make it, Jake," Slim said as I let the door close behind me. He held a large-caliber automatic in his hand. "Where's your compatriot?"

"He decided he wasn't up to wrestling any gods today."

"I can't blame him. What's with the snake-charmer outfit?"

"Play games with me and you'll find out."

Slim enjoyed a little laugh, and I moved to the sealed chamber. Heidi's eyes were closed, her perfect features calm under the oxygen mask, her body motionless. Cables disappeared under her blouse, and an injector pack ringed her neck.

"You bastard," I said, pressing my hands against the frigid glass. "You said if I came down you wouldn't kill her."

"I lied!" Slim giggled.

I turned on him. "Bring her back or I'll kill you."

"I'm afraid you haven't that option," Slim snarled. "If anyone's going to do any killing here, it's going to be *me*." He smiled. "Just like I killed your buddy Nu."

Rage flashed through me, but I fought it down and shifted my eyes to Herb. "Bring her back, Herb. *Now*."

Herb's nervous eyes turned to Slim, who smiled. "I'm afraid you're not giving orders around here anymore, *Commander*."

"C'mon, Herbert," I said, my voice rising. "Don't get me mad."

"It's *Herb*," Herb blurted out. "And you damn well know it!"

"It's Herbert now, Herbert."

"Stop that!"

"Herbert! Herbert! Herbert!"

Herb teetered on the brink of a conniption fit until Slim backhanded him.

Silence returned and Slim regained his smile. "Go ahead and bring her back," he said, then looked to me. "We were going to do it anyway. I just wanted to see you squirm over losing your little Jezebel slut."

Herb went to work on the control panel, his face red with the slap. After a moment he jabbed the red shock button.

Heidi jumped, then lay still.

"Come back, baby," I whispered, watching her face. "C'mon back."

Fluid jetted into her neck, and Herb slapped the button again. The body jumped again, but the heart line stayed dead flat.

"What's wrong?" Slim asked nervously, moving next to Herb.

"Sometimes it just takes a little longer," Herb said, but I could see he was nervous, too. He hit the button again, then a fourth time without effect.

"You better tell me what's going on," Slim said in a high, dangerous tone.

"She's not responding to defibrillation," Herb wailed. "Let me try Bretylium." More fluid jumped into Heidi's neck, and he shocked her again. The heart line didn't even twitch. Herb looked at us helplessly. "Sometimes they don't come back."

"Listen to me, you dirty quack," Slim said, his face shiny with sweat, putting the gun to Herb's temple. "Either she comes back, or you'll effing join her."

"I'm doing all I can!" Herb cried, his shaking fingers fumbling on the control board.

"Do more!" Slim screamed, the big automatic trembling in his hand. "Or I'll send you to One right now!"

I saw my chance. I took two swift steps and swung a roundhouse kick at Slim's head. As he twisted away, my boot caught his shoulder, spinning him around. I drove right and left jabs into his kidneys, and he fell onto Herb. They both collapsed to the floor, and I jumped on top of Slim's gun hand with both boots. Slim screamed, and the pistol scuttled across the floor. I rushed over and picked it up while Slim and Herb untangled themselves.

I pointed the pistol at both of them. "Get back behind the board," I snapped at Herb. Slim got to his feet, and I shoved him against the wall and patted him down. I found a small hideaway revolver in an ankle holster. I popped open the cylinder, checked the load, then dropped it into my pocket. I shoved Slim hard, and he sprawled to the floor. He glared up at me, grinding his teeth and cradling his injured hand.

Herb poked at the control board, but he seemed a little on the unmotivated side.

"Get to it, Doc," I warned.

"There's not much more I can do, Commander. I've tried everything."

"Try something else."

He shook his head sadly. "She's gone, Commander."

I leveled the gun at his head. "Then I guess there's no reason to keep you around."

"Wait a minute!" he cried. "We can do one more thing." His hands fumbled beneath the panel, and he came up with an injector gun. "It's still experimental," he said. "We'll have to pop the lid."

"Do it."

Herb stabbed at the panel, and the lid hissed up, releasing a wave of warm air. He leaned inside and pressed the gun against Heidi's rib cage. "It probably won't work."

"Do it!" I shouted, and the injector hissed. Herb stared at the monitor, then leaned both hands on her sternum, compressing her lungs. After three presses he ripped off the oxygen mask and breathed twice into her mouth.

I watched the little dot of the heart monitor intently. It continued its slow, even trek across the screen. "Jump," I whispered. "Jump you bastard, jump!" And it jumped.

Heidi arched her back and gasped, drawing a huge breath of air. Her eyes flickered open, and she began to sob. Herb backed away, crying happily, and I helped Heidi out of the chamber, removing the disks and injector pack. She coiled her arms around my neck and sobbed into my shoulder, shivering as if we'd pulled her from an icy river. "Oh, Jake, you wouldn't believe what I saw! It was so wonderful!"

"We can talk about that later," I said, looking at my chrono. "Right now we have forty-five minutes to stop One from making his move. How do you feel?"

"A little dizzy, but I'm okay."

"Good. Take this," I said, handing her Slim's hideaway revolver. "Keep them covered while I figure out what happens next." I addressed Slim and Herb with my eyes.

Herb stopping crying and backed away. "You can't kill me after I just saved her."

"Sure he can," Slim said, getting up from the floor. "He's a killer. It's what he does best."

I turned the pistol to Slim. "You're right," I said. "I believe I owe you something for Nu. Are you ready to meet your god?"

Slim spread his hands and smiled. "I'm a martyr. I'm always prepared to claim my place in paradise. But I guess the bigger question is, are *you?*" His eyes shifted meaningfully to my left. I glanced over to find Heidi wasn't pointing the pistol at Herb and Slim anymore. She was pointing it at me.

30

She said, "Drop it, Jake."

I gaped at her. "Did that death box convert you, Heidi?"

She laughed. "Not converted, Jake. Coordinated. You see, I had to go out and make certain One would be on hand for the show."

I laughed uneasily. "Don't worry. You're just suffering from a bad case of postdeath trauma. Now, why don't you put that gun down."

"You idiot," she said. "You still don't get it." She reached up with her free hand and grabbed a handful of her hair. With a single rearward pull, the blond wig slipped off and fell to the floor. A hairnet followed, and long black locks tumbled down. She touched each eye with a finger, the tinted contacts came out, and concrete gray eyes became tar black. She finished with a wicked smile, and the transformation was complete. Prim but murderously deranged Heidi had become sinister but lovable Jackie.

"Well, Jake," she said. "What do you think?"

"I think I liked you better as a blonde."

She frowned, and there was perhaps the slightest taint of jealousy in her eyes. "Well, that's just tough. Give Slim the pistol."

Slim started toward me with his hand out, wearing a big

sloppy grin. I stopped him in his tracks with a twitch of the automatic's barrel. "I think I'll hold on to it."

"I'm not screwing around, Jake," Jackie said, firming up her grip on the revolver. "Drop it or I pull the trigger."

I sighed with skepticism. "Yeah, right."

Jackie sighted down the barrel. "I'll do it, Jake."

"You wouldn't kill me," I said with a confident smile. "You love me too damn much."

"Goodbye, Jake," she said, and squeezed the trigger.

The revolver clicked. She pulled the trigger again, but I was still smiling.

"I emptied the cartridges when I took it from Slim," I explained.

"Huh?" she said, still clicking the gun at me with vain hope. "What for?"

"Your act isn't as tight as you thought," I said. "It took me a while, but I finally figured it out. It was a lot of little things. The empty cupboards, the dead flowers, a few slips of the tongue, the doctored picture, the many subtle coincidences. And Slim here seemed a little too excited about bringing you back to life."

My smile turned bitter. "Yeah, I see it all now. It was a big setup from the start—you had big sap Jake coming and going. You were my client, target, lover and confidante all wrapped up into one nasty little package. First to get the data chip, then to train your killers." I enjoyed a mean laugh. "You're not a very nice girl, Jackie."

Jackie shrugged. "You were just a tool to be used. Just like the rest of us."

"All for One and One for himself, eh? Is that why One sold out to the Party?"

"*They* sold out to *One*," Jackie snarled. "They're just a means to an end. Let's face it, people just aren't taking to the Party too well—it's deficient in too many ways. The set, on the other hand, appeals to every facet of life, vice and virtue, body and soul. Just as Christianity subjugated the Roman Empire, the set will flower from the corpse of the Party."

"Well, it sounds like you had some big plans." I gestured with the pistol. "Why don't you get over there with Slim and Herbert?"

"Herb," Herb said.

"Shut the fuck up."

Jackie sauntered over to Herb and Slim. "I can't believe you'd kill me, Jake. Not after all the good times we've shared."

"Are you speaking as Jackie or Heidi?"

"Whichever."

"Right. Didn't one of you just try and shoot me a minute ago?"

"I was aiming at your gun arm." She smiled demurely. "Can't you forgive me?"

"I'm afraid that well has run dry, baby. I'm not going to kill you anyway. I think you'd make a better ticket into the show alive than dead. But as for you," I said, turning the pistol to Slim, "your ticket has already been punched. How does paradise look now?"

Slim stared at the open mouth of the pistol, and the wall of confidence caved in. He raised a shaking hand in front of him and made a strange clawing gesture. His eyes rolled back, and his jaw began to chatter. "I'm not ready yet, not ready…"

"No one ever is. Here comes your karmic reward, Slime."

The door burst open behind me, and I was knocked to the floor amid a cloud of colored powder. The pistol jarred from my hand and slid away. I struggled beneath the weight that pinned me to the floor and stretched for a pistol that was no longer there.

"Looking for this?" Jackie asked. I looked up into the barrel of the big automatic.

"As a matter of fact, I was. May I please have it back?"

"Screw you. Get up."

Zach rolled off my back, and we both got to our feet.

"Well," Jackie said, "it looks like we got the whole tribe."

Zach blinked at the pistol then looked to me. "Did we screw up?"

"We screwed up," I assured him.

"You're darn right!" Slim shouted hysterically. "Shoot him, Jackie! Shoot the dirty rotten blasphemer!"

"Jackie wouldn't shoot me," I said. "Not after all the good times we've shared."

"He's right," Jackie said.

I smiled triumphantly and Slim gaped. "Well, let me do it, then," he said, reaching for the gun.

"No, shooting him would be too messy." She stepped away from the chamber and gestured at it with the gun. "Why don't you climb inside?"

"Why don't I not?"

She thumbed back the trigger. "Because I'll shoot you."

I took my time walking to the chamber. I touched the glass shield speculatively. "Are you sure this thing's safe?"

"Safe enough for where you're going. Get in."

I looked into Jackie's eyes, searching for reprieve. "You won't meet a man like me again."

"Not if I'm lucky."

I sat on the edge of the chamber and swung my legs up. "Plenty of room in here," I said, slapping the padding. "Sure you don't want to hop in?"

"Positive. What's that in your belt?"

"Oh, yes, I almost forgot," I said, drawing the knife. "I believe this is yours."

She stared at the blade with what appeared to be genuine bewilderment. "I've never seen it before."

"Sure you have," I said. "You murdered your parents with it."

"I didn't murder my parents," she snarled. "*She* did."

I stared at her rage, and a point hit home. "I see."

"Just drop it."

I dropped the knife to the tiles, and Jackie moved to the panel.

I held up my hand. "Before you do that, I'd like to ask one last question."

Jackie sighed impatiently. "Okay, let's hear it."

"I was waiting for the right moment to ask you, but I guess this is as good a time as any. Jackie?"

"Yeah?"

"Will you marry me?"

She laughed and shook her head. "I'm too young to be a widow."

"Are you saying my ticket for this thing is one-way?"

"I'm afraid so. So long, Jake, have a nice trip." She stabbed at the panel, and the cover hummed over me.

I'm a man in desperate need of a quality plan, I thought, watching Jackie converse with Slim for a moment, their voices too muffled to understand. She walked over to the glass and looked at me for a moment. She leaned over and planted a kiss on the glass, leaving a lip-shaped red smear. She waved sadly, pointed the pistol at Zach and marched him out of the room.

Slim walked to the glass like a strutting rooster, hands behind his back, monstrous grin on his face. He waved at me, then leaned his face to the glass. "How you doing in there, Jake?"

"Up your ass," I shouted back at him, and banged the inch-thick glass with a fist. The shield felt solid. I braced my back against the bed, then launched both knees at the glass. I succeeded in making my knees throb with pain and nothing more.

Slim rapped on the glass and scolded me with a finger as he paced maniacally in front of me, giggling. It was obvious he intended to savor the moment, squeeze out every last drop of pleasure. He vanished for a moment, then popped up like a jack-in-the-box, giggling hysterically. He walked away from the chamber then returned, swinging his hips. He bent over the glass and kissed the lipstick smear left by Jackie, waved solemnly, then minced away to double up with laughter. The show was starting to drag, so I arched my neck until I could see Herb. He shrugged at me from behind the panel. I turned back around to see Slim's face pressed grotesquely against the glass.

"I'm going to turn the gas on now," he said in a slow, muffled voice. "When I do, I want you to tell me exactly how it *feels*."

He moved to the keyboard, shoving Herb out of the way. He grinned at me, then dropped a finger.

I sucked in a deep breath and held it. Slim walked over to the glass and watched me casually. After two minutes my lungs began to ache, but I held on, fighting the howling panic loose in my skull. *These are my golden moments,* I thought grimly, *and I have to treasure them.* I waited for the highlights of my life to start playing, but apparently my brain couldn't find any good footage.

Slim rapped on the glass as my lungs began to tighten. "How does it feel?" he asked. "Does it feel *good?*"

I gestured obscenely and he started laughing. My lungs felt about to implode, my stomach tied up in knots, and a little voice inside said *fuck it*.

I opened my mouth and sucked in air greedily, nearly hyperventilating, waiting to inhale enough poison to die. A moment later my breathing returned to normal and I was still alive.

Slim opened his mouth into an O and clapped his cheeks with feigned surprise. "I think I pushed the wrong button!" he shouted, then howled with laughter until tears streamed down his face.

Screw this, I thought. He'll get no more pleasure out of me. Though tragic and unfortunate circumstances had prevented my living a life of grace and virtue, I would at least die with some semblance of dignity. I interlaced my hands over my stomach and let my body and mind relax. I'd had my fun, and now it was time to shake the Reaper's hand.

Slim went back to the panel and began circling his index finger above the board as if searching for the proper button, his brow creased with feigned confusion. Finally he smiled, waved at me and pushed a button.

A tiny hissing sound filled the chamber, and I fought back the urge to take a deep breath. I didn't hoard air, yet neither did I breathe; I relaxed my lungs and let the air within them lie dormant and still. The faint smell of peppermint touched my nostrils, but I ignored it. I would slip into the afterlife gracefully, on my own terms.

Slim rapped on the glass and gave me a thumbs-up, then the okay sign. He backed away and doubled up with laughter.

Red blood cells sucked the last molecules of oxygen from my bronchial tubes, and my stomach began to tighten and turn. I unbuckled my belt and drew it from around my waist. I wrapped it tightly around my right hand, the fat steel-and-turquoise buckle over my knuckles.

Some gas slipped into my nose, and I could feel a tingling sensation spread through my chest. *Ah,* I thought, *this is really it, no turning back now. I will concentrate and I will refuse to blink out.* All panic slipped away, and I breathed rapidly, sucking in the poison, psyching myself up for the afterlife. There was just one more thing to do.

Slim moved close, and I focused on his face, just inches beyond the glass. I concentrated until the glass became nothing, just a shimmer of light, a thin wall of smoke.

"I want you to give a message to One for me," Slim said solemnly, fighting back a smile. "I want you to tell him it was I who sent you, I who sent down the first resident of his new hell."

I reached out with my hand, the turquoise buckle passed through the wall of smoke, and I grabbed Slim's throat. He clawed at the hand, then braced his own hands against the chamber as he realized my intentions. I braced my knees and with my last ebb of life, pulled Slim's horrified, screaming face to the jagged hole in the glass.

"Tell him yourself," I croaked, then died.

FROM HIGH ABOVE, I watched Slim struggling against a dead man's grip. He slapped frantically at the shield, wailing and sobbing, his face cut horribly by the jagged glass.

I floated near the ceiling of resurrection room thirteen, ethereal, weightless and hugely relieved. *I didn't blink out,* I thought, *but what's next?*

An irresistible force began to tug at me, and I knew my question was about to be answered. *Here we go,* I thought, and I hurtled out of the room and into a field of darkness. *Now comes the tunnel,* I thought. The tunnel, then judgment.

But instead of shooting down a dark tunnel to a being of brilliant light and ultimate wisdom, I found myself standing in front of a drab gray door. A completely unremarkable drab gray door, except it was surrounded on three sides by howling infinity. I opened the door and looked inside.

A heavy, dough-faced Mongoloid sat behind a desk deep in the dim gray room. His misshapen head bent over a small human-shaped figurine in his hands, and the light from the ceiling bulb made his face appear inscrutable and skull-like. A large round office clock ticked on the wall behind him.

I leaned in the doorway. "You seen a tunnel around here?"

His monstrous head lifted slowly, and he regarded me with the dull, unblinking gaze of the incurably retarded. He stared for a moment, then returned to his toy.

I stepped inside, closing the door behind me. "I suppose this is the processing room for hell," I said conversationally.

He continued to play with the doll, poking and pinching like a cat toying with a wounded mouse.

I looked up at the ticking clock. It was a strange one. Instead of the usual twelve hours, the numbers and tick lines stopped at exactly 8:31. It was presently 8:02.

"That's a screwy clock," I said.

The dough-faced man blinked up at me with a dumb expression, then turned around and looked up at the clock. In a slow, dumb voice, he said, "No, it's right."

The ticking of the clock seemed to be getting louder. I walked to the room's lone window, which looked out on the howling black nothingness of infinity. "So," I said, "you're One."

"That's what they call me."

"And this isn't hell?"

"Oh, no. Only the things you believe in are real. Everything else—" he shrugged his big shoulders "—isn't."

I listened to the clock tick, each tick minutely louder than the last. I studied his reflection in the window, sizing him up. He had the heavy, powerful build of a sumo wrestler, but he also looked slow and dim. I figured I could take him.

"It's funny," I said, "you look just like I imagined you would."

"Of course. What else *could* I look like?" He slapped the doll cruelly against the desk, and I thought I heard a tiny cry. I turned around to see the doll whip around in his hands, and One tightened his grip, smiling cruelly. I heard a small, high-pitched scream and realized the doll was alive. As I walked to the desk, One turned the doll's tiny face toward me. It was a face I knew, the face of a nice suburban kid I'd taught to kill.

"Do you know him?" One asked, his eyes moving to mine.

"Give him back," I said, holding out a hand.

One started to hand him over, then suddenly jammed him into his mouth. With a gruesome slurping sound, Nu's torso, legs, then tiny feet disappeared into One's mouth. One burped, then patted his stomach. "That was a very tasty soul," he said, licking his greasy lips. "Most of the ones I get are so *dirty.*"

"You son of a bitch," I said, frozen with surreal horror.

"It was your fault," One said, smiling his cruel, idiot smile. "He never believed until you told him *you* believed. It's all your fault."

"Cough him back up," I demanded.

"Sorry," One said, patting his belly. "All gone!"

I screamed and lunged over the desk. I clawed for his throat, and for an instant my fingers closed on hot, oily flesh. The next thing I knew I was standing next to the door with my hand on the knob.

"Sinn was sure right about you," he said from across the room. "He sure was."

"I'll never work for you," I swore. "I'll burn in hell before I serve in your heaven."

One smiled. "Yes. Could you send the next soul in?"

"Still hungry, One?"

He giggled. "I'm *always* hungry."

I stepped outside and saw a long line of faces. Hunched and quivering with fear, Slim was first in line.

"What's he like?" Slim stuttered. "Is he a *good* god?"

"He's just what you expected," I said, and stepped into darkness.

31

I sat up in the open chamber, shivering against a chill that went right to the marrow. I felt as if I were put together with wire and corkscrews, and my heart burned with pain, racing and slowing at sickening intervals, beating at my rib cage like a wild animal trying to get out. Slim lay dead on the floor, and Herb stood in front of me, arms folded, a satisfied look on his face.

"Why?" I stuttered, my teeth chattering.

"I'm a Faith No More operative," he said quickly, helping me out of the chamber. "Junes said to tell you you're even."

"But how…"

"No time to explain," Herb said, hustling me toward the door. "You only have twenty-three minutes to stop them."

"Hold on," I said, leaning against the wall. I felt like a boxer who'd spent twelve rounds on the ropes, and there was a ticking in the back of my head. "I need a moment to get it together." After a few deep breaths I felt marginally worse. "Are you still an atheist?" I asked.

Herb frowned. "What difference does that make?"

"Just curious."

"Yes, yes, of course I am," Herb said impatiently. "But let's hurry, you've less than twenty-two minutes now."

"Sure," I said weakly, driving a fist into Herb's stomach, dropping him to his knees. He struggled to get up, and I kicked him in the face, sprawling him on his back. He pulled an automatic from his lab coat, but I kicked it out of his hand, then dropped a knee into his solar plexus. He groaned with pain, and I crossed the room and picked up the pistol, catching up with him before he could crawl out the door. I stepped on his right hand and pinned his neck to the floor with the barrel of the automatic. He lay on his belly and stopped moving. "You have a funny way of showing your gratitude," he grated.

"I'm a funny guy," I said. "Only I'm not laughing anymore. Why'd you bring me back?"

Herb twisted his head around, and one round, terrified eye looked up at me. "To stop Sinn."

"Why? You work for Sinn."

"I told you, I work for Faith No More, I…"

"You're no more an atheist than I am. Sinn turned you. You're his double agent. You're the one who finked about Junes's headquarters. So why'd you bring me back?"

"I don't know what you're talking about."

"You're not concentrating," I said, grinding my heel into his hand.

"I'm telling the truth!" Herb gasped, his face contorting with pain.

"Tell me a lie, then."

Herb pressed his lips together and told me nothing. I leaned my full weight on the back of his hand, grinding my heel until the bones of his hand began crackling like melting ice. Herb wailed and tried to pull his hand free.

I pressed the barrel of the pistol to his temple where his eye could see it. "Last chance, Herb. Are you sure you're ready to meet One? He's not a very nice guy, you know. And his table manners are atrocious."

Herb closed his eyes and tears welled out. "All right," he whined. "It's all a setup. Get off my hand and I'll tell you everything."

I removed the pistol from his temple and stepped back. Herb rolled over slowly, holding his crushed hand.

"Let's hear it," I said, crouching next to him.

Herb nodded, covering his face with his hands and sobbing quietly. "I don't know what to say except...*this!*" His good hand sprang from his face and grabbed the barrel of the pistol. He tried to pull it away, jerking the trigger against my finger. A single shot rang out, and Herb collapsed to the floor, his right breast bubbling blood from a punctured lung.

"Oh, shit," he cried. "I'm shot!"

"You're dying, Herb. It's time to come clean."

"Clean for who?" He giggled deliriously. "I hope you don't mean *God*." He tried to seal his lung with his fingers without much success. "Shit, I've pushed so many over the edge into death, *thousands,* and now here I am on the brink, and you know, it's frigging *scary.*"

"I know," I said. The ticking in my head was growing louder, and I checked my chrono. The curtains parted in seventeen minutes. "Well, I've an appointment to keep."

"No! Don't leave! You have to tell me what it's like. You've been there, you know One."

"All right," I said. "I'll tell you. But only if you tell me some things first."

"Yes, yes, anything."

"Why did you resurrect me?"

"It had to happen this way. One had to approve of you."

I looked down at his fevered face and tried to make

sense of his words. "Why? Sinn knows I won't command the martyrs."

"No, no, it has nothing to do with that. That was just a smoke screen from the start. Early on Sinn became convinced a favored man would rise through the ranks, be given all, only to turn on his generous masters. A great betrayer, delivered by the hands of destiny and fate, would be exposed and destroyed by Sinn's own hand the same moment as One rises triumphant."

"What the hell are you talking about?"

"There has to be a counterbalance, an opposing force to keep One from eating everything." He coughed fitfully and drew a great, racking breath. "Now you have to tell me everything about One."

"All right," I said. "One isn't real. Stop believing in him right now. Believe in Jehovah, Brahma, Thor or the goddamn Whispering Coyote god, believe in anything but One."

"It's too late for that!" he wailed. "I know too much, I've seen too much proof not to believe." He started to cry in earnest. "Oh, shit, it's true, then. He's real and he's going to eat me!" Suddenly desperate hope jumped into his eyes, and he grabbed at my arm. "Hold on, Jake. I've helped you, haven't I? I told you the truth, I brought you back, right? You owe me one, right? Don't you?"

"Sure," I said.

"Say it, then. Say you owe me!"

"All right," I said. "I owe you. But you're going to have a hard time collecting where you're going."

The terror drained from his face, replaced by a smile of bliss. "Oh, don't worry about that." His smiling, loving eyes looked into mine. "I believe in you, Jake, I really do." Herb quivered once, then let go.

I studied his dead smile, trying to think. After a moment I stood up stiffly, crossed the tiles and picked up the butcher knife.

I LURCHED down the abandoned hall like an exhausted cripple, delirious with hot and cold flashes, hounded by the ticking in my head. I staggered into Jackie's office, holding my skull in my hands, my brain feeling as if it were a time bomb about to explode any second. I leaned against the desk and tried to regain control of a body gone amok, tried to focus a blurred brain. I looked at my chrono. It read 8:16. I pushed off from the desk and began gathering the things I'd need, then took the elevator up.

Through the glass of the God Hall I watched the congregation of the powerful and greedy, those who just hours before bowed to no greater mantle than their own. They now leapt and danced as giddy children, waving their arms and chanting "One God! One God!" at the behest of their new prophet, who paced before the red curtain, wearing the cruel smile of a cat who'd huckstered the mice into believing cats were vegetarians. Sinn flapped his arms wildly and shouted, pumping them up and urging them on until the mob's voice shook the floor of the God Hall. The pheromones were so thick I could smell them two stories up. I spotted Jackie in the aisles with Zach, gun at his back. The big clock read nine minutes.

I laid down the things I'd taken from Jackie's office. I tied one end of the hemp stripped from the rope chair to the middle of the Mau Mau spear of vengeance. Taking the spear in both hands, I drove its thick shaft deep into the wall. I tied on the Tonton Macoute demon mask to protect my eyes and face, then straddled the hemp, looping the rope around my hip, over my shoulder and under the opposite arm. Drawing the pistol, I stepped back against the wall and fired six bullets into the floor of the God Hall.

A hole the size of a manhole cover opened up and I stepped into it. I let the hemp drag through the fingers of my left hand and, like a monkey falling from heaven, I rappeled to the stage in the wake of a shower of broken glass, landing ten meters from Sinn.

"Ah-ha!" I croaked, pointing the pistol at him.

Sinn stopped pacing and blinked at me. The chanting died with a collective gasp.

"Is that you, Jacob?" Sinn whispered, a smile twitching at his lips. "Is it really you?"

"That's *right!*" I snarled menacingly, stripping off the mask. "Just in time to save the whole damn universe!"

"Well, what a *super* entrance." Sinn beamed and began to clap. The audience picked it up until it became a roar; they apparently thought I was *with* the program. "Listen to the crowd!" Sinn cried out. "You're a hit!"

I sensed black movement to my right, and martyrs surged from the wings, bristling weapons.

"No!" Sinn howled at them, throwing up his arms. "Nobody hurt him, and keep those cameras rolling!" Sinn turned his lunatic smile back to me. "Oh, that mask, beautiful, a wonderfully beautiful touch. I couldn't have choreographed it better myself."

"Wait a minute," I said, upset my heroic entrance wasn't having the derisive effect I'd anticipated. "You're reading from the wrong script, bozo. I'm pulling the goddamn *plug* on this goon show."

Sinn rolled his head back and laughed. "You *still* don't understand, do you? How marvelous, how perfect. Your date with destiny, and you're still acting like a comic-book character. Don't you know who you are, Jacob?"

"Of course I know," I said. "I'm the hero and you're the villain, so quit acting like we're on the same side and start cowering and cringing like you're supposed to."

Sinn bellowed with laughter. "But we *are* on the same side. Oh, Jacob, can't you see this moment has always been here, waiting for you, since the day you were born?"

"It's true," Jackie said, stepping forward, hands clasped in front of her. "It was always you, Jake."

"What the hell are you talking about?" I asked, pointing the pistol at her vindictively. "You had me *killed* twenty minutes ago!"

"I didn't kill you, Jake," she purred. "I introduced you to One. He had to approve of you. And he did approve."

"He didn't approve anything!" I shouted, and the ticking in my head doubled in volume, stabbing into my concentration like a jagged dagger. "I didn't even fill out an application!"

"He must have approved," Jackie said, smiling. "He let you come back."

Sinn took a step toward me. "I knew it was you from the moment I shook your hand," he said. "We've groomed you for this position from the start, cultivated you like a deadly nightshade. Oh, Jake, I almost envy you. Just think of the power you will hold!"

"Shut up!" I shouted, trying to fight the ideas and pheromones stabbing at my brain. "I'm not falling for your… your lies and religious con-man crap. This party is *over.*"

"Oh, but it's just begun. We've been waiting for you, our honored guest. But where are my manners?" Sinn said, turning to the crowd. "It's time proper introductions were made. Ladies and gentlemen!" he roared, his voice booming across the auditorium. "I promised to show you the face of One tonight. And I shall. But what is the white without the black? What is light without darkness? Ladies and gentlemen, *what is a god without a devil?*"

Sinn turned a hand to me. "Loyal children of One, I present to you our own fallen angel, the one man, who, given everything, would turn against the one god who would save him from eternal damnation. I present to you Jacob Wolfgang Strait, *the Anti-One!*"

The clapping began tentatively, the crowd uncertain if meeting the Anti-One was something to applaud. Then, with more encouragement from Sinn, doubt was cast aside, and the vast room filled with applause and cheers. Sinn turned to me, beaming like a proud parent.

I stood alone in the big crowded room and a dark, heavy wave rolled over me. Each strand in the vast web of contradiction and deceit became lucid and defined, as all the pieces that didn't fit twisted into place to form a big, ugly picture. All of Sinn and Jackie's contradictory behavior now appeared subtle and clever manipulations, all directing me to this singular, damning end. I'd been as deftly manipulated as the drugged winos who'd ripped apart plastic-and-neon Jesus. I looked back on the monstrous deception and realized I'd been right about only one thing from the start: I *was* going to hell. *My* hell.

"But I don't wanna be the devil," I protested.

Sinn stopped a meter away, his face stern and loving. "There's no turning back now, Jacob. From cradle to grave, all the days of your life in exchange for this golden moment." He clenched a fist between us and squeezed it tight. "And with this golden moment you can buy *eternity!*"

"I've seen eternity," I said, stepping back and raising the

pistol. "It begins right here, where it ends. I'm stopping this right now."

Contempt flashed across Sinn's face. "And how do you propose to do that, you terrible little man?"

I raised the pistol. "For starters, I'm going to shoot you."

"Mensch!" Jackie screamed.

"Your magic is gone, witch," I sneered.

"Don't worry," Sinn said to Jackie. "Jacob won't shoot me." He held out his hand. "Now, give me that toy."

"Sure," I said. "One bullet at a time." The room boomed with an explosion, and the bullet smacked into Sinn's chest, knocking him to the floor. I shot him once more in the heart to be sure, then turned the pistol on Jackie and the martyrs grouped behind her. They stared at Sinn, paralyzed with the fall of their master. I turned to the audience. "The show's over," I shouted. "One couldn't make it. Go home."

People in the crowd looked at each other with confusion, then began to rise. Half out of their seats, they suddenly froze, staring with horror and hope at something directly behind me. An icy jolt ran up my spine, and I turned around to find Sinn getting to his feet.

It's a frigging nightmare! I thought, and shot him again. He staggered back a step but didn't go down. I shot him again and again, but he walked toward me like a man fighting a gusty wind.

"Do you see?" he hissed, so close I could smell the sharp, acrid scent from the cordite burns on his thick robe. "Do you see the power of a *god?*" He took the pistol from my paralyzed hand and pushed its hot barrel into my belly. "Now take what is yours."

I swayed on the brink of eternity, sensing the darkly glittering mantle being offered to me; if I reached out, it would be mine. Instead, I reached for something else.

"I got it," I said.

"Well," Sinn grinned, "I guess it's time for you to go, then."

"All right," I whispered, putting my left hand on his shoulder. "But you first." I drove Jackie's butcher knife through his spider-silk robe, up under his rib cage and into his right lung. Sinn staggered back, dropping the pistol.

"Kill him," he gasped to Jackie, grabbing the hilt of the knife. "Send him to hell before it's too late!"

Jackie drew her pistol and, like a Gila monster launched from a catapult, Zach barreled through martyrs and jumped on Jackie's back, howling mantras, knocking the pistol from her hand.

The auditorium filled with clanging alarms and shrieking sirens, and pandemonium broke out. I looked up at three blinking zeros, and the red velvet curtains began to part.

"It's time!" Sinn cried, pulling the knife from his chest and dropping it to the floor. He staggered toward the screen, leaving a trail of blood. "One is here!"

The curtains spread wide, revealing a wall of flashing light and twitching color, pulsating like a quickening heart.

"One! One! One!" the crowd chanted, and an energy crackled through the room, an almost physical power that pushed and shoved its way in. The crowd shuddered and screamed as a single mad beast, flailing and howling to greater and greater heights of violent orgasm, their minds snapping under the sheer weight of the cataclysmic moment. The screen mirrored the anarchy, reaching to a chaotic crescendo of color that churned into a howling vortex, spinning faster and faster until it became...

…a perfect cotton whiteness. The shouting and fighting stopped, and a terrible silence gripped the room. For ten mean seconds the screen remained glaringly blank, sucking at eyes like a vacuum, and even Sinn's gruesome smile began to crumble.

Then, slowly, like mud bubbling up from the black bottom of a deep lake, hues began rising to the pristine surface, corrupting the perfect whiteness, and a shape began to form, an oval boiling with shadows. Slowly the shadows became eyes, a nose, then a mouth around which a beard grew. It was an old human face with flowing white beard and hair and piercing blue eyes infinite with wisdom.

The crowd went wild, and Sinn threw his hands in the air. "The face of One is revealed!" he cried, and I could hear the hysterical shouts of newsmen screaming into microphones.

The face of One shimmered, then bloated into the chubby countenance of a smiling Oriental.

"The second face of One!" Sinn shouted a little less enthusiastically, and the crowd roared again.

The Oriental face twisted and churned, narrowing into the features of a handsome, mother-eyed woman that grew horns and turned into a drooling, fire-eyed bull's head, in turn replaced by the dumb, menacing mask of the idiot god I had met, succeeded by a baying goat. The faces formed and faded with increasing velocity; the thousand faces of God came and went until they became a wild blur, a congealed shimmer of color. The crowd's ecstasy dissolved into confusion, then chaos until the screen flashed like a monstrous flashbulb and the rushing images vanished, replaced by a perfect, shimmering mirror.

"I knew it," Sinn whispered to the silence, stumbling toward his reflection, held up by Jackie. "It's me!" He collided with the screen, pawing his image, his lips kissing his god's. "It was always *me*."

One by one, then in groups, the audience stood up and looked into the mirror, into the face of their own gods.

I stepped closer to the screen and my image moved to meet me. Ten meters away I stopped and picked up Jackie's pistol. My image raised his pistol and said, "Now there's a god I don't like."

I pulled the trigger, blowing a hole in my face, drilling the screen. There was a hollow pop and the screen hissed like an angry snake, then exploded violently, blowing glass into the crowd and knocking me off my feet. I covered my eyes with a hand and with a final shriek of circuitry like the wail of a dying god, the monstrous screen tumbled forward.

Martyrs swarmed around the collapsed screen, looking for their prophet who had disappeared beneath its monstrous weight. After a moment of confusion, they turned their guns to the fleeing audience, and for a moment I thought they were going to open up on them just for something to do. When the auditorium had cleared, they turned their guns to me.

For a long, breathless instant they stared, black suited as if in mourning, orphans who did not know how to cry, only to kill.

"Go home," I said, knowing they had no home. "It's all over."

They looked at each other and shifted their weapons as minutes ticked by beneath the blinking zeros of the big clock. Then one martyr nodded, and they began backing toward the aisles, looking lost and bewildered, without master or reason.

I helped Zach to his feet. He stood unsteadily, shaking

off pulverized glass. "You're lucky you weren't cu___
I said.

"I would have been if I hadn't erected a protection bubble around my body when the screen exploded," he said, wincing as he moved his left arm. "Except for my arm—my arm was outside the bubble." He winced again. "And my right ankle must have slipped out." He balanced on his left foot and looked around the wrecked stage. "What happened to Sinn and Jackie?"

I nodded toward the screen. "Under there."

"Whew. The bastard just reached out and grabbed them."

"Yes," I said, staring at the toppled screen, feeling tired and empty. I knew it was wrong to feel any loss at all. She'd used me like a chump from the start, meanly and without emotion, but it didn't change the way I felt. I knew then not all bridges were meant to be burned; some should be left as monuments to emotions greater than the man. "I'll miss you, Jackie," I whispered.

"What?" Zach asked.

"Nothing," I said. "Let's go get a drink."

Epilogue

She walked into my office two weeks later, as resplendent in white as the day I'd first met her. She sat on the love seat across the desk from me.

"I'm sorry I haven't been in touch," she said, "but I've been out of town." She took an envelope out of her purse and set it on my desk. "Inside is a check for the past four weeks' work." She returned hand and eyes to her lap.

"Do you know what happened?" I asked.

"I saw it on TV." She started to cry, then turned away. Her face looked bruised under the heavy makeup. "I know you tried your best. I only wish she could have been saved."

"Jackie didn't want to be saved, Miss Pan. At least not in the sense you might think."

"Oh?" She dabbed her eyes with a handkerchief. "Did you get to know my sister well?"

"I was in love with your sister," I said, and Heidi's eyes flashed. "Well, at least part of her."

"Which part?"

"I don't know. I haven't figured it out yet."

"I'm surprised you got to know her at all. She was such a cold, fickle creature, poor girl." Heidi finished crying and put away the handkerchief. After a moment of silence she said, "Jackie didn't try and pose as me, did she, Mr. Strait?"

"I'm afraid she did."

"Damn her, I knew she would. She always does." She sat for a moment, then rose. "Well, I guess I'll be going."

I came around the desk. "Heidi?" I said.

She turned around and faced me. "Yes?"

"Your father must have really hurt you," I said. "To drive you and Jackie apart."

She bowed her head. "He wasn't such a bad man. Only Jackie hated him."

"Is Jackie really dead, Miss Pan?"

She looked up at me, startled. "I don't know what you mean."

"Her body was never found."

Her big gray eyes found my eyes, and we swayed almost imperceptibly toward each other, as if drawn by a pulsating magnet.

"She's gone," she whispered breathlessly, and the magnetism vanished.

I nodded slowly, turned around and walked to the window. "If she comes back," I said to glass, "I'd like her to call me."

"I don't know if I'll be able to tell her."

"It's all right. She'll know."

I listened to her walk to the door, a slight limp in her step. The door creaked open, and she said, "She just might. Goodbye, Mr. Strait."

"Goodbye, Miss Pan."

A minute later a tall, lovely woman in white scarf and coat came out of the building, pausing to wave up at me.

I waved back, not sure who she was.